WATER PLANET

EAST CAROLINA UNIVERSITY GEOGRAPHY DEPARTMENT

Kendall Hunt
publishing company

Cover image © 2011, Shutterstock, Inc.

Kendall Hunt
publishing company

www.kendallhunt.com
Send all inquiries to:
4050 Westmark Drive
Dubuque, IA 52004-1840

ISBN 978-0-7575-9270-6

Printed in the United States of America
10 9 8 7 6 5 4 3 2 1

Contents

Chapter 1

THE WATER PLANET – AN INTRODUCTION

INTRODUCTION

"Water, water, every where, nor any drop to drink." Sure, it is a line from a famous poem, but does it hold true today? Where is all of Earth's water? What does it do for people and other living creatures? How much of the water is actually drinkable? What kind of power does water have on landscapes and on people? What can it create or destroy? How and why is it so sacred? How do people agree, or not, to use this water?

In The Water Planet course at East Carolina University, we will cover these questions and more. This course is unique to our campus and yet it seems like a pretty obvious choice of topic to study given the local and world events related to water that are publicized in the news each day.

The Water Planet course is taught by Geography Department faculty who will each highlight various topics from tropical weather to hazards mitigation, pollution impacts, beach processes, and water supply management. The purpose of this book is to provide a solid grounding in these topics through relevant readings and assignments that allow for exploration of water-related issues. All of the course instructors, however, emphasize the core topic of water as the one vital element found everywhere on Earth that ties together all peoples through an amazing assemblage of physical, environmental, and social processes.

Geographic Analysis

One of the rather special features of this course is that we look at water-related phenomena through a Geographic perspective. This brings up a basic question: What is Geography? Not all Geographers agree, but for this class a basic working definition can be that Geographers study the relationships among geographic areas, environmental systems, society, and cultural activities. We identify these as spatial relationships because locations and the interactions between them matter. Within the discipline of Geography, researchers typically align themselves with one of four traditions as they start their examination of any topic. These four traditions are:

- regional geography, in which comparisons are made on various characteristics of regions
- applied geography, where research is conducted with an emphasis on quantitative or statistical analyses
- physical geography, which involves field or laboratory studies into environmental processes, and
- human-environment interactions, which look at our human activities affect, and are in turn affected by, our Earth's processes.

For this course, we incorporate all four main Geographic traditions because water can—and should!—be studied from a variety of perspectives to give decision makers the widest possible range of expertise about this vital topic.

Within any and all of these traditions lies the fact that Geographers are interested in two major ideas. First, we examine the 'where'—or distribution and patterns—that shows us how things vary across Earth. These things can be groundwater wells, hurricane tracks, diplomatic water conflicts, or almost anything you can imagine. Today, much of the 'where' question is handled using a combination of fieldwork where data are gathered through surveys or interviews of people, by laser (LIDAR) analysis of landscapes, or other methods, and all the data points are tied to latitude and longitude on Earth by use of Global Positioning Systems (GPS or SatNav). These data can then be transformed into computer generated maps through various styles of software called Geographic Information Systems (GIS). GIS allows us to combine as many layers of data as necessary to show distributions and patterns that allow for further analysis of the connections across Earth's places.

The bigger research task is to think critically about the processes that create or change those distributions. Therefore, the second big question Geographers study is 'why,' to identify and understand the processes that connect and control the distributions we mapped. For example, to appreciate the likely causes and potential impacts of a drought, a Geographer can use GIS to study current weather systems, landforms, vegetation cover, land uses, and population density in the drought-impacted region. Geographic inquiry combined with GIS then suggests hypotheses to investigate further through statistical analysis, development of computer models, additional fieldwork, surveys or interviews, laboratory studies, or other forms of scientific analysis.

Usually when Geographers conduct such analyses, there are five underlying themes that help direct the nature of their research, including location, place characteristics, relationships between places, movement of people, culture, or physical matter, and regional understanding. Location is of first importance as that helps set the stage for everything else that follows and is tied to questions of distribution, to discover where other similar places or phenomenon are located across the globe. Place characteristics can help identify what makes places unique or similar and is the starting point for identifying how they are connected to the world, physically, culturally, or economically. These relationships are tied to the movement of goods, services, or physical features such as how animals or sand dunes move within a place and to new locations. And finally, we can answer how particular characteristics of some place qualify it, or define it as being contained within, a larger region.

For example, imagine you are interested in studying the human impacts related to areas where hurricanes form on Earth. You could start with the knowledge that hurricanes often make landfall on the south-eastern U.S. coastline. This gives you an original location and then you can expand your research to find other places where hurricanes develop and also strike land, and now you have a hurricane distribution map. Use of the distribution map and further study of local ocean and weather processes can help identify factors contributing to hurricane formation and these factors can be used to locate coastal cities most at risk from hurricane paths. If you are interested in human impacts resulting from hurricanes, then you could examine how at-risk coastal cities prepare emergency response teams and evacuation routes, how much money is lost in a given city due to hurricane-caused business or structural damage, or how flooding from hurricanes can lead to water-borne disease outbreaks. Results from these studies could then be compared with, or applied to, other regions of the world that experience hurricane activity.

LOCATION, LATITUDE AND LONGITUDE

Before progressing with this kind of analysis, however, it is a good idea to interject a discussion of place and location, since those concepts are basic to Geography and integral to this course. There are two different ways to identify a particular place. Often, we will use a relative description of a place. For example, if you tell a friend from New York City that Greenville is located between Raleigh and the Atlantic Ocean, this says that our location is related to these other places, if only through directional means. Relative locations are great for giving others a rough idea of where a place is located, but in this example, those relationships might not be enough to direct your friend if she's driving to Greenville. To be more accurate, we use absolute locations, such as providing street addresses for mail deliveries or using latitude and longitude as part of a geographic grid system to map places on Earth. Most of the technologies today including cell phone applications and internet-based maps use latitude and longitude even though those coordinates are not necessarily visible or recognizable.

The following brief description on how to use relative and absolute location concepts, particularly of latitude and longitude, will be useful as you read through this book and participate in classroom discussions. There is an exercise after this chapter that allows for some practice of these concepts. Knowing where a place is located on Earth is the first step toward identifying and understanding the relationships between that place and its physical, environmental, and social characteristics.

In this course, several very important variables such as the amount of sunlight, types of vegetation, global wind belts, locations of hurricane formation, and landforms such as deserts and glaciers are all significantly related to particular latitudinal regions, so it is worth taking a moment to review these concepts. Latitude describes a line that runs east and west around the Earth parallel to the Equator, which is at 0°. These lines, also called parallels, are used to indicate the location of place in terms of its angle in degrees north or south of the Equator. If you live in the northern hemisphere, you can be anywhere between 0° and 90° North, as shown in Figure 1.1. Folks in the southern hemisphere live between 0° and 90° South. The poles are each at 90 degrees of latitude.

Other important latitude lines are the Tropic of Cancer at 23.5°N and the Tropic of Capricorn at 23.5°S. Locations between these lines indicate the tropical region, which tends to get significant amounts of sunlight and therefore many places in the region experience very lush vegetation and higher humidity. Really cold places with little to no sunlight in winter tend to be north of 66.5°N, the Arctic Circle, or south of 66.5°S, the Antarctic Circle. Locations from 23.5°N to 66.5°N and from 23.5°S to 66.5°S are considered mid-latitude or temperate locations that tend to have definite seasonal changes. More information on weather patterns associated with latitude can be found in Chapters 3 and 4 and vegetation and climate distribution patterns based on latitude are described in Chapter 6.

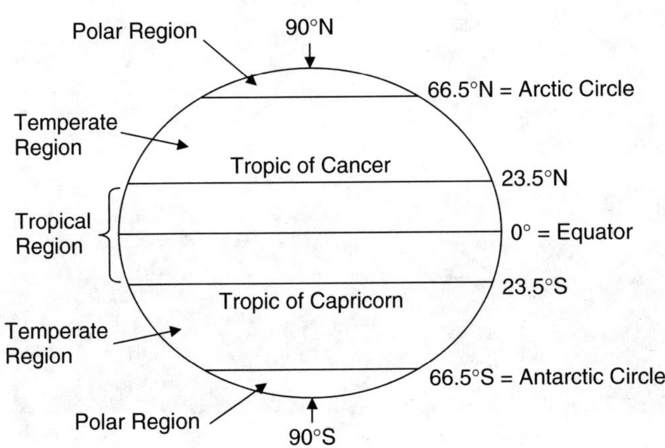

Figure 1.1 Important latitude locations and related regions on Earth.

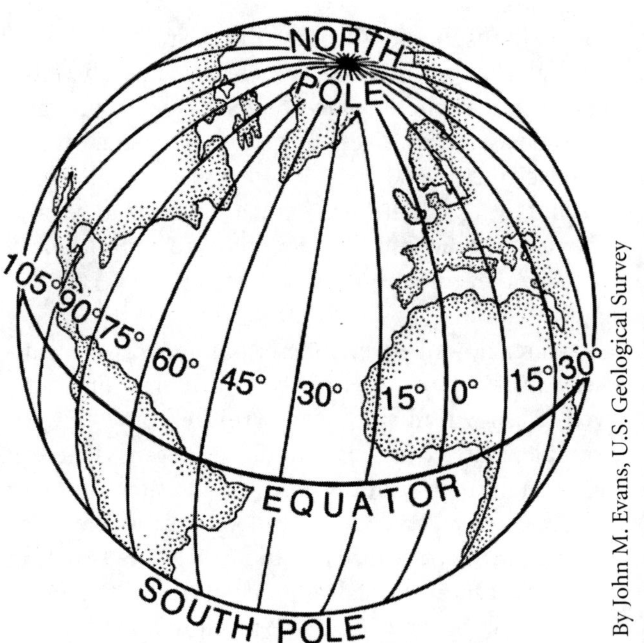

Figure 1.2 Diagram indicates how lines of longitude run from the poles north and south across Earth. Source: Pearson Scott Foresman, donated to the Wikimedia Foundation.

The second component of the geographic grid, longitude, helps identify whether a location is east or west of 0°, a line on Earth called the Prime Meridian, as shown in Figure 1.2. The 0° longitude line runs through Greenwich, England and also parts of France, Spain, and several countries in western Africa. Longitude can be used to indicate if a place is located from 0° to 180°East or from 0° to 180°West of the Prime Meridian, so it defines the eastern and western hemispheres. Longitude is not closely tied to environmental processes in the same way as latitude, but it does help determine time zones. In fact, the start of each Earth day happens at 180° of longitude.

HYDROLOGIC CYCLE

This chapter is also a good place to provide a bit of background about water properties that make it so special for promoting and maintaining life on Earth. We generally discuss water moving through four spheres, which include:

- the atmosphere, which refers to the air in, on, or above the planet,

- the lithosphere, which refers to the rocks and minerals that produce the land areas and ocean beds,
- the hydrosphere, which refers to bodies of water such as oceans, rivers, and lakes or water stored as glacial ice,
- and the biosphere, which refers to all creatures and plant-life, whose life functions are supported by the other three spheres.

Water flows between these four spheres continuously in a system we call the hydrologic, or water, cycle, as shown in simplified form in Figure 1.3. For example, water exists as a liquid in oceans, where it can evaporate and become a gas, as water vapor in the atmosphere. From there, the water vapor can condense, turning back into a liquid or become frozen in the form of snow, and fall as precipitation onto land or other bodies of water. Once the precipitation hits land, it can become frozen and stored in the form of snow banks for a season or, on longer time scales, solid water can be stored in glaciers and ice sheets. As a liquid, precipitation can runoff the land into rivers that flow back to oceans or it can be stored in lakes. If it is able to infiltrate into the land surface, water can be stored as groundwater in aquifers, and can also flow out of the ground into rivers or lakes where it can then evaporate back into the atmosphere. Water falling on land can also be used by plants, which can then release water back into the atmosphere through evaporation and transpiration processes. A more complete discussion of the hydrologic cycle as it relates to creating weather is given in Chapter 2.

Often, we take this process for granted on Earth, but it is really quite a special and amazing cycle that is able to exist because water can be found here in all three states: gas, liquid, and solid. Most other liquids do not change states at the same temperatures or pressures as water and so are not found in all forms naturally. But, as we know, water boils at 100°C (212°F) and freezes at 0°C (32°F), so water can change states

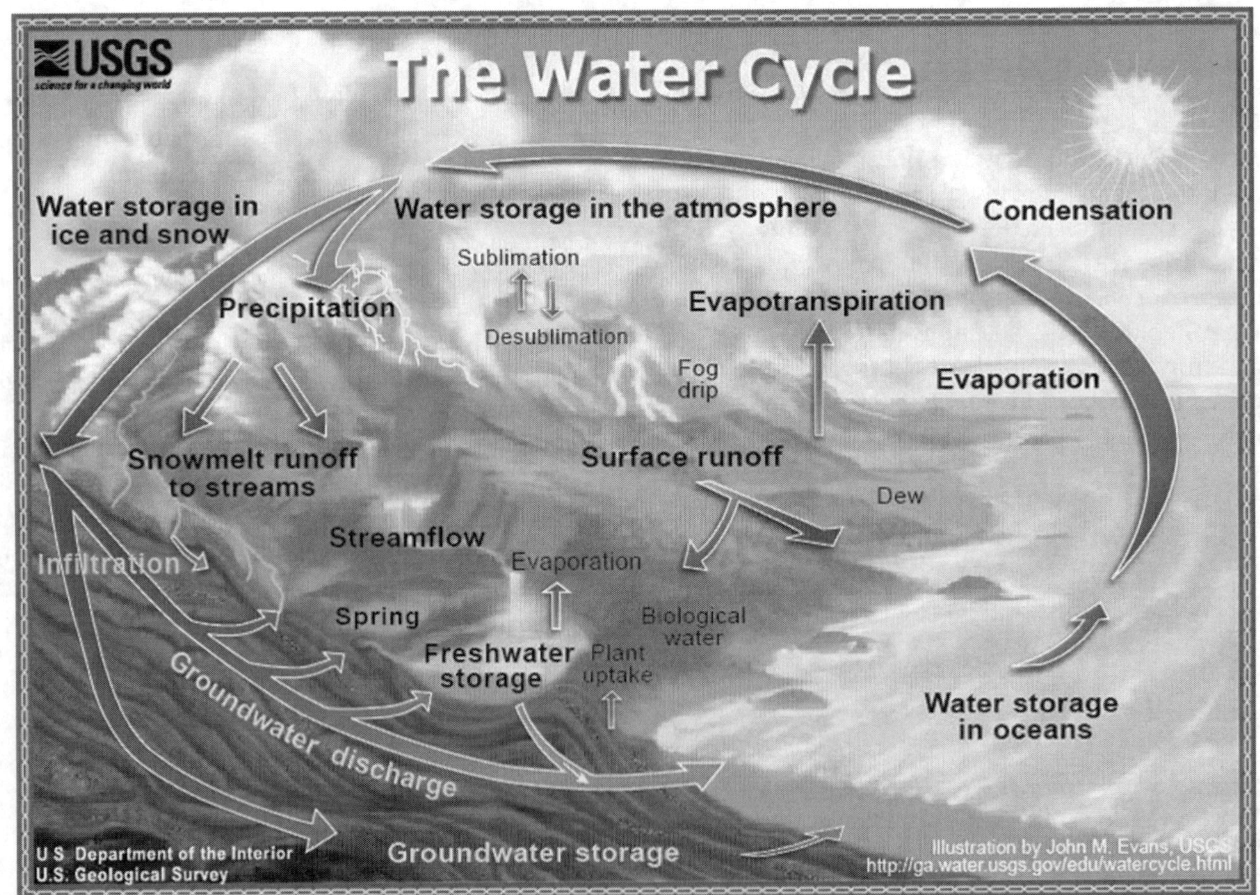

Figure 1.3 A simplified view of the water, or hydrologic cycle, showing typical flows of water as solid, liquid, or gas throughout the four spheres, the lithosphere, biosphere, atmosphere, and hydrosphere.
Source: U.S. Geological Survey http://ga.water.usgs.gov/edu/watercycle.html

quite simply under Earth's environmental conditions. Another property of water that can be seen operating throughout the hydrologic cycle is the fact that water can dissolve many substances so that as it flows over or through the land or even the atmosphere, it can take with it minerals such as salts to deposit in the oceans. These and other chemical properties such as water's high specific heat values, ability to expand upon freezing, and molecular attraction are discussed in more detail in Chapter 10.

Humans are completely dependent on the hydrologic cycle for nearly everything we do! We need water to live and to grow plants for food, we use water for manufacturing all the items we use and then we rely on water to transport much of those items across thousands of miles of rivers or oceans. On the other hand, humans can also impact the operation of the hydrologic cycle in many ways, including:

- Building dams to store more water on land
- Withdrawing groundwater from aquifers by use of wells
- Clear-cutting forests, interrupting local evaporation and transpiration processes
- Removing water from rivers or lake for use as irrigation or drinking water
- Altering the chemical composition of the atmosphere, allowing for changes in evaporation and condensation processes
- Covering the land surface with concrete during urbanization and development, preventing evaporation of water from soil and reducing vegetated areas

This Water Planet course will look at these human and environment interactions, pertaining to the uses and modification of water on Earth. How we use water and manage it as a resource is a human endeavor that must consider politics, economics, cultural beliefs, religion, history and many other social science based factors. Many processes connecting people to water as part of the hydrologic cycle are typically studied by physical or Earth scientists. This book, therefore, intends to provide some introduction to the physical processes as well as exercises and chapters connecting these processes to social concerns so that you can more deeply understand the problems and issues related to water faced by society today.

WATER PLANET EXERCISE 1

Name: Busra Burce

type it up! 8.23.12 1week due 30th

Mapping Our World and Water Places

Purpose: This exercise gives you a chance to use a basic online map tool to explore absolute location concepts of latitude and longitude while locating some of Earth's interesting water features. Hopefully, it also illustrates how it is possible to use a combination of spatial information from maps and aerial photographs to geographically describe and compare:

- Place characteristics such as presence of vegetation, topography, or political units;
- Regions, including land masses, oceans, and dry versus humid areas;
- Movements of people or water between places;
- Distributions of variables such as water in liquid or frozen states.

To start, get on the Internet and go to www.bing.com/maps

Part I – Location, Location, Location:

In the search box, enter: Greenville, NC. Just below the town's name at the top left, you should see some numbers like this: 35.6071950495243 -77.3802246898413.

All the decimal places make this a very specific latitude and longitude address, but for this exercise we are only interested in the first two or three places beyond the decimal. This gives us an address for our city of 35.607, –77.380. Cool! We're on the Geographic Grid!
Hm . . . but what does that negative sign in front of the 77.380 mean? Let's find out.

1. At the Bing Maps search box, type in 35.607, 77.380. To identify this place, you may need to click on the – and + signs (Zoom Out or Zoom In buttons) at the top of the map and Zoom Out – a lot! Where did you go?
   China, Huldi, in the Kunmin mountain range
2. So, site 35.607, +77.380 is located in which hemispheres? Eastern & Northern
3. We (at 35.607, –77.380) are located in which hemispheres? Western

To play around with this concept a bit more, find these locations and describe them by their continent or ocean and any nearest features you can identify.

4. Enter –35.607, +77.380
   Describe: Indian Ocean, dark blue.
5. Enter –35.607, –77.380
   Describe: South Pacific Ocean (Chile)

It is important to know whether you intend a + direction (N and E), which are assumed by the computer program, but you must type in negative (–) signs for S and W locations.

Alternatively, you can type in cardinal directions; for example, to get back to Greenville, NC, you could enter 35.607N, 77.380W or to find Sydney, Australia enter 33.867S, 151.209E.

6. In the Bing Maps search box, enter "North Pole." What is the latitude and longitude here according to Bing? What should it be?

7. Hm, that wasn't fun . . . let's look for something else on land. Search for "Antarctica." What latitude and longitude do you get?

Part II – Comparing Landscapes and Movements

Online mapping tools can be powerful aids for understanding geographic differences. Let's look at some river deltas to explore this function.

In the Bing Maps search box, type in "Mississippi River Delta" and then Zoom Out (the negative Zoom button above the map) until you see the Gulf of Mexico and also New Orleans.

8. What is the latitude and longitude you are given for the delta? 29.3 N latitude and 89.28 W longitude

9. How would you describe the shape of the delta? bird's feet

10. At the top of the map, you should see a drop-down arrow next to the word "Road"—click on that and select "Bird's Eye View" to overlay an aerial photograph of the region onto the map. Now, what color is the delta region? dark green Why? It's how it looks from a plane.

11. Now type in "Nile River Delta" into the Bing Map search box. What is the latitude and longitude? 30.9000°N, 31.1167°E

12. Leave the map in the "Road" map view first. What shape is the Nile Delta? Can you tell? arc shaped

13. Now, go to the "Road" menu and click on the "Bird's Eye View" again to view the aerial photograph. What color and shape is the delta?

14. How does the Nile River Delta compare to the surrounding lands in Egypt?

15. What do you think is the reason the Mississippi and Nile River regions look so different?

16. For one last delta comparison, type into the Bing Maps search box "Amazon River." What latitude and longitude do you get?

17. In what country is this point located?

But wait . . . the Amazon River flows into the Atlantic Ocean, not the Pacific close to Peru!

18. Type into the search box "Macapa"—a city near the Amazon River Delta. What is the latitude and longitude here?

To explore how big the Amazon River is, click on the word "Directions" (left of the map) and type in (or cut and paste) the latitude and longitude of your first "Amazon River" search and make sure "Macapa" is in the second box. This should give a driving route from the headwaters to the delta.

19. How many miles is this route if taken by auto?

20. If you'll look closely, much of this route goes far south of the actual Amazon River. Why?

Part III—Human-Environment Interactions

For a preview of a water and climate-related problems addressed in this class, look up one more location.

21. Search in Bing Maps for "Chacaltaya."
    What is the latitude and longitude? ______________________________
22. Next, click on the Bing link to "Wikipedia Article" and read the introduction
    What is the elevation of Chalcaltaya? ______________________________
23. Look back at the Map using the "Bird's Eye View."
    What is the terrain like? ______________________________
24. According to the Wikipedia article, why was this area once famous or important to this part of Bolivia?
    ____
    ____
25. What happened in the last few decades to change this place and what are the effects of that change?
    ____
    ____

Chapter 2

THE ROLE OF WATER IN WEATHER

In 1986, a scientist at the University of Iowa theorized that comets the size of a house routinely crash into the earth's atmosphere (and harmlessly vaporize high above the planet). If they exist, these "snowballs" from space would be millions of times smaller than big comets like Halley's or Hale-Bopp.

Thought to originate from just beyond the orbit of Neptune, these small comets are (theoretically) composed of ice, much like their bigger cousins. Although the theory does not address how long these comets have been thrown at our planet, it is possible that there has been a cosmic snowball fight underway for over four billion years! If this is true, then small comets may have been responsible for importing a fair share of our planet's water supply (the small-comet theory purports that about 30,000 bombard the earth's atmosphere every day).

The high variability of water vapor compared to the other variable gases sticks out like a sore thumb. Even over warm tropical oceans, concentrations of water vapor seldom exceed four percent of the total atmospheric composition. Yet, this seemingly paltry amount is enough to fuel ferocious hurricanes such as Katrina in late August 2005 (see Figure 2.1).

The quirkiness of water doesn't end there. All three phases of water—liquid, solid (ice) and gas (water vapor)—can coexist in the same environment at exactly the same time. Although the bluish icebergs floating in a fjord need no further comment, we point out the overcast of low clouds in the background. They attest to the presence of water vapor in the air.

Courtesy of NOAA

Figure 2.1 Powerful Hurricane Katrina takes aim on the central Gulf Coast on August 28, 2005.

Formally, a **cloud** is a vast collection of tiny water drops and/or ice crystals (assuming all or the upper portions of a cloud is sufficiently cold). Clouds form when water vapor (which is invisible) condenses onto tiny airborne particles called **condensation nuclei**, or, in the case of very cold clouds, when water vapor "deposits" onto **ice nuclei**, which are small airborne particles that encourage the production of ice crystals. The simultaneous existence of the three phases of water in the atmosphere sets the stage for the Bergeron-Findeisen process, an in-cloud, give-and-take between

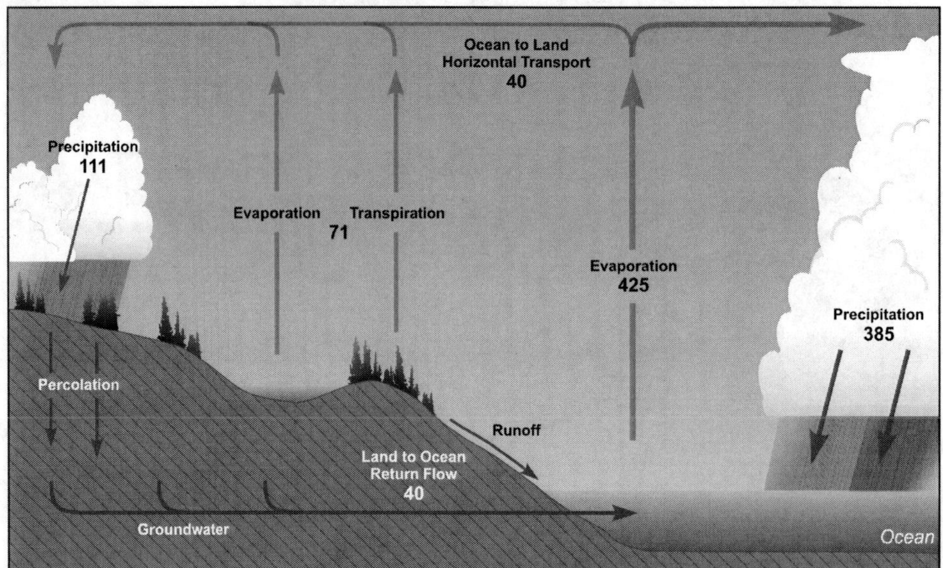

Figure 2.2 The hydrologic cycle. Numbers are expressed in units of thousands of cubic kilometers of water transferred per year. Note that, in terms of the volume of water transferred, evaporation and precipitation are the dominant processes.

water, ice, and water vapor that creates much of the precious precipitation that falls to earth.

In Figure 2.2, much of the water vapor that condensed to make cloud droplets (or deposited to make ice crystals) probably evaporated from the ocean. Meanwhile, the icebergs, having broken off or "calved" from a great glacier, may have eventually drifted out into the Atlantic, where they may have threatened the shipping industry before gradually melting away.

The tracing of the journeys of water, ice, and water vapor as they change phase and shuttle back and forth between the earth and the atmosphere is called the **hydrologic cycle**—a maze of possible paths that water molecules can take on their many varied voyages (see Figure 2.2). Let's go for a loop.

HYDROLOGIC CYCLE: TORTOISE AND THE HARE

The volume of water contained in earth's oceans is enormous, more than one billion cubic kilometers. That's a staggering figure indeed, so let's add some perspective. Think of a perfectly smooth, spherical planet equal in size to earth. If all of the water in earth's oceans were spread uniformly over this hypothetically smooth planet, the water would be about 2.5 km (1.7 mi) deep!

About 97 percent of all the water on or close to the earth's surface lies in the oceans. Of the remaining few percent, approximately three-fourths is locked in the ice caps of Greenland and Antarctica, about one-fourth can be traced to lakes and groundwater, and (drum roll, please) only about 1/3000 resides in the atmosphere. Of the atmosphere's seemingly paltry allotment of water, almost all of it is water vapor. To add further perspective: If all the atmospheric water vapor suddenly and completely condensed into water, and was then brought down to cover the earth's surface uniformly, the water would only be a little more than 2.5 cm (1 in) deep.

What little water vapor the atmosphere has at any given moment, it doesn't have for long. For water to evaporate into the air, move with the wind for a distance, ascend in a rising current of air, condense to help form a cloud droplet, and precipitate back to earth—only eleven days elapse, on average. Indeed, once in the atmosphere as vapor, water speeds through the hydrologic cycle like a hare. Returning to the surface, water may quickly recycle into the atmosphere or it may have a short layover as it makes its way through groundwater, lakes, or rivers (see Figure 2.3). In contrast, the oceans have quite a hold on their water—the average time any water molecule resides in the sea is about 2,800 years, a lengthy stay reminiscent of the pace of a tortoise.

In the hydrologic cycle, only relatively few water molecules get taken out of circulation for longer periods—those that fall as snow over the polar ice sheets can get buried in glaciers for tens of thousands of

Figure 2.3 This view from space on September 22, 2004, shows runoff from the flooding rains of Hurricane Ivan carrying silt into the Chesapeake and Delaware Bays from the Susquehanna and Delaware Rivers. Runoffs from rivers are part of the hydrologic cycle.

years. It is sobering to think about the "ill-fated" snow that fell over Greenland, became buried and turned to ice under the increasing pressure of more accumulating snow, flowed slowly seaward in a tortoise-like glacial river, calved into an iceberg and then toured the Davis Strait, drifted south in the Labrador Current, and then sank the mighty Titanic in 1912, taking perhaps hundreds of thousands of years to complete its sinister mission.

The hydrologic cycle is called a "cycle" for another good reason. Consider that mean annual precipitation, averaged over the globe, is about one meter (39 in). Because the amount of water that resides on or near the earth's surface is essentially constant over relatively short time scales, average global precipitation must be, for all practical purposes, balanced by average global evaporation. In other words, over the course of a year, water vapor that gets into the air must be nearly balanced by water that falls out of the air. Now that's a cycle!

Besides evaporation, there are two other ways to introduce water vapor into the hydrologic cycle: **transpiration**, the process by which plants release water vapor to the air, and **sublimation**, the process by which ice changes directly to water vapor (think of the decreasing size of ice cubes left in a freezer for a few weeks). But evaporation remains by far the atmosphere's most prodigious supplier of water vapor. Meteorologists generally define **humidity** as the amount of water vapor in the air at any instant (later in this chapter, you will learn that we differentiate between humidity and relative humidity). As you probably know through experience, humidity can vary greatly in time and space: oppressively high humidity along the Gulf Coast in summer to low, lip-chapping humidity in northern Minnesota during winter.

As we already mentioned, most of earth's water is held in detention in the ocean. Relatively speaking, only a few select water molecules get paroled to take a whirlwind leave into the free atmosphere at any given time. Over the next few sections, we will follow water on its temporary leave from evaporation to precipitation.

EVAPORATION: WATER MOLECULES CAN CHECK OUT, BUT THEY CAN NEVER LEAVE . . . WELL ALMOST NEVER

We've already used the term *evaporation,* appealing to the experience you already have with this process. For the record, **evaporation** is the process by which water molecules break their bonds with their neighbors and escape to the air as a gas (water vapor).

At very high altitudes, intense solar radiation can **dissociate** water vapor. By "dissociate," we mean that the Sun's energy breaks water molecules apart into constituent hydrogen and oxygen. Once freed from oxygen, hydrogen is sufficiently light to escape the earth's gravitational pull and move out into space. Losing hydrogen to space is tantamount to losing water because hydrogen is a building block for water molecules.

Scientists estimate that earth loses the equivalent of a small lake to space each year. Not to worry. The total loss of water over geologic time probably amounts to less than 0.2% of the water contained in all of the oceans, an infinitesimal loss at the time scales at which earth's present-day hydrologic cycle operates. Temperature, however, changes on much shorter time scales, and the hydrologic cycle responds accordingly.

Temperature: The Warden of Evaporation Rates

Water molecules are like captives in minimum security detention—the bonds that bind them to the liquid phase are relatively lax. Thus, water molecules can get time off for kinetic behavior whenever their molecular vibrations break these bonds, allowing them to take a furlough in the free atmosphere in the form of water vapor. As we just mentioned, less energetic molecules imprisoned in the rigid lattice of ice—they're doing "hard time"—also can be paroled to the vapor state.

How are these liquid bonds broken? Every now and then, a water molecule gets enough of a boost in energy from its neighbors that it can overcome their attraction and escape into the air above the water. Think of water molecules in a puddle of water as a crowded dance floor with couples rockin' to a fast song. Given the fast tempo, it's inevitable that dancers bump into each other, and, occasionally, a dancer gets knocked off the dance floor. And so it is with water molecules that evaporate.

Like air molecules, water molecules oscillate faster as the water temperature increases. In turn, this boost in kinetic energy allows more water molecules to break free from their liquid bonds. In terms of our dance metaphor, the beat quickens and couples bump into each other more frequently (and more "energetically"). Thus, the rate of evaporation quickens as water temperatures increase.

The bottom line here is that water temperature is a primary controller of the evaporation rate, which is the number of water molecules evaporating from a given area of water over a specified time. Qualitatively, a puddle of water evaporating from a street once the sun returns after a brief summer shower is an example of a relatively high evaporation rate. In contrast, water sitting in a vase of flowers on the kitchen table evaporates at a slower rate.

Whatever its rate, evaporation is a cooling process. That's because water molecules with the greatest kinetic energy are more likely to wriggle free and break their molecular bonds. The loss of these highly energetic molecules lowers the average kinetic energy of the water, which, in turn, translates to a lower water temperature. As an apprentice weather forecaster, you will need to be concerned about the effects of evaporation on air temperatures. In fact, some of the most difficult temperature forecasts arise when precipitation is slated to occur.

You may have noticed that surface air temperatures often decrease once it starts to rain. That's because some of the smallest raindrops evaporate on descent toward the ground. The heat energy required for small raindrops to evaporate is extracted from the air surrounding the drops. As a result, the air usually cools when it rains. To see this **evaporational cooling** in action, consider Figure 2.4, a "before-rain" and "during-rain" example of the temperature and dew point profile of the atmosphere between the ground and the base of a precipitating cloud. In Figure 2.4a ("before" rain begins), the temperature and dew point are far apart below the cloud base. Figure 2.4b shows the situation once rain reaches the ground. The temperature between the cloud base and the ground decreases in response to evaporational cooling, while the dew point increases as some raindrops evaporate before reaching the ground.

All weather forecasters worth their salt weigh the effects of evaporational cooling on predicted air temperatures when they expect precipitation to fall. If forecasters anticipate high evaporation rates, they know that the effects on temperature can be dramatic. When precipitation is underway during winter, for example, relatively high rates of evaporation at altitudes near 1500 m (about 5000 ft) can sometimes cool the air enough to tip the scales toward frozen precipitation instead of rain.

It's just not humanly possible to measure evaporation rates by simply counting the number of water molecules escaping to the air over any period of time. But we can infer evaporation rates by calculating the rate that heat energy is lost from water with a specified surface area. Scientists refer to this rate as the flux of heat energy, or simply **heat flux**. The standard units

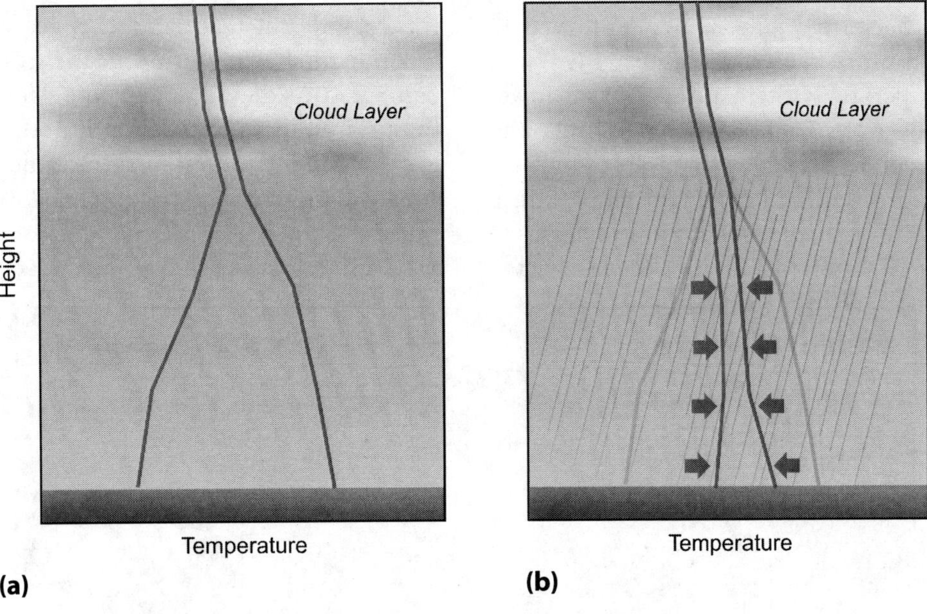

Figure 2.4 Sample temperature (right) and dew point (left) profiles of the atmosphere between the ground and the base of a cloud (a) before rain begins; and (b) after some rain has reached the ground.

of heat flux are watts per square meter (W/m^2). Watts correspond to a flow of energy per second, so, in the context of evaporation rates, watts per square meter represent the loss of heat energy per second from water (or wet ground) that has an area of one square meter.

Climatologists sometimes use average heat flux as a proxy (substitute) for evaporation rates when they classify the regional climates of the world. This "stand-in" for evaporation rates is called the **potential evaporation**. Figure 2.5a shows the annual average of potential evaporation (in W/m^2) over the land masses of the earth. Think of potential evaporation as the evaporation rate from wet ground that has an unlimited water supply (in other words, it has the same wetness over time). Of course, such an assumption is not realistic, but it affords climatologists a way to quantify differences in climates across the globe.

For example, note that the highest evaporation rates occur over the subtropical deserts (the Sahara in northern Africa, for example). Not surprisingly, this is one of the hottest regions of the world, as Figure 2.5b shows. And the lowest potential evaporation, in general, occurs over polar regions, where average temperature is lowest. So there clearly is a firm relationship between potential evaporation and temperature. But note that there are also places where the correlation isn't as iron-clad, such as along the equator in Africa, where evaporation rates are noticeably lower despite average temperatures that remain relatively high. What's up with that?

Conclusion: There must be other controllers of evaporation rates besides temperature. Let's investigate.

Water Vapor and Temperature: The Keys to Solving the Puzzle of Potential Evaporation in Africa

Our assertion that the potential evaporation in the Sahara is high might have caught you off guard simply because there isn't much water in the Sahara (see Figure 2.6). Not surprisingly, there is little rain over much of this vast desert that covers North Africa (see Figure 2.7). Without much water to evaporate, concentrations of atmospheric water vapor are relatively low, although from time to time the wind transports a little water vapor over the Sahara from other regions. Despite the lack of water, there is a high *potential* for evaporation in a hot and dry climate.

Now let's shift south from the Sahara to Africa's wet equatorial region. Much of the great rain forests in the Congo River Basin coincide with the equatorial swath of high precipitation rates shown in Figure 2.7. Until human intervention during the twentieth century, these great forests once stretched pretty much unbroken across much of equatorial Africa (see Figure 2.8).

Now look back to Figure 2.5b. Notice that, despite the location of these forests near the equator, average temperatures there are somewhat lower than readings over the Sahara. Indeed, clouds and rain help to moderate daytime temperatures in these equatorial rain forests. And these lower temperatures account, in part, for the reduced evaporation rates in this region. But there's another reason for relatively low potential evaporation in the Congo River Basin compared to the Sahara: There's more water vapor in the air in these tropical rainforests. But why would greater concentrations of atmospheric water vapor over wet equatorial Africa mean lower evaporation rates?

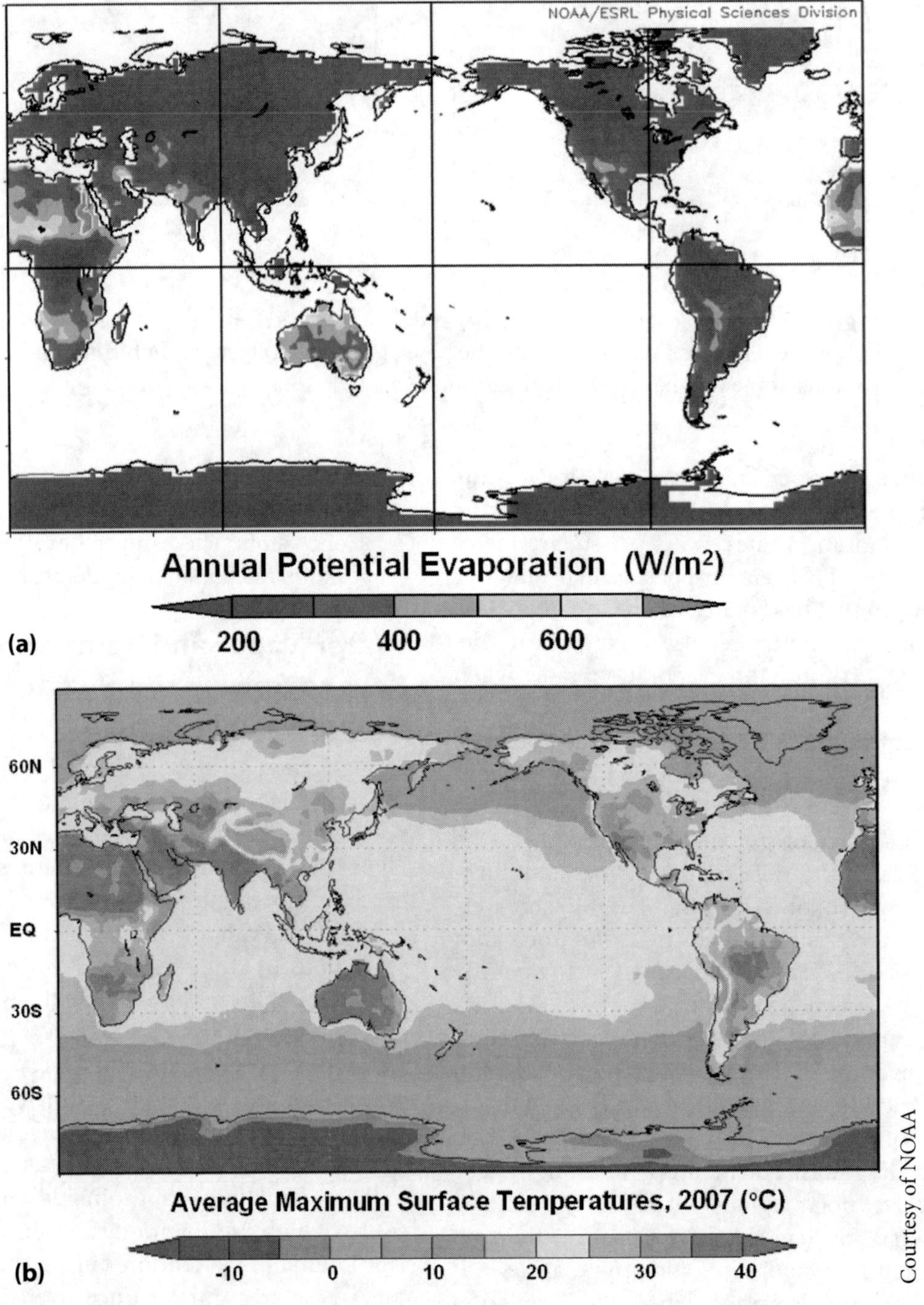

Figure 2.5 (a) The annual average of potential evaporation for the land masses of the earth, in W/m^2 (courtesy of NOAA); (b) Average maximum temperatures in 2007, in °C.

Shutterstock © Oleg Znamenskiy

Figure 2.6 Sahara Desert.

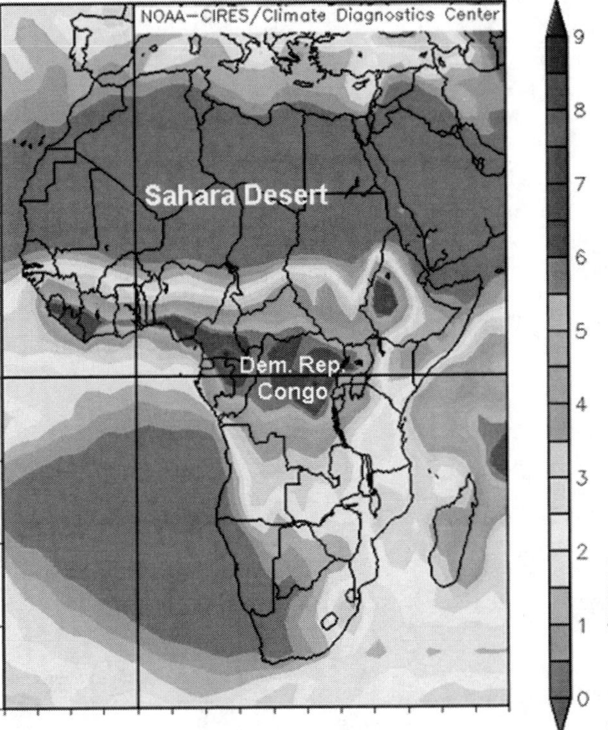

Courtesy of NOAA

Figure 2.7 Average precipitation rates across the African continent, expressed in mm/day (25 mm is approximately one inch). Note that rainfall rates over the Sahara are close to zero.

Shutterstock © Larsek

Figure 2.8 Light piercing forest.

Courtesy of the Hurricane Research Division,

Figure 2.9 A photograph inside the eye of Hurricane Katrina during aircraft reconnaissance in late August 2005.

Net Evaporation: Evaporation Edges Condensation

Formally, **condensation** is the process by which water vapor returns to the liquid state (you could say it's the "reverse" of evaporation). Even so, it turns out that evaporation and condensation usually take place at the same time. Figure 2.9 is a photograph taken by aircraft reconnaissance from inside the eye of Hurricane Katrina in August 2005. Note the relatively low overcast in the eye of Hurricane Katrina (yes, the eye of a hurricane can be rather cloudy at times). Here, condensation rates exceeded evaporation rates, so there was **net condensation**. In other words, clouds formed. Above this layer of clouds inside the eye, the sky was clear. Indeed, in this clear part of the eye, net evaporation ruled because evaporation rates exceeded condensation rates.

It's often said that a picture is worth a thousand words. But, in the case of Hurricane Katrina's eye, it's not obvious that both evaporation and condensation were in progress at the same time. Let's conduct a simple experiment to satisfy our scientific curiosity.

Consider a closed container like the one shown in Figure 2.10a. Although there are no such containers suspended in the real atmosphere, we'll use this idealized example to make a point. We'll assume that initially, the closed system contains only dry air (no water vapor). But because we plan to add some water to the container, we'll need to make provisions for keeping track of it.

For sake of argument, let's suppose that we are able to count water molecules as they move back and forth between the liquid and vapor states. Because vapor molecules will bounce off the walls of the container, each will exert a pressure; collectively, the pressure they exert is called, appropriately enough, **vapor pressure**. To understand this concept, we first need to briefly introduce you to the concept of air pressure. We've already established that all air molecules

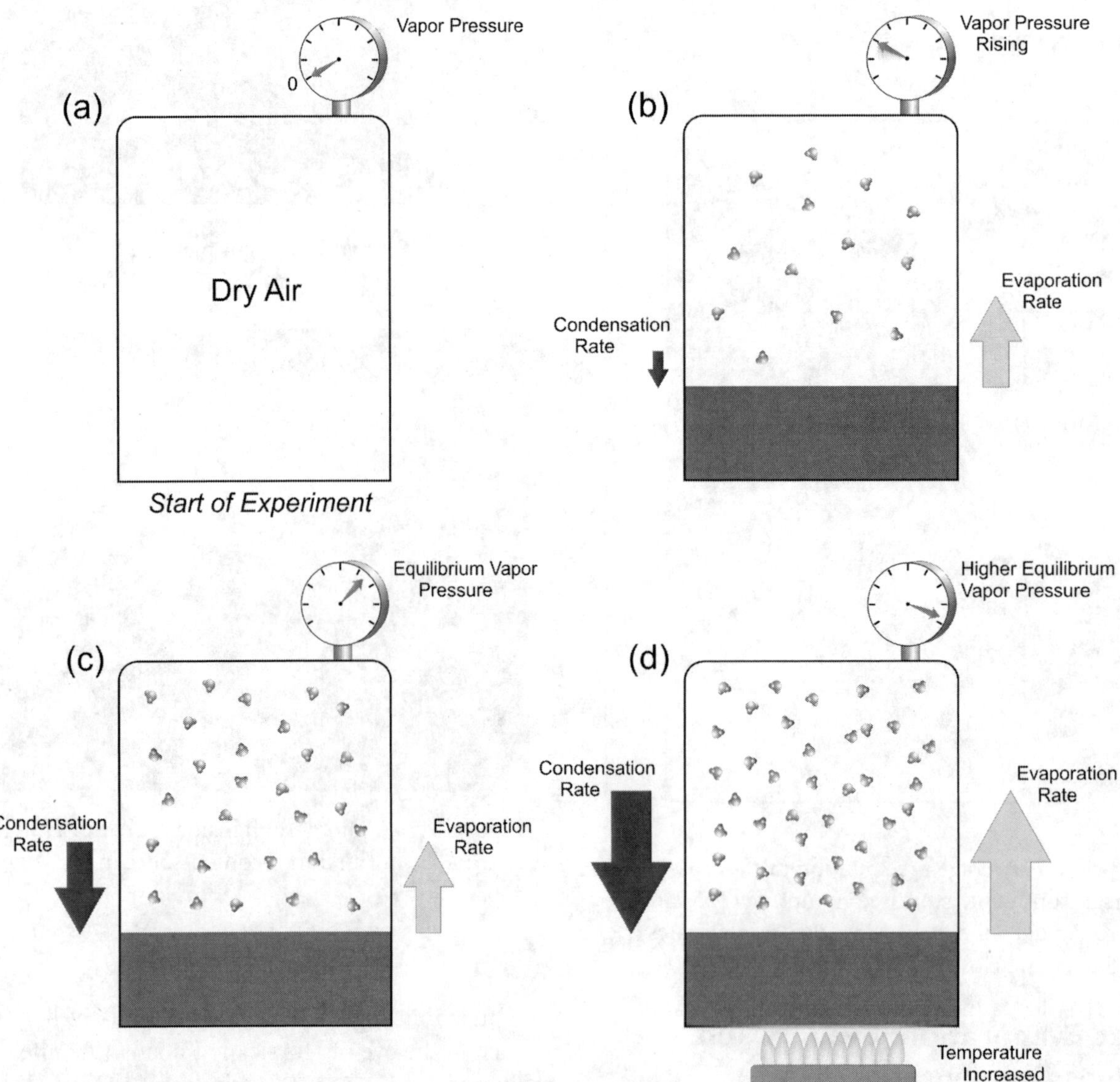

Figure 2.10 At the start of the experiment, with just dry air inside the container, the vapor pressure meter reads zero; (b) When water is poured into the container, evaporation dominates condensation at first, and the vapor pressure of the air increases; (c) Eventually, an equilibrium is reached when condensation and evaporation are equal; at this equilibrium, we say the air is saturated; (d) If the temperature of the water is increased, a new equilibrium state is achieved with greater rates of evaporation and condensation, and thus a greater equilibrium vapor pressure

(be they oxygen, nitrogen, argon, water vapor, and so on) have kinetic energy. Because air molecules are in perpetual motion, they collectively exert a force when they strike objects. Air pressure is simply the force exerted per unit area on an object. And vapor pressure is the part of the total air pressure exerted by water vapor.

Now let's add water at a temperature of, say 60°F (16°C), to the container (see Figure 2.10b). Within a short time, some water molecules break their bonds with their neighbors and evaporate. As they do, these molecules pass through the water-air interface, a very thin partition between the two mediums that theoretically has the properties of both water and air. In this interface, we hypothetically monitor evaporation rates by counting molecules on their way from the liquid to gaseous state. We also monitor condensation rates, as a few vapor molecules inevitably also reenter the interface on their way back to the liquid phase. Initially, the evaporation rate exceeds the condensation rate (there is net evaporation), and the vapor pressure increases.

But as the number of water vapor molecules in the air increases, the chances that vapor molecules will recross the water-air interface and condense increases. Eventually, an equilibrium between rates of evaporation and condensation will be established (see Figure 2.10c). We define the **equilibrium vapor pressure** to be the vapor pressure associated with this balanced state. Moreover, we refer to this balanced state, when the evaporation rate equals the rate of condensation, as **saturation** (the equilibrium vapor pressure is sometimes referred to as the saturation vapor pressure).

When we increase the water temperature to, say, 80°F (27°C), things change. At this higher temperature, water molecules have greater kinetic energy and thus are more likely to easily break their bonds with their neighbors and evaporate. So, in quick fashion, the evaporation rate increases (and, in turn, so does the vapor pressure). In response to increasing water vapor, the comeback-kid condensation rate rises to the task, and the frequency of water vapor molecules entering the water-air interface increases. Eventually, there's a new balance between evaporation and condensation rates, only this time at a higher equilibrium vapor pressure (Figure 2.10d).

Carrying out the experiment at a myriad of different temperatures yields the curve in Figure 2.11, which shows the equilibrium vapor pressure as a function of temperature. For any given temperature, points that lie below the curve have vapor pressures that fall short of equilibrium. In other words, below the curve, the rate of condensation can't match evaporation—there is net evaporation. In contrast, points that lie above the curve have vapor pressures that exceed equilibrium—there is net condensation and, ladies and gentlemen, a cloud is born!

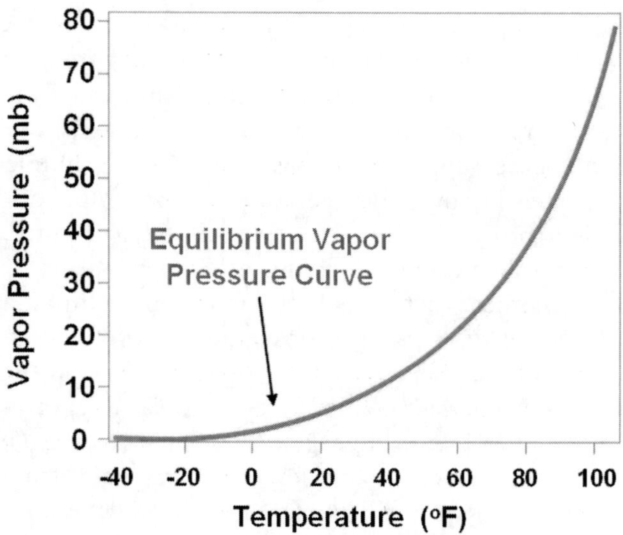

Figure 2.11 The equilibrium vapor pressure (the vapor pressure when the rate of condensation equals the rate of evaporation) increases as water temperature increases. This curve, called the equilibrium vapor pressure curve, formally quantifies the relationship between temperature and equilibrium vapor pressure.

Clearly, water temperature is a primary player in determining evaporation rates. Thus, the water vapor content of the air over and near warm bodies of water such as the Gulf of Mexico is, on average, relatively high. On the other hand, vapor pressures over and near relatively cool bodies of water, such as the offshore waters of the Pacific Northwest, are low, on average.

But as our experiment shows, the amount of water vapor already in the air also matters because some water vapor condenses into water and essentially slows down the evaporation rate. Now the question becomes: How do meteorologists gauge the degree to which condensation will affect the overall evaporation rate?

Vapor Pressure Gradient: A Proxy for the Net Evaporation Rate

Right after we first introduced water into the experiment with the closed container, evaporation had the upper hand (big time) because there was no water vapor in the air that could condense into water and offset evaporation. Had there initially been water vapor in the air, equilibrium would have been reached sooner and, consequently, the amount of water lost from its initial supply would have been less. Thus, when the air is already humid, net evaporation is reduced. Your experience supports this observation: On a humid summer day, overall evaporation of sweat from your skin (a process that helps to cool your body) is limited. As a result, most people feel uncomfortably warm.

Another way to look at this discussion is through the eye of the **vapor pressure gradient**, which is the difference in vapor pressure between the air and the water-air interface. When there's little water vapor in the air, the vapor pressure gradient is large because the vapor pressure of the air is low and the vapor pressure of the moist air-water interface is high. So net evaporation is large. In contrast, when the air is humid, the vapor pressure gradient is small because the vapor pressure of the air is high and the vapor pressure of the air-water interface is also high. So net evaporation is small.

Wind also affects the vapor pressure gradient. If wind blows over the water (imagine screen walls in the closed-container experiment), it would whisk water vapor away, keeping the vapor pressure of the air relatively low. Thus, the vapor pressure gradient would remain relatively large, setting the stage for large net evaporation. This observation is also consistent with your experience: Wet swimsuits hung outside typically dry more quickly when the wind blows, and the faster the wind, the faster the clothes dry.

We began this discussion intending to determine why evaporation rates in equatorial Africa were noticeably lower than those in the Sahara Desert. Yes, temperature is a primary factor. But so are vapor pressure gradients. Over the Sahara, vapor pressure gradients are typically high, so evaporation can proceed like gangbusters (where there is water, of course). Over equatorial Africa, vapor pressure gradients are typically smaller, owing to the larger concentrations of water vapor in the air.

Now that you have a sense of what makes evaporation and condensation tick, let's look at the next intermediate step in the hydrologic cycle—clouds.

NET CONDENSATION: A CLOUD IS BORN

At any given moment, nearly half of the earth is covered by clouds. Some are short-lived, evaporating in seconds, like the fleeting cloud from your breath on a cold winter's day. Others are long-lived—the low,

Shutterstock © Condor 36

Figure 2.12 A towering cumulonimbus cloud (background) drifts over Swifts Creek in Victoria, Australia. Note the rising, turbulent turrets associated with developing cumulus clouds in the foreground (courtesy of Henry Firus, Flagstaffotos, http://www.flagstaffotos.com.au/gallery2/main.php).

precipitation-barren clouds left in the wake of deep low-pressure systems of late autumn and winter can last for a week or more. In terms of the recycling mission of the hydrologic cycle, both of these cloud types fail, dissipating without ever having produced a drop of precipitation. Other clouds, such as tall, regal cumulonimbus (see Figure 2.12), can produce flooding summer rains in a matter of tens of minutes. Such prodigious rainmakers are employees held in high esteem by the administration of the hydrologic cycle.

Clouds and Relative Humidity: There's Nothing Magical about 100%

One winter day a few years ago, a hot-water pipe burst above the second floor of the meteorology building at Penn State University. After flooding several rooms, a fog formed above the standing warm water. One of the authors quickly snapped a picture (see Figure 2.13) that he knew would illustrate the foggy consequences of high evaporation rates (let's face it, folks, some meteorologists are simply "weather weenies"—they eat, sleep, and drink the science).

Figure 2.13 Fog forms in a classroom at Penn State University after a hot-water pipe burst during the winter of 2001.

This indoor flood of warm water affords us an opportunity to introduce the concept of relative humidity (you've probably already heard this term many times). To define it, let's return to the experiment we conducted in the closed container. **Relative humidity** is the ratio of the actual vapor pressure and the equilibrium vapor pressure (at the observed temperature), converted to a percent; in other words, it's the former divided by the latter, times 100%. If we apply this definition to the state of saturation in the closed container, the relative humidity is 100%. For the record, the relative humidity in the foggy, flooded classroom was 100% as well.

There's one important stipulation underlying this definition of relative humidity that sometimes gets overlooked. This definition applies to the air space above a *flat* surface of *pure* water. Why do we make

WEATHER FOLKLORE AND COMMENTARY

Human Hair and Relative Humidity

In the popular vernacular of the 1990s, a humid, damp day is a "bad-hair day." Indeed, human hair is very sensitive to changes in atmospheric moisture. When humidity rises, for example, human hair (as well as many other organic substances such as wood) absorbs a proportional amount of moisture and its length increases. For people with curly hair, the extra length means that there will be extra curl. In the 1970s, such hair was referred to as the "frizzies." Added length from increasing moisture can also cause hair to "lose its body" and look limp.

There is an instrument that measures relative humidity by taking advantage of hair's response to changes in atmospheric moisture. It is the hair hygrometer and its design is relatively simple (**hygrometer** is the general term for an instrument that measures the amount of moisture in the air). A bundle of hair is attached mechanically to a pointer. As relative humidity ebbs and flows, hair length decreases and increases, causing the pointer to pivot over an indicator calibrated between 0% and 100% (see Figure 2.14). Typically, hair length varies 2 to 3% as relative humidity varies from 0% to 100%.

Blond is the color of choice because it responds more quickly to changes in relative humidity. Even so, one of the major drawbacks of hair hygrometers is that they do not respond quickly enough,

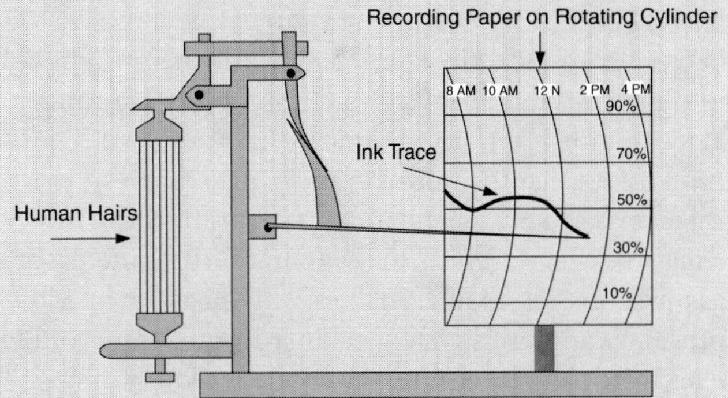

Figure 2.14 A hair hygrometer. As relative humidity changes, the strands of hair contract and expand in length. Using a series of levers, the changes in hair length are amplified so that changes in relative humidity move the pen and trace a time series.

particularly at low temperatures. Hair hygrometers have other shortcomings, too. They are not as accurate as other types of hygrometers such as hygristors (used in radiosondes) which depend on changes in electrical resistance. Plus, hair hygrometers are in constant need of calibration.

So if you desire carefree measurements of relative humidity and really don't want to spend money on a more sophisticated instrument, relax. The limpness of your own hair is a reliable indicator of high relative humidity and the possible arrival of rain.

these distinctions? If the truth be told, cloud droplets are neither flat nor pure. As a result, it is actually possible to have relative humidities in the atmosphere that exceed 100%. In fact, the relative humidity inside a cloud is, on average, a few tenths of a percent above 100%! So the common reference that clouds form when the relative humidity reaches 100% (in other words, the air reaches saturation) is generally not true in the strictest sense. What's up with all of this?

To answer this question, you'll need a little background regarding the size of atmospheric particles. Cloud droplets are spherical with typical diameters on the order of 10 μm (recall that 1 μm = 0.000001 m). Figure 2.15 helps to put this size in perspective. The average diameter of the finest drizzle or the tiny drops that make up fog is about 100 μm. Small raindrops are about 1000 μm in diameter, while large raindrops may reach 5000 μm.

Now let's consider the fate of the tiniest, embryonic cloud droplets, much smaller than even those shown in Figure 2.15. If no other processes were at work except for evaporation and condensation, the relative humidity of their environment would have to be very high (actually about 300%) for them to grow into mature cloud droplets and not rapidly evaporate. Why would the relative humidity have to be so high? It turns out that the rate of evaporation from a spherical drop is much higher than the evaporation rate from a flat surface. Moreover, the evaporation rate increases as the drops get smaller. So there would have to be a lot of water vapor, relatively speaking, around embryonic cloud droplets to ensure net condensation (which is the situation necessary for cloud droplets to grow).

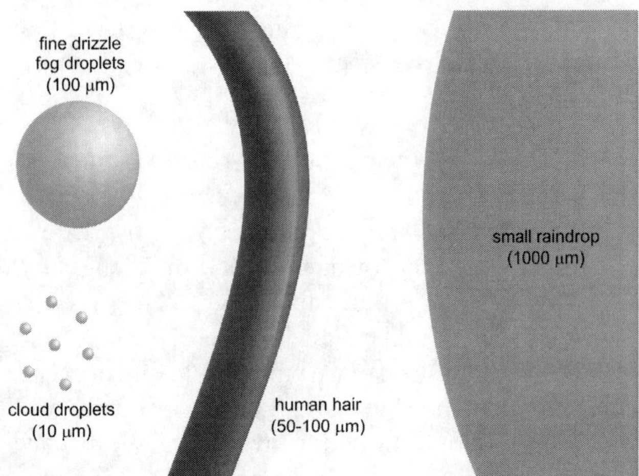

Figure 2.15 The relative sizes of cloud droplets, drizzle and fog droplets, and small raindrops, compared to the diameter of a typical human hair.

However, relative humidities on the order of 300% simply do not exist in the real atmosphere. Fortunately for life on earth (which ultimately depends on the precipitation produced by clouds), such high relative humidities aren't necessary. That's because the natural presence of condensation nuclei, those microscopic particles of dust and dirt onto which water vapor readily condenses, allows net condensation to occur at much less inflated values of relative humidity. Many of these condensation nuclei are **hygroscopic**, which means that they tend to attract water vapor (salt is hygroscopic, for example). As a result of this propensity for water vapor, hygroscopic condensation nuclei generally reduce the relative humidity required for clouds to form to just a few tenths above 100%.

That's not to say that net condensation doesn't occur at lower relative humidities. For example, when relative humidity in the lower troposphere exceeds 70% or so, fine particles of soil, smoke, sea salt, and pollution begin to swell by net condensation, forming **wet haze** (see Figure 2.16). Wet haze, a hallmark of summertime in the eastern United States, reduces visibility and gives the sky a milky-white appearance. Although some people associate hazy skies with the good times of summer, the appearance of haze often translates to poor air quality, which poses a risk to public health.

We're pretty sure that the notion of relative humidity exceeding 100% inside a cloud is not very intuitive for you. So here's a more straightforward approach: For a cloud to form, the rate of condensation must simply exceed the rate of evaporation (or, more succinctly, there must be net condensation). Recall that the relative humidity equals 100% at saturation, when the rate of evaporation equals the rate of condensation. Thus, when net condensation occurs, the relative humidity must be slightly greater than 100%.

It's now time to apply what you've learned to the real atmosphere.

A Tried-and-True Recipe for Clouds: A Pinch (of Nuclei), a Dash (of Vapor), Then Chill

So, how does net condensation occur in the atmosphere? The most common way to achieve net condensation is to cool the air.

As air temperature decreases, water vapor molecules slow down. As they become increasingly sluggish, more and more of them huddle closer to condensation nuclei

(a)

(b)

Figure 2.16 (a) The view of the mountains surrounding State College, PA, is sullied as humid southwesterly winds imported pollution from the Ohio Valley, setting the stage for wet haze to develop; (b) The same view on a day with a fresh air mass from Canada.

(of course, the same is true of other air molecules, such as oxygen and nitrogen, but when it comes to cloud formation, we don't care about them). Once there's a "quorum" of water vapor molecules, the stage is set for net condensation. It's actually pretty straightforward.

Along these lines, some television weathercasters wrongly suggest that the reason clouds form as air cools is that there's "not enough room for water vapor" in cold air or that "cold air can't hold water vapor." The implications are that the air (which is predominantly composed of nitrogen and oxygen) takes some sort of active role in determining how much water vapor can occupy any given space. That's simply not true. Cold air is not like a hotel that hangs out a "No Vacancy" sign once all the rooms for water vapor are filled. To the contrary, net condensation occurs when cooling causes a sufficient number of sluggish water vapor molecules to huddle close around condensation nuclei. This may sound like an argument over semantics, but the idea that there is "limited space" in the air is simply unscientific.

When concentrations of water vapor are relatively small, cooling must be relatively substantial to reach net condensation (especially when the air is warm and water vapor molecules are very energetic). On the other hand, when concentrations of water vapor are high, less cooling is needed to achieve net condensation.

Now the question becomes: What are the mechanisms for cooling the air?

Lifting the Air: Caution! Air Molecules at Work

When parcels of air rise, they expand and cool (see Figure 2.17). To understand this basic tenet of meteorology, we first observe that air pressure is greatest near the earth's surface. Let's explore this idea.

Figure 2.18 shows a climber viewing the summit of Mount Everest and nearby Mount Nuptse At an elevation of 29,035 ft (8849 m), the amount of available oxygen can barely support life. Not surprisingly, the overall density of air (the number of air molecules per unit volume) at this altitude is low, providing evidence that air density decreases with increasing height. Air pressure follows suit, mirroring the vertical profile of air density; in a nutshell, fewer air molecules in a

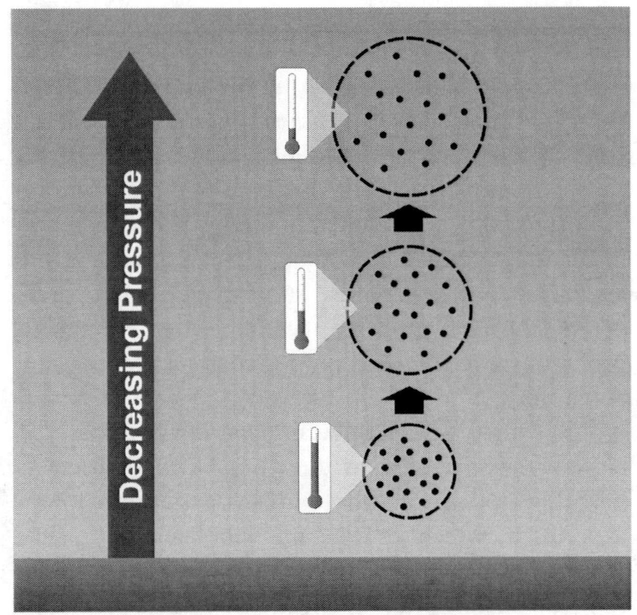

Figure 2.17 When a parcel of air rises, it expands as it moves through air of lower pressure. As the parcel expands, it cools.

Shutterstock © Daniel Prudek

Figure 2.18 View of Everest and Nuptse

given volume translates to lower air pressure. So air pressure decreases with increasing altitude. Now hold this thought for a moment.

Let's look more carefully at an air parcel as it rises. Initially at rest near the ground, the air parcel is in balance with its environment—the air pressure inside the parcel equals the air pressure outside the parcel. As the parcel rises, it moves through air that has a lower pressure (recall the thought we just asked you to hold onto). Once the parcel starts to rise, the balance in air pressure is lost because the pressure inside our idealized parcel is greater than the pressure outside the parcel. To try to achieve a new balance, air molecules inside the parcel push out the sides—in other words, the parcel expands. In pushing out the sides of the parcel, air molecules lose some of their kinetic energy (the work required to push out the sides of the parcel comes at an expense—there are no free passes in the atmosphere). As a result, the temperature decreases inside the parcel. This cooling proceeds as long as the air parcel continues to rise and expand. If the parcel contains water vapor and it is lifted high enough to produce sufficient cooling, net condensation occurs and a cloud is born.

Of course, we can't ride along on a rising parcel of air to witness net condensation, but we can do the best next thing—simulate what happens. So it's time for an experiment, which we'll document in Figure 2.19. Let's start with a glass bottle with a little water on the bottom (upper-left photograph). A rubber stopper seals the top of the bottle, although plastic tubing fastened to the center of the stopper allows us to blow air into or suck air out of the bottle.

Like any good chef who follows a recipe, one of the authors added some condensation nuclei by sucking air out of the bottle through the plastic tubing and then pinching off the tube to prevent air from immediately rushing back in (upper-right photograph). Then he blew out a match (which he lit beforehand), holding the extinguished match close to the open end of the plastic tubing. Then he quickly released his pinch on the tube. Because the air pressure inside the glass container was now less than the air pressure in the room (an imbalance), air rushed into the glass bottle to regain balance. In the process, particles of combustion were drawn into the bottle.

Simply adding condensation nuclei was not enough to make a cloud because the rate of condensation on these newly introduced suspended particles obviously did not exceed the rate of evaporation. Somehow, in order to make a cloud, he had to tip the scales toward a state of net condensation.

Next, the author blew hard into the tube (lower left photograph), thereby increasing the air pressure (he added more air molecules). Then he pinched off the plastic tubing. Once he released his pinch, air rushed out of the tubing like air escaping from a bicycle tire that's been punctured. In the process, the escaping air expanded. As you just learned, air cools when it expands. As a result, the rate of evaporation, which strongly depends on temperature, decreased dramatically.

How about the rate of condensation? Though some water vapor was lost as air rushed out of the bottle, some water vapor was also added from the author's hot, moist breath. Nonetheless, the rate of condensation also likely decreased. But the real loser was the rate of evaporation, which is tied so strongly to temperature. The now-lowered temperature of the air inside the bottle (from expansion) meant that the rate of condensation was able to exceed the markedly reduced rate of evaporation. Translation: There was net condensation, and a cloud was born (lower-right photograph).

To drive home our point about the consequences of cooling the air by expansion, carefully observe a bottle of soda whenever you open it. The air in the neck of the bottle above the soda, which has a greater air pressure than the air outside the bottle, rapidly expands when you remove the cap (listen for the "whoosh"), cooling the air and paving the way for a fleeting cloud to form in the neck of the bottle.

We confess that the cloud that forms in the neck of a soda bottle is a bit different than the one we made in our experiment because there aren't any condensation

Figure 2.19 Like a genie, one of the authors makes a cloud in a bottle. The bottle has a layer of water in the bottom, and condensation nuclei are added in the upper right photograph. The air is cooled (bottom left), and a cloud forms (bottom right).

nuclei in the air above the soda. But, after you open the soda bottle, the cooling of the expanding air is so dramatic that water vapor molecules become really sluggish. By chance, sluggish water vapor molecules congregate and initiate net condensation without the benefit of condensation nuclei. Such clouds do not form in the atmosphere because there are always foreign particles suspended in the air.

Now that we've convinced you that air cooling by expansion during ascent can lead to clouds, let's briefly discuss a few common lifting mechanisms. Low-pressure systems and their attendant fronts regularly lift the air to produce clouds and precipitation (there's more to come on lows, fronts, and lifting throughout the book). Convection is a form of lift, with uneven heating of the ground caused by differences in surface covering (for example) leading to the positive buoyancy of some air parcels (see Figure 2.20). And mountains, which act as barriers to the wind, are "heavy" lifters, forcing air moving horizontally to abruptly ascend the sloping terrain.

Formally, the forced lifting of air by the terrain is called **orographic lifting.** In mountainous areas, this process is the dominant cause of precipitation. In fact, some of the snowiest and rainiest places in the world are located on the **windward** side of mountains—the side that faces into the prevailing winds. The opposite side of the mountain is known as the **leeward** (or lee) side. Originally, windward and leeward were nautical terms, as sailors referred (and still refer) to the side of the sail catching the wind as the windward side and the side sheltered from the wind as the lee side (see Figure 2.21).

Given prevailing winds from the west, it is possible to prediict the annual precipitation patterns in Califronia based on the state's topographic map as shown in Figure 2.22. For the record, the prevailing winds blow from the west over California. Note how, in general, precipitation amounts increase as the terrain slopes

Courtesy of National Weather Service, Huntsville, AL

Figure 2.20 Clouds formed over the Tennessee Valley as air parcels rose over heated ground. Note the lack of clouds over cooler rivers.

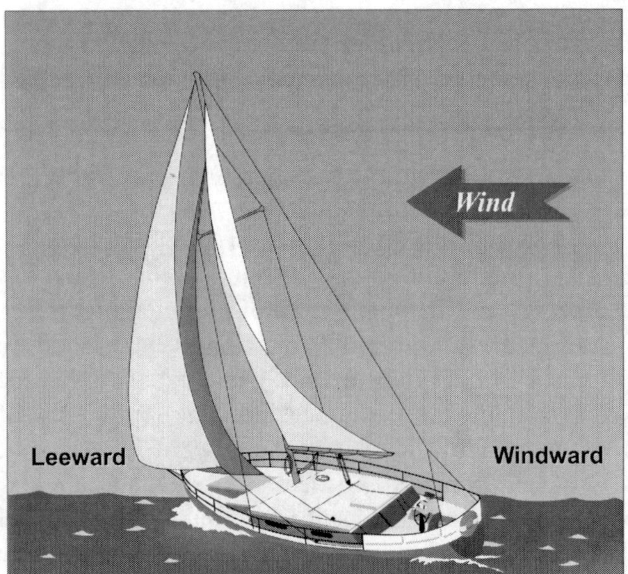

Figure 2.21 The windward side of a sail is the side that catches the wind. The lee (or leeward) side is sheltered from the wind.

upward and decrease as the terrain slopes downward. In other words, relatively heavy precipitation generally falls at the highest elevations or where the terrain slopes upward. The Central Valley of California, where air tends to downslope off the mountains to the west, is a relative minimum in precipitation. When a precipitation minimum occurs on the lee side of a mountain range, the zone is called a **rain shadow**. To the east of the Central Valley, precipitation increases again as the prevailing westerly wind flow encounters the Sierra Nevada Mountains. There's an indication that extreme eastern California is the gateway to the vast rain shadow that is the Great Basin, which lies to the east of the Sierras.

There are a couple other ways to produce clouds without forcing the air to rise. Let's investigate.

Clouds without Lifting: Special Recipes

On a clear night with light winds, the ground can impart a big chill to the overlying layer of air (primarily by conduction). When the nocturnal chill is spread throughout a sufficiently deep layer by light winds (only a few miles per hour), net condensation can occur and **ground fog** forms by dawn. A typical ground fog (sometimes called **valley fog**) is shown in Figure 2.23. However, to get you thinking about this process, consider that the fog in the room shown

Figure 2.22

Figure 2.23 Valley with fog.

Figure 2.24 Fog formed over lake.

in Figure 2.13 dissipated after the window had been opened for several minutes.

Fog can also form over lakes and streams, particularly during early autumn, when water is still relatively warm and nights are chilly (for an example, see Figure 2.24). Given that the water in the lake was warmer than the overlying autumnal air, a completely different mechanism must have caused this **steam fog** to form. Indeed, steam fog is a type of **mixing cloud**. As its name suggests, a mixing cloud forms when warm, moist air mixes with cooler drier air. In the case of Figure 2.24, the mixing occurred between warm, moist air in the water-air interface over the lake and cooler, drier air above.

The most common example of a mixing cloud is the fleeting cloud that forms from the exhalation of your breath on a cold winter's day. Conditions must be optimal because, on other days or indoors, you won't see "your breath." To gain insight, we must refer to the equilibrium vapor pressure curve in Figure 2.25, which is sort of an operator's manual for determining whether a cloud will form or not.

In Figure 2.25a, let point A represent the temperature and vapor pressure of your breath (approximately body temperature and very moist) while point B represents the temperature and vapor pressure of the air on a typical winter day (cold and very close to, or at, equilibrium). The points on the line connecting A and B represent all possible states that might result from the mixing process. Note that all the points lie above the curve within the jurisdiction of net condensation. Voila! You see your breath as a cloud. As another example, consider Figure 2.25b, where point A still represents your breath but point C represents the conditions inside your house (taken to be 70°F (21°C) and not even close to saturation). Now note that all points on the line connecting A and C lie below the curve, where net evaporation dominates. Sorry, you won't see your breath.

Like your breath on a cold day, the hot, moist exhaust from jet aircraft mixes with cold, relatively dry air, forming mixing clouds called **contrails** (short for *con*densation *trails*). In Figure 2.26, note the clear gaps between the jet engines and the contrails, indicating the zone where the mixing occurred. Sometimes, contrails will rapidly evaporate when the air is very dry. At other times, they spread out horizontally into a long ribbon of high, wispy clouds. Ultimately, the life span of a contrail depends on the relative humidity of the air at cruising altitudes. If the air is close to saturation, for example, the contrail may persist for hours (although winds may spread it out or break it up). Around busy airline hubs like Atlanta, GA, long-lived

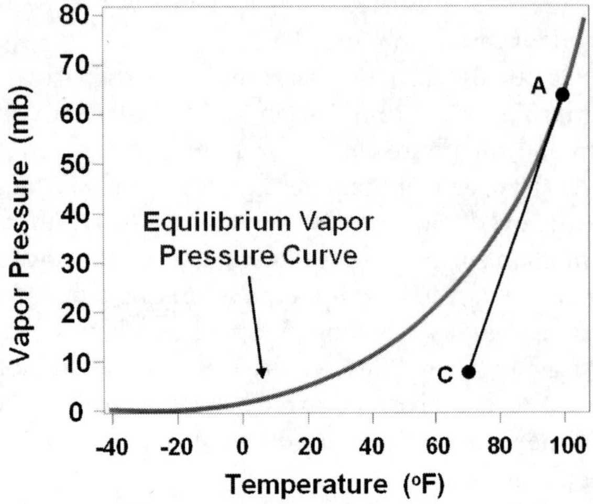

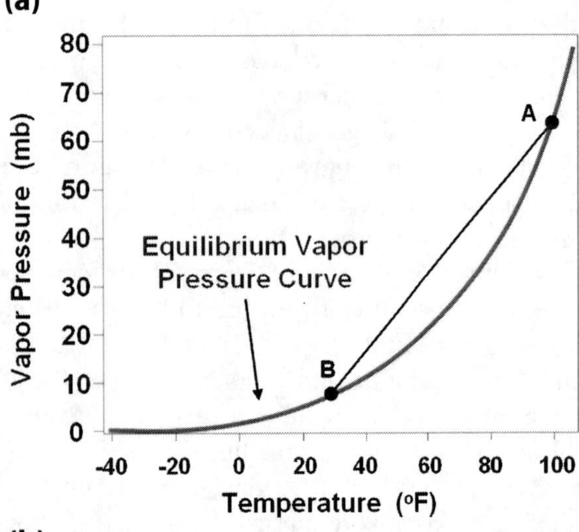

Figure 2.25 Whether a mixing cloud forms depends on the temperature and vapor pressure of the air involved in the mixing. (a) Mixing of warm, moist air from your breath (represented by point A) and the outside air on a cold winter day (represented by point B). All points on the line connecting A and B lie above the equilibrium curve, indicating net condensation. Thus, a cloud forms; (b) Mixing of warm, moist air from your breath (point A) and the warm dry air from inside your house (point C). The line connecting points A and C lies below the equilibrium curve, so no cloud forms.

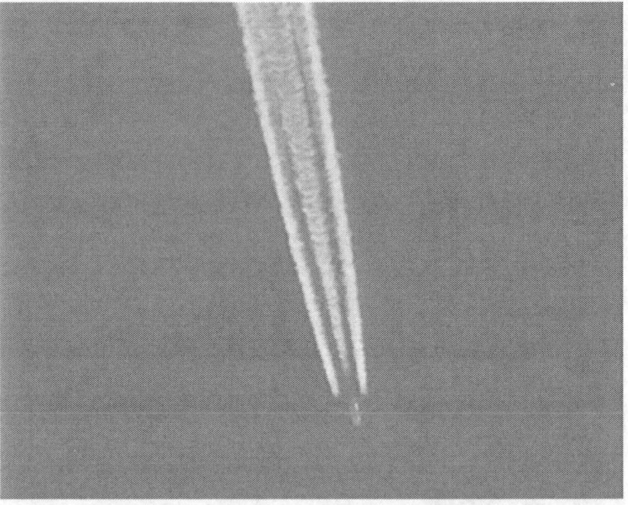

Figure 2.26 Contrails form as the hot, moist exhaust from a jet engine mixes with colder, drier air. Note the clear gaps between the jet engines and the contrails, indicating the zone where the mixing occurred.

Courtesy of NOAA

Figure 2.27 This view from a weather satellite shows persistent contrails over the southeastern United States.

contrails can dramatically increase high cloud cover (see Figure 2.27).

If you read the last paragraph closely, you probably noticed that we initially stated that contrails can form in air that's relatively dry. Then we said that contrails persist when the air is close to saturation. Are these two statements contradictory? Not at all, if you consider that measures of moisture can be relative (as in relative humidity) or absolute. Read on.

ASSESSING MOISTURE: APPLICATIONS TO WEATHER FORECASTING

When the water vapor content of the air is low, the relative humidity can be very high. Before you think that the authors have lost all their moisture marbles, let us explain.

Relative Humidity versus Dew Points: To Each His Own

Recall the definition of relative humidity ("RH") that we introduced earlier in this chapter: RH is vapor pressure divided by equilibrium vapor pressure, multiplied by 100% (in order to change the ratio into a percent). Recall that the denominator in this quotient depends on temperature. What this means is that we have a (so-called) measure of atmospheric moisture that is not totally governed by the amount of moisture in the air. So relative humidity, despite its popularity as a crutch for some television weathercasters, is not an *absolute* measure of moisture in the air—it is a *relative* measure because it depends on temperature.

With this caveat in mind, let's return to the brain teaser we posed at the start of this section. On a chilly December morning in New England, under the control of a dry Canadian high-pressure system, for example, the relative humidity may be quite high (see Figure 2.28). Yet the air feels crisp and far from humid. The apparent paradox results from the low morning temperature, which dictates that the equilibrium vapor pressure is also low. So the actual vapor pressure, which is low (remember, this is a dry Canadian air mass), divided by the low equilibrium vapor pressure, yields a relative humidity that's pretty high.

There's another rub to relative humidity. If the actual vapor pressure remains constant throughout the day, then the relative humidity will change as temperature changes. That's because the numerator in the expression for relative humidity doesn't change, but the denominator increases (decreases) with increasing (decreasing) temperature. So a low vapor pressure divided by an increasing (decreasing) equilibrium vapor pressure results in a decreasing (increasing) relative humidity. This roller-coaster behavior of relative humidity is depicted schematically in Figure 2.29.

Before we move from the relative to the absolute, let us say something positive about relative humidity. A relative humidity near 100% gives us a clue that the air is close to saturation and that additional cooling will produce net condensation. Thus, relative humidity (near the ground and aloft) is a tool that forecasters use to predict the formation of fog and clouds. For example, Figure 2.2 is a meteogram that includes the time trace of relative humidity (blue line, in percent) at Red Bluff, CA, beginning during the pre-dawn hours on a December day. Note that fog formed as the relative humidity reached 100%. But relative humidity alone cannot tell us how much water vapor is in the air.

So what measure do forecasters routinely use to represent the absolute amount of water vapor in the air? Answer: the dew point, which is the temperature to which air must be cooled (at constant pressure) in order to reach saturation. To understand this concept, think of a clear, calm autumn morning with dew on the grass. How did the dew get there? The previous night, air in contact with the chilling ground cooled to the temperature at which saturation was reached, and then a tad lower so that net condensation began and dew formed. The temperature at which dew formed on the grass is the dew point. Now look back to Figure 2.30 and note that, as the temperature (red line) fell toward and eventually reached the dew point (green line), fog formed as net condensation occurred in a layer of air just above the ground.

When the dew point is low [say 40°F (4°C)] and the temperature is much higher [say 80°F (27°C)], a

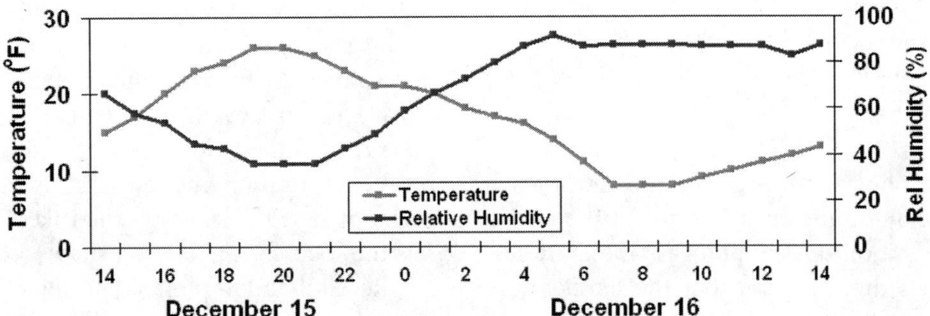

Figure 2.28 The time traces of temperature (red line, left axis in °F) and relative humidity (blue line, right axis in percent) at Orange, MA, from 14Z on December 15, 2004, to 14Z on December 16. Note that the relative humidity in the pre-dawn hours of December 16 was close to 90%. Yet the temperature was near 10°F, and the frigid morning air was far from feeling humid.

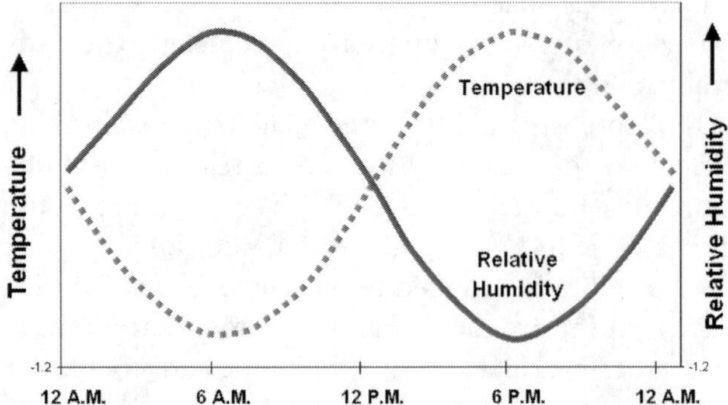

Figure 2.29 Suppose, for sake of argument, that the actual amount of water vapor in the air near the ground remained nearly constant on a particular day. Even so, the relative humidity would still change throughout a typical day, but only be-cause temperature varies. Early in the morning on such a day, the relative humidity would reach a maximum because the temperature is lowest. On the other hand, relative humidity would be lowest when the temperature is highest—in the late afternoon.

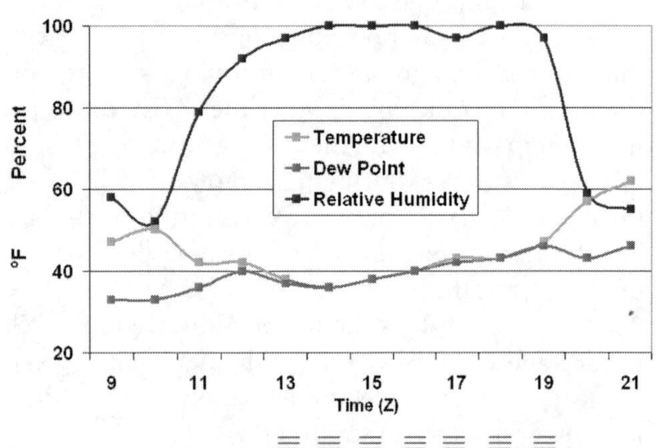

Figure 2.30 Meteogram showing temperature (red line, in °F), relative humidity (blue line, in percent), and dew point (green line, in °F) at Red Bluff, CA, from 09Z to 21Z on a December day. All three variables share the numerical axis labels on the left. Obstructions to visibility are shown along the bottom. Note that fog formed at 13Z as the relative humidity neared 100%.

great deal of cooling is required for the air to reach saturation. The amount of water vapor in the air (in light of the definition of dew point) is therefore low and the air feels dry. Suppose that the temperature is the same but the dew point is now high [say, 70°F (21°C)]. In this case, not as much cooling is required to reach saturation—there is ample water vapor in the air and it feels very humid. Air starts to feel a bit humid when the dew point reaches 60°F (16°C). By the time the dew point reaches 65°F (18°C), most folks would agree that the air is humid. At dew points near 75°F (24°C) or higher, the air feels oppressive and stifling.

The dew point seldom exceeds 80°F (27°C). Of course, there are exceptions to every rule. Check out the 21Z analysis of surface dew points on July 25, 2007 in Figure 2.31. Before you recoil at the sight of so many **isodrosotherms** (isopleths of dew points), we point out that this is a mesoanalysis, which is a highly detailed array of isopleths whose aim is to identify important small-scale features. The isoplething interval here is 2°F, which is less than what is typically used for dew point. Speaking of small-scale features, look in northern Minnesota near the U.S.-Canadian border. Dew points here were near 80°F. Wow! When we first noticed these extreme values, our first reaction was that we couldn't remember the last time we saw dew points this high so far north! By way of explanation, persistent winds had been blowing from the Gulf of Mexico, which was, not surprisingly, quite warm in July (so evaporation rates were high). In turn, these steadfast southerly winds allowed a pool of very humid air to travel exceedingly far north.

Before we close this section on dew point, we note that when the air temperature is 32°F (0°C) or less, the **frost point** becomes the absolute measure of moisture in the air, although many meteorologists continue to loosely use "dew point" at such low temperatures.

Patterns of isodrosotherms such as the one shown in Figure 2.31 always change in time, particularly across the middle latitudes. So it behooves weather forecasters to understand the processes that control surface dew points.

How to Change Dew Points: From Up, Down, and All Around

The most obvious way to change the dew point is to simply evaporate water into the air. For example, chilly, dry Canadian air moving over the relatively warm Great Lakes in autumn and winter creates large vapor pressure gradients just above the water surface. As a result, evaporation rates are large and the Canadian air gets moistened as it crosses the Lakes. This moistening sets the stage for "lake-effect snow" (see Figure 2.32).

Recall that dew points typically increase below the base of clouds after the onset of precipitation because some raindrops evaporate on the way to the surface. For folks driving or hiking in the Rockies or Appalachians, there are implications. Indeed, when it rains or snows in mountainous regions, the cloud base (ceiling) often lowers below the peaks as increasing dew

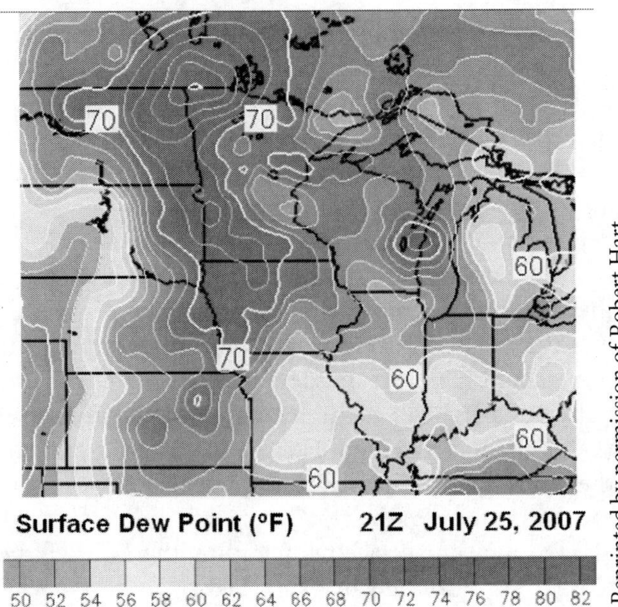

Figure 2.31 The 21Z meso-analysis of surface dew-point temperatures on July 25, 2007, shows a small pocket along the U.S.-Canadian border with dew-point temperatures near 80°F.

Figure 2.32 Outside the National Weather Service office in Buffalo, NY, in the aftermath of lake-effect snow that brought in excess of 80 inches to parts of Erie county in late December 2001.

points and decreasing temperatures bring the air closer to saturation. As a result, ridge-top fog often shrouds mountain peaks during wet weather.

Another way for surface dew points to change is for eddies to mix drier air downward from altitudes of a few thousand meters (this is more noticeable during summer). Water vapor is like oxygen and nitrogen; concentrations generally decrease with increasing altitude. Thus, on a sunny, hot and humid summer day,

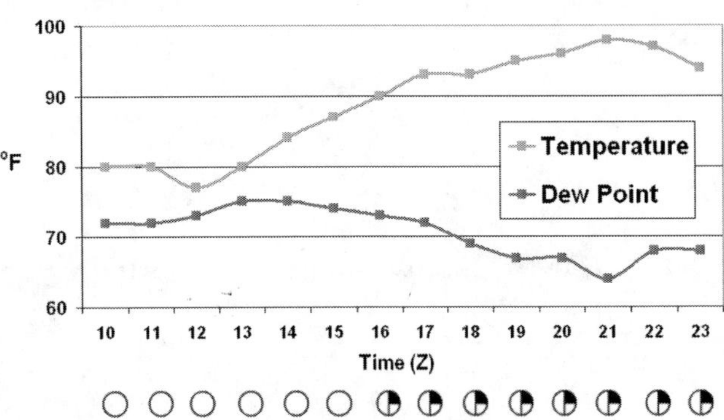

Figure 2.33 An August day started off warm and very humid in Dallas, TX, with a temperature of 80°F and a dew point of 75°F at 13Z. But as the mercury rose toward 100°F (lighter line) on a mainly sunny day (see cloud portion of meteogram), convective eddies mixed drier air toward the ground, causing dew points (darker line) to decrease to a more comfortable 64°F by 21Z.

dew points can decrease a bit in the afternoon when eddies generated by solar heating mix drier air from higher up toward the ground.

Figure 2.33 shows this process in action. It's a portion of the meteogram for Dallas, TX, on an August day dominated by a hot and humid air mass. Note that the dew point started off at a very muggy 75°F (24°C) at 13Z. As the day grew hotter, dew points gradually decreased, bottoming out at a less sultry 64°F (18°C) at 21Z [the same time that the temperature peaked at 98°F (37°C)]. Lower dew points could be traced to heights around 1800 m (6000 ft), about the highest altitude from which eddies generated by major-league solar heating circulated drier air toward the ground.

Of course, moist or dry air can also be transported horizontally into a region by the wind, causing dew points to increase or decrease in time. For example, **dry advection** typically follows on the heels of a cold front, as the portion of the meteogram for Atlanta, GA, illustrates in Figure 2.34. A cold front moved through Atlanta between 11Z and 12Z on this December day. In response, the dew point (and temperature) started to decrease beginning at 12Z in response to the west-northwesterly winds in the wake of the cold front. Also note that **moist advection** took place prior to the frontal passage as dew points increased in concert with southerly winds from the Gulf of Mexico.

The overall message that you should take from this discussion is that dew points are an absolute measure of the amount of moisture in the air. In addition to giving a sense of how humid or dry the air feels, dew points also play a pivotal role in other facets of weather

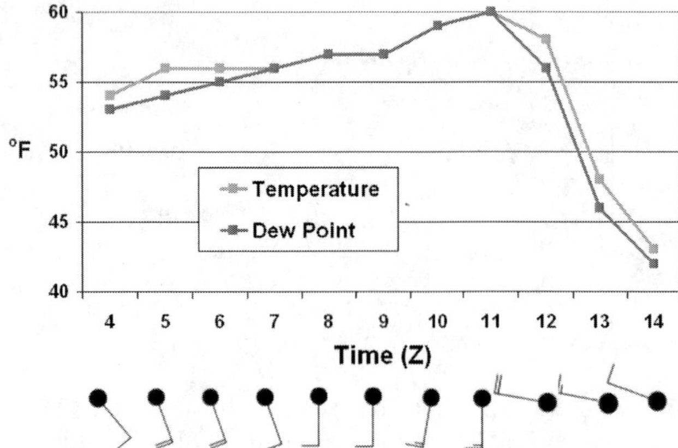

Figure 2.34 The temperature (lighter line), dew point (darker line), cloud cover, and wind portion of the meteogram from Atlanta, GA, from 4Z to 14Z on a December day. A cold front moved through around 11Z. Ahead of the front, moist advection occurred on southerly breezes, and the dew point increased. Behind the front, westerly and northwesterly winds imported drier air, and the dew point decreased. Note that from 7Z to 11Z, the air was saturated so the temperature and dew point curves overlap.

forecasting. We'll finish the chapter by discussing a few of these applications to further enrich your forecasting apprenticeship.

Dew Points and Weather Forecasting: A Few Applications

In case you haven't noticed in the examples we've given so far, the dew point always seems to be less than or equal to the air temperature. After all, look at its definition: Dew point is the temperature to which the air must be cooled (at constant pressure) to reach saturation. For net condensation to occur, however, there must be a little extra cooling. Indeed, the air temperature must fall ever so slightly below the dew point whenever clouds form. We really can't measure this difference on a thermometer because it's so small. So don't be fooled. When clouds form, the temperature is a "gnat's eyelash" lower than the dew point.

For all practical purposes, however, meteorologists can assume that a parcel of air rising from the ground will achieve net condensation when the temperature decreases to the dew point (again, because we really can't detect that the temperature is ever so slightly lower than the dew point when clouds form). You will learn later that the temperature of a rising, unsaturated parcel of air decreases at a rate of about 10°C per kilometer of ascent (about 5.5°F per 1000 feet). As it turns out, the dew point of an ascending parcel also decreases, but at a much smaller rate.

The exact numbers aren't important here. What's important is that the temperature of a rising air parcel decreases faster than its dew point. And that means that the temperature has a better chance of reaching the dew point (and thus a better chance for clouds to form). The altitude where the temperature falls imperceptibly below the dew point (they are essentially equal) is called the **lifting condensation level** (LCL for short). In Figure 2.35, you can get a sense of the level of the LCL over State College, PA, by eyeing the flat bottoms of the clouds.

For a given surface temperature, the LCL will be closer to the ground when surface dew points are relatively high. That's because higher dew points translate to more water vapor in the air, which means that less cooling is required to reach net condensation; in other words, air parcels do not have to rise as high for clouds to form.

Conversely, in the western United States where surface dew points are often very low, the LCL tends to lie at a higher altitude, especially during late spring and early summer when temperatures are high and dew points are relatively low. When high-based thunderstorms erupt in this environment, the raindrops that fall from their bases often evaporate before reaching the ground. That's because they have to fall through a thick layer of relatively dry air below the cloud base. Thunderstorms with lightning but no rain can spark wildfires, so it behooves weather forecasters to alert the public when high-based thunderstorms are likely. Dew points play a pivotal role in making these kinds of forecasts.

The forecasting utility of dew points doesn't end there. On clear, calm evenings, the dew point often serves as a lower bound for the upcoming night's low temperature, provided weather conditions stay pretty much the same throughout the night. For example, Figure 2.36 shows the temperature, dew point, cloud cover, and wind components of the meteogram for State College, PA, on the night of December 17–18, 2004. The dew point at 00Z (7 P.M. local time on December 17) was 16°F. With clear skies and light winds for the rest of the night, the temperature lowered toward the dew point, which stayed fairly steady through the night. The official low temperature was 18°F, so the dew point gave forecasters a solid first guess at the overnight minimum.

Figure 2.35 The flat bottoms of "pancake cumulus" clouds over State College, PA, are found at an altitude called the lifting condensation level.

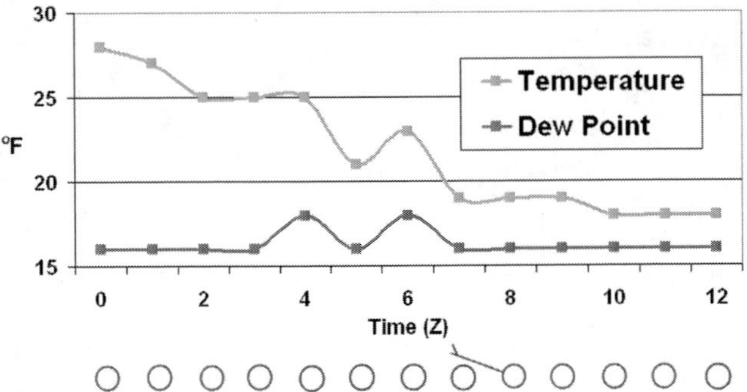

Figure 2.36 The temperature (red line), dew point (green line), cloud cover, and wind portions of the meteogram from State College, PA, on the night of December 17–18, 2004. The dew point, which remained relatively steady through the night, was a reasonable estimate for the low temperature on this clear, calm night.

Finally, analyses of dew points also help weather forecasters to pinpoint areas at risk for severe weather (such as damaging winds, large hail, and/or tornadoes). For example, Figure 2.37a shows the pattern of isodrosotherms at 23Z on April 20, 2004. Note the surge of higher dew points into Missouri, Illinois, and Indiana, indicative of moist advection associated with southerly winds ahead of a cold front (the front lies at the eastern edge of the relatively large gradient of dew points from Oklahoma to Wisconsin). The high dew points indicated plenty of moisture that served as fuel for powerful thunderstorms, which appear as red blobs on the corresponding radar image (see Figure 2.37b). These storms produced a swarm of tornadoes, primarily across Indiana and Illinois (tornado reports appear as red dots in Figure 2.37c). You will learn more about severe weather later in the book.

Of course, relatively high dew points in the lower troposphere also can signal the potential for flooding, particularly during summer when slow-moving thunderstorms can produce prodigious rainfalls in relatively short periods of time. We'll delve into flooding from thunderstorms in Chapter 9. Until then, we'll end this chapter with a brief overview of the instruments that meteorologists use to measure precipitation.

RAIN GAUGES: PUTTING THE PRECIPITATION PUZZLE TOGETHER

On the night of June 6–7, 2008, heavy thunderstorms deluged a relatively small portion of southwestern Indiana with as much as eleven inches of rain, causing severe flooding. Most of the heaviest rain fell in rural areas, but based primarily on measurements taken from the cooperative observing network, the National Weather Service was able to put the pieces together and get a good sense of the pattern of rainfall (see Figure 2.38).

Among cooperative weather observers, the most common instrument used to measure rainfall is the standard National Weather Service rain gauge, shown

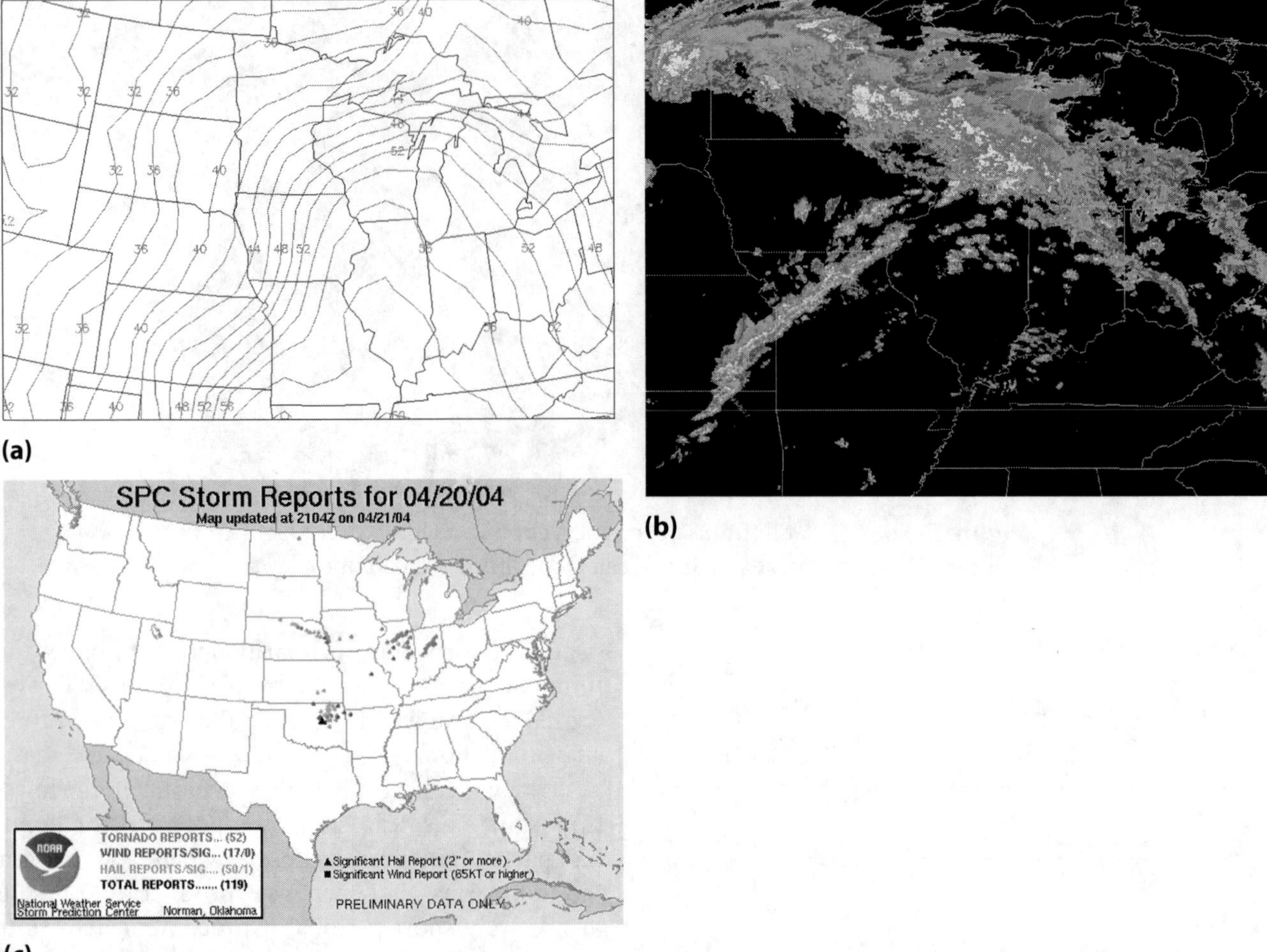

Figure 2.37 (a) An analysis of isodrosotherms at 23Z on April 20, 2003, shows a tongue of high dew points surging into Illinois and Indiana (courtesy of Plymouth State University); (b) The corresponding radar image at 23Z shows powerful thunderstorms (the blobs) erupting in Illinois and Indiana; (c) The powerful thunderstorms produced a swarm of tornadoes over Illinois and Indiana, indicated by dots in this storm report from the Storm Prediction Center in Norman, OK (All images courtesy of NOAA).

in Figure 2.39. The outer shell of this standard rain gauge is an eight-inch diameter cylinder with a funnel on top. Inside the outer shell lies a second cylinder (just over 2.5 inches in diameter) into which rain funnels. Given that the cross-sectional area of the outer cylinder is ten times that of the inner cylinder, rain funneling into the smaller cylinder will rise to a height ten times the actual rainfall. This horizontal "squeezing" of collected water translates to a vertical "stretching." Thus, a meager one-hundredth of an inch (0.01″) of rain balloons to a depth of one-tenth of an inch (0.10″) on a measuring stick, making the otherwise unwieldy task of obtaining accuracy to one-hundredth of an inch a lot easier. When the forecast calls for snow, weather observers remove the inner cylinder, allowing snow to accumulate in the outer cylinder. They then determine the liquid equivalent of the snow by taking the gauge indoors, melting the snow, and pouring the liquid into the small cylinder to accurately measure its depth (observers similarly obtain the liquid equivalent of hail and sleet this way).

Another instrument for measuring rainfall is the tipping-bucket rain gauge (see Figure 2.40). This gauge works by collecting rain and funneling it into a two compartment bucket; 0.01″ of rain will fill one compartment and overbalance the bucket so that it tips, emptying the water into a reservoir and moving the second compartment into place beneath the funnel. As the bucket tips, it completes an electrical circuit which then records the rainfall.

There are several other kinds of rain gauges. A few are very sophisticated, such as optical rain gauges,

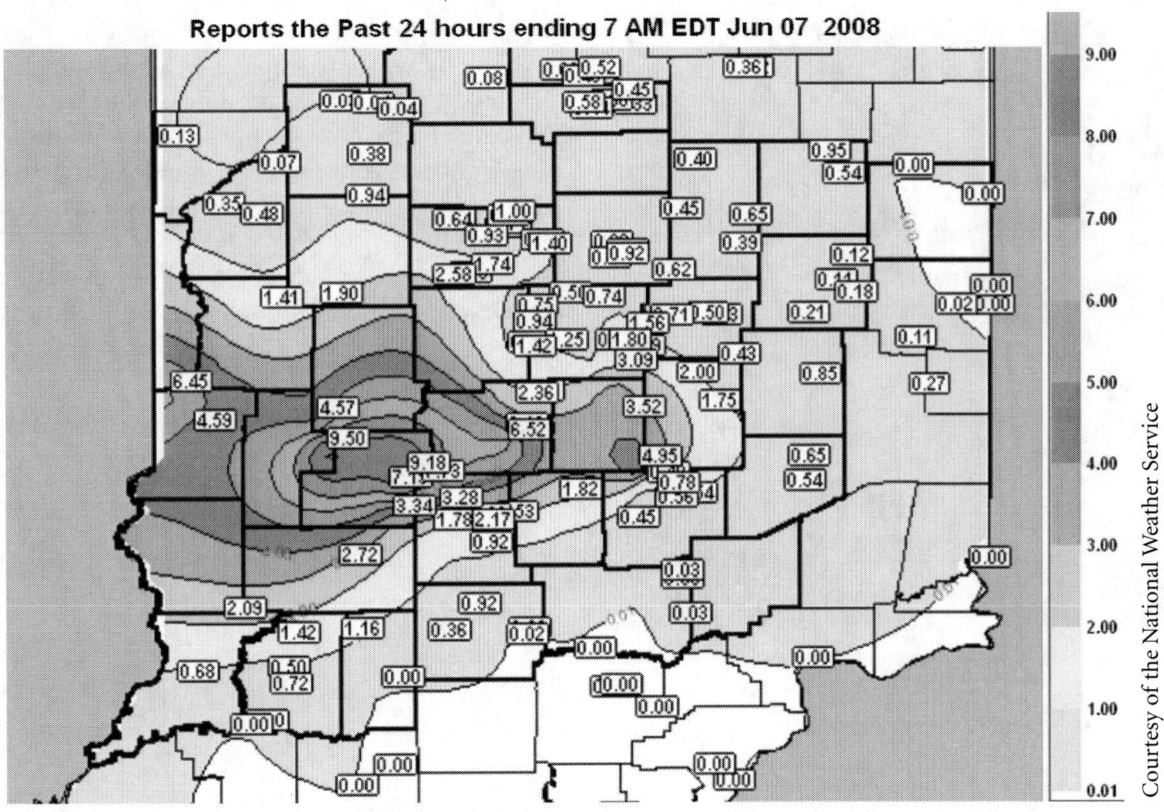

Figure 2.38 Rainfall in Indiana during the 24-hour period ending at 7 a.m. EDT on June 7, 2008. More than nine inches fell in parts of Owen county, between Bloomington and Terre Haute. The primary source of data used to prepare this map was the cooperative observing network.

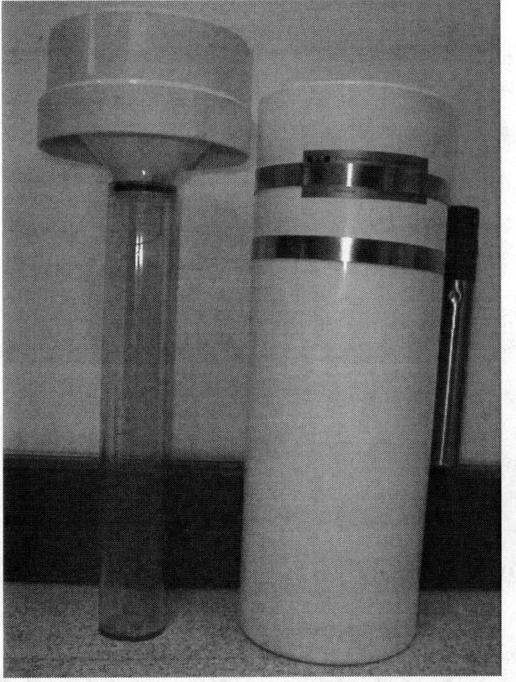

Figure 2.39 The standard National Weather Service rain gauge.

Courtesy of the National Weather Service

Figure 2.40 A tipping-bucket rain gauge.

which measure rainfall using a laser. Others operate in a simpler way. For example, a weighing gauge collects rain and funnels the water into a hole, below which is a catch bucket. As water accumulates in the bucket, its weight gets converted to a liquid-equivalent depth. Routinely, a mechanically driven pen scrolls across a chart attached to a rotating drum and traces out a record of this depth as a function of time (the drum rotates once every 24 hours).

FOCUS ON TOPICS

The Color of Clouds: Of *Star Trek* and Milk

In the 1960s, the popular television series *Star Trek* always prided itself on the quality of its scientific content. But, on a few episodes, writers and producers committed "Bad Science." In the near-vacuum of space (yes, there are some nomadic molecules wandering the galaxy), visible light from phasers fired by the Starship Enterprise should not have been able to be seen by any neutral observer because there aren't enough molecules in space to scatter light to the observer's eyes. Only if an observer assumed a position in the line of fire, looking directly at the incoming phaser energy, would the observer be able to see the light. And taking such action would not be a prudent way to prove a scientific point.

Back on Earth, the scattering of visible light plays a crucial role in determining the color of clouds perceived by sky gazers. Some clouds are white while others are not, and we'll try to shed some light on the differences.

Let's start with a tall glass of milk (homogenized, of course). Milk contains lots of fat globules, which are more efficient at scattering the shorter wavelengths of visible light than the longer wavelengths. Thus, when "white light" (which, like sunlight, contains the wavelengths of the visible spectrum) impinges on milk, these fat globules scatter shorter wavelengths efficiently and longer wavelengths not so efficiently. But, because there are so many globules, longer wavelentghs, after rattling around a bit, eventually get their "scattering due" (as do the other wavelengths of visible light), and white light emerges from the milk. Thus, the glass of milk looks white! (As a side note, if you have nothing else to do over the breakfast table, stare at a glass of skim milk—depending on the background, you should be able to detect a touch of blue color because there aren't enough fat globules in skim milk to sufficiently scatter longer wavelengths of visible light.)

And so it is with clouds. Trillions of tiny water drops (and some ice crystals) act like milk globules to scatter white light to our eyes. Think of a smattering of puffy, fair-weather cumulus clouds (see Figure 2.41) as just glasses of milk in the sky.

(*Continued*)

Figure 2.41 Fair-weather cumulus clouds.

Figure 2.42 A thick cumulonibus could (rain shaft on the right) has a very dark base.

From above, clouds always look white, but the view from below can sometimes be as different as day and night. The bases of cumulonimbus and cumulus congestus clouds (see Figures 2.12 and 2.42), which are tall and thick, typically appear dark to a nearby observer on the ground.

We again turn to milk for our explanation. Check out Figure 2.43, which is a sequence of four photographs of an experiment we conducted to convince you that thick clouds transmit very little sunlight. The upper-left photograph shows a plain bottle of water. We then began the experiment by mixing in just a little milk (upper-right photograph). Although the bottle looks a bit "milky," you can still see right through the mixture because visible light from the window behind the bottle was largely transmitted to our camera. In other words, the relatively few milk globules back-scattered a little visible light, but not enough to prevent some light from getting through. The bottom line is that you can't see through the bottle as well as you could before we added milk.

Figure 2.43 The upper-left photograph shows a bottle filled with plain water. From the upper-right to the lower-left and then finally to the lower-right photograph, an increasing amount of milk was added. In this order, the albedo of the mixture increased. As a result, light from behind the bottle was increasingly back-scattered by more and more milk globules, and less light was transmitted to the camera. Thus, you cannot see through the bottle in the lower-right photograph because the albedo of the mixture is so high.

Next, we added more and more milk (lower-left and then lower-right photographs). In each case, the greater number of milk globules back-scattered an increasing amount of light, to the point that you cannot see through the bottle. In effect, the mixture with the greatest concentration of milk globules extinguished light from the window behind the bottle. In turn, the mixture in the lower-right photograph looks relatively dark.

(*Continued*)

FOCUS ON TOPICS *(continued)*

Now think of the mixture of milk and water in the lower-right photograph as a thick cumulonimbus cloud. If we liken the camera to the eye of a nearby observer on the ground looking at the base of the cloud, you'll understand why its base looks dark to the observer: The "optically thick" cloud extinguished (back-scattered) a lot of sunlight.

This dark perception is enhanced when the observer views these clouds against a brighter background. Indeed, we cannot say enough about the importance of background in determining the perceived shade and color of clouds. One of the authors just went outside with his "white" handkerchief to prove a point. The handkerchief looked very white against the dark green siding of a house, but appeared almost pink against the bright white backdrop of freshly fallen snow.

And so it is with clouds. A single cloud that might appear gray or dark against a surrounding brighter sky might look almost white if it were viewed against the backdrop of an approaching dark thunderstorm. Yes, background can make a world of difference in how clouds appear. Figure 2.44 shows the swirling cloud of a waterspout that looks dark against a bright background. Meanwhile, Figure 2.45 shows a tornado whose funnel cloud looks bright when viewed against the dark backdrop of the optically thick parent thunderstorm.

Writers and producers of *Star Trek*—don't get your hopes up! Even though the backdrop of space is pitch black (save for some tiny, distant stars), you still won't be able to see the phasers of the Enterprise unless you're directly in the line of fire. And that view won't last very long.

Figure 2.44 A waterspout looks dark against the bright background.

Figure 2.45 TA white tornado.

Answer the following question using these maps.

1. What regions of the country tend to have a water surplus (precipitation exceeds evaporation)?

2. What regions of the country tend to have a water deficit (evaporation exceeds precipitation)?

3. What is the general relationship between precipitation and evaporation across the country?

4. Fill in the table below. If you click on the location dot for each city, the relevant data are shown on the scale below each map.

	Precipitation	Evaporation
Tucson, AZ		
Miami, FL		
Denver, CO		
Philadelphia, PA		

5. Which cities have a water surplus?

6. Which cities have a water deficit?

7. How can Denver have 1.16 cm of runoff if annual evaporation exceeds annual precipitation?

Chapter 3

AIRMASSES AND FRONTS

AIRMASSES

An ***airmass*** is a large body of air with relatively uniform thermal and moisture characteristics. Airmasses cover large regions of the Earth, typically several hundred thousand square kilometers, and can be as deep as the depth of the troposphere or as shallow as 1 to 2 km. Airmasses form when air remains over a relatively flat region of the Earth with homogeneous surface characteristics for an extended period of time. Areas with relatively uniform surfaces include continental arctic regions such as Canada and Siberia, cool oceanic regions such as the North Atlantic and Pacific, deserts such as the Sahara and the American southwest, and tropical oceanic regions including the equatorial Atlantic and Pacific, as well as smaller water bodies such as the Caribbean Sea and the Gulf of Mexico. The atmosphere "acquires" the thermal and moisture properties of the underlying surface as heat is transferred between the surface and the atmosphere and moisture evaporates into the air from the surface.

Meteorologists classify airmasses according to their thermal and moisture properties. Airmasses characterized by bitter cold temperatures are classified as ***arctic airmasses,*** cold temperatures (or cool in summer) as ***polar airmasses,*** and warm-hot temperatures as ***tropical airmasses.*** Airmasses that form over oceans are called ***maritime airmasses*** and those that form over continents are ***continental airmasses.*** Continental airmasses are normally drier than maritime airmasses since there is relatively little surface water evaporating into air over the continents.

Figure 3.1 identifies the typical airmass source regions of North America. Arctic airmasses develop over Canada and the frozen Arctic Ocean in wintertime, generally poleward of about 60° N. Extremely cold airmasses can form as air continually cools in the near-perpetual darkness of winter. Continental polar airmasses continually develop over the northern parts of the North American continent in all seasons of the year. Maritime polar airmasses develop over the North Atlantic and North Pacific Oceans. The oceans moderate wintertime temperatures within these airmasses. Maritime tropical airmasses originate over the tropical Atlantic and Pacific, the Gulf of Mexico, and the Caribbean Sea. Continental tropical airmasses develop over the desert regions of Mexico and the southwestern United States.

The centers of cold airmasses are associated with high pressure on surface weather maps. High pressure develops in response to cooling. In winter, high-pressure centers form and are the dominant feature over the northern parts of the continents of Asia and North America. In summer, when the oceans are cooler than the landmasses, large high-pressure centers are the dominant feature of the atmosphere over the North Atlantic and Pacific Oceans. The high-pressure center over the Atlantic is called the ***Bermuda high*** because it is centered near Bermuda, while its Pacific counterpart is called the ***Pacific high.***

The centers of very warm airmasses appear as semi-permanent regions of low surface pressure. These low-pressure areas appear over desert areas such as the

American Southwest in summer, and in Southeast Asia, central Africa, and near the equator. In winter, semi-permanent low-pressure centers appear over the northern oceans. The semi-permanent low over the Pacific is called the ***Aleutian low,*** while its Atlantic counterpart is called the ***Icelandic low.*** Semi-permanent low-pressure centers differ substantially from migrating tropical and extratropical cyclones, although the latter often migrate into the areas of the semi-permanent lows.

Airmasses do not remain over their source regions indefinitely. As storms move about the globe, airmasses move out of their source regions and over other areas. Arctic airmasses can move as far south as the Gulf of Mexico during a cold air outbreak. Maritime tropical air can extend well into Canada in midsummer. The arrows in Figure 3.1 show the typical paths North American airmasses take as they move out of their source regions. Once out of their source regions, the temperature and moisture characteristics of airmasses change as they begin to acquire the thermal and moisture characteristics of the new surfaces over which they reside. For example, in summer warm humid air over the Gulf of Mexico typically moves northward over the central United States. Over land, this air may heat several degrees and acquire additional moisture from crops through a process called evapotranspiration. By the time the air moves far inland, it can be considerably more uncomfortable than along the coast.

Not all airmasses are in contact with the ground. An example is the stratosphere, a large airmass that covers the entire globe. Airmasses exist aloft in the troposphere, residing on top of other airmasses in contact with the surface. Airmasses are three-dimensional, and the boundaries between airmasses are often quite sharp and distinct. These boundaries, called ***fronts,*** are meteorologically important because much of the precipitation in the middle latitudes, and most severe weather, occurs in their vicinity.

Check Your Understanding 3.1

1. How large and how deep is a typical airmass?
2. What characteristics make a region a good source for airmasses?
3. What is the relationship between airmasses and fronts?

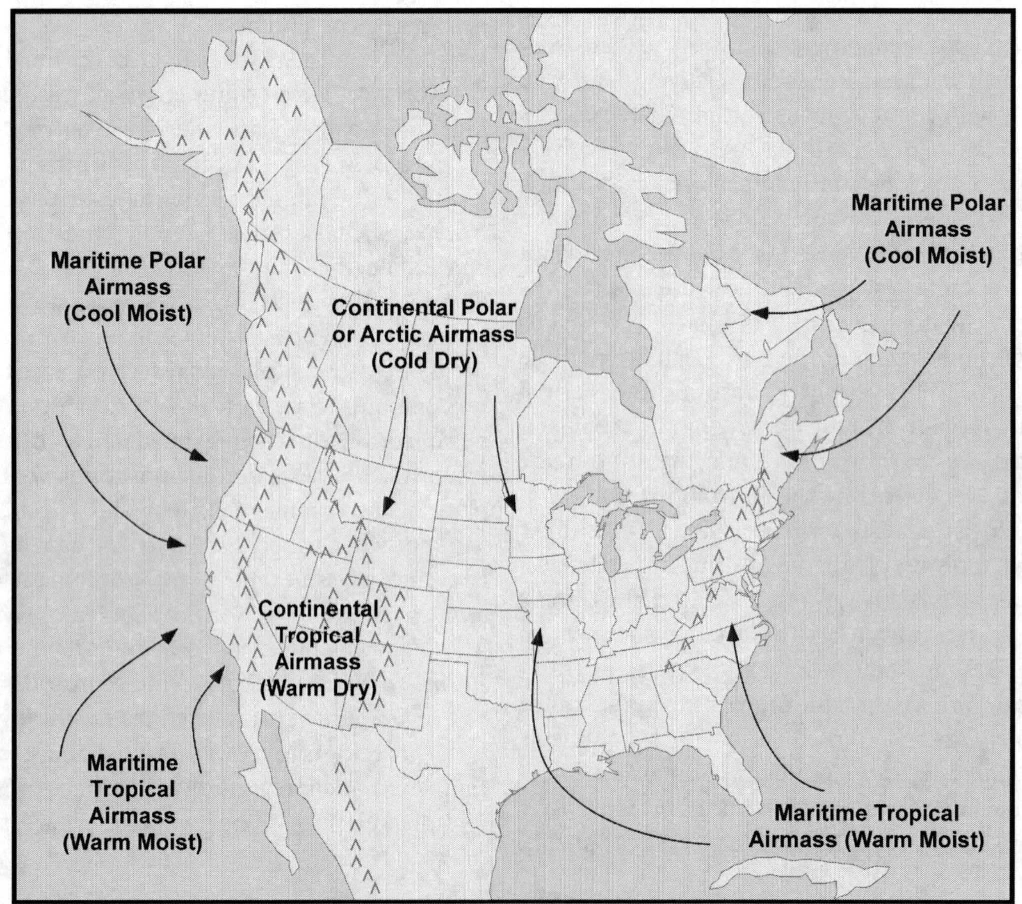

Figure 3.1 Airmass source regions for North America and the typical tracks airmasses take out of their source regions.

FRONTS

Meteorologists classify fronts based on the thermal and moisture characteristics of the airmasses, the direction of movement of the airmasses, and whether the boundary between the airmasses is in contact with the ground (a surface front), or can only be found aloft (an upper level front). In most cases, two airmasses in contact with one another will have different thermal properties, one cold and the other warm.

Cold Fronts

We call the boundary between two airmasses a ***cold front*** if the cold air is advancing forward, lifting the warm air. The leading edge of the cold airmass typically has a shape like a dome, as shown in Figure 3.2A. Note that, because of the tilt of the airmass boundary in Figure 3.2, the front's horizontal position varies with elevation. The type of precipitation that will occur along a cold front depends on the characteristics of the warm air ahead of the front. If the warm air is moist and conditionally unstable, lifting ahead of the front can trigger thunderstorms. These thunderstorms will often form in a line, called a squall line, along the front. In some situations, supercell thunderstorms may form along the front with tornadoes, hail, and damaging winds. On the other hand, the atmosphere may be stable ahead of the cold front (Figure 3.2B). In this case, the clouds that form by lifting may only produce light rain, or no rain at all. In some cases, the warm air ahead of the front is dry (Figure 3.2C). In this case no clouds will form at all. *Regardless of the cloud formations, we say that the front is a cold front if the cold air is advancing, lifting the warm air ahead of it.* When extratropical cyclones (low-pressure centers) form in the Northern Hemisphere, air flows around the low-pressure system counterclockwise. Cold air on the west side of the cyclone advances southward and then southeastward. For this reason, cold fronts are typically located in the southwest quadrant of a cyclone early in its lifetime (see Figure 3.3). Cold fronts that mark the boundary of extremely cold airmasses in wintertime are called ***arctic fronts.*** Arctic airmasses are normally much more shallow than airmasses associated with spring and fall season cold fronts.

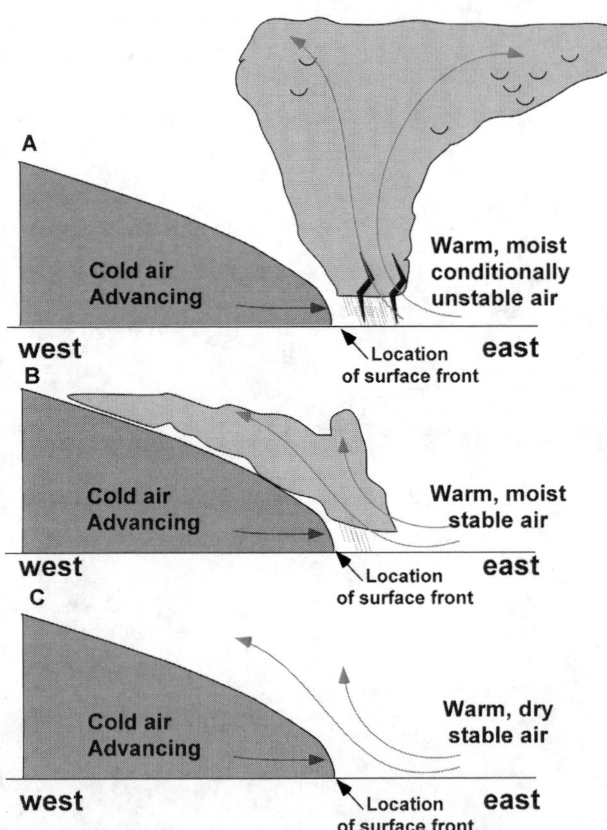

Figure 3.2 Cross section through three cold fronts. In A, the air ahead of the front is conditionally unstable and forms thunderstorms when lifted. In B, stable moist air is lifted along the frontal surface. In C, dry air is lifted, so clouds do not form. In all cases, the cold air is advancing into warmer air.

Warm Fronts

A boundary where the cold air is retreating and the warm air is advancing is called a ***warm front.*** Since warm air flows northward on the east side of a cyclone, warm fronts are normally found in this location (see Figure 3.3). The cold air, in this case, still has a dome-like structure, although the cold air dome typically slopes more gradually ahead of a warm front than behind a cold front (see Figure 3.4). The warm air flows toward the cold air, rising over the dome as it progresses northward. The type of precipitation that occurs along a warm front again depends on the moisture and thermal characteristics of the warm air. In eastern North America, warm air gliding upward along a warm front typically originates over the Gulf of Mexico or the Atlantic and is normally moist. As the warm air glides upward over the cold air dome, widespread layered clouds will develop. These clouds are deepest just north of the frontal boundary and progressively become thinner and higher toward the north. Precipitation is heaviest closer to the frontal boundary where the clouds are deep, and lighter to the north where the clouds are shallow. The intensity of the precipitation depends again on the stability of the warm air. If the warm air is conditionally unstable,

FOCUS 3.1

Frontal Symbols

Meteorologists indicate the location and type of front on surface weather charts using a heavy line with either barbs or half circles along the line. Solid lines are used when a front is obvious, while broken lines are used to indicate that a front is either forming or dissipating. Although a frontal symbol exists for an upper-level front, it is rarely used. Recognition of the importance of upper-level fronts in severe weather is relatively recent in meteorology. The symbols for all of the fronts discussed in this chapter appear in Figure 3A.

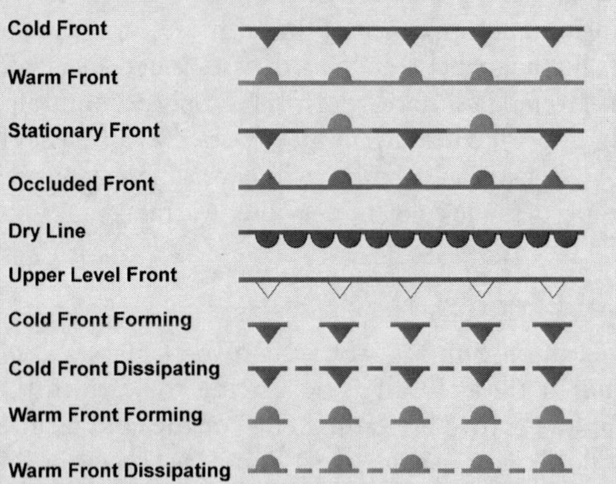

Figure 3A Frontal symbols used on surface weather maps.

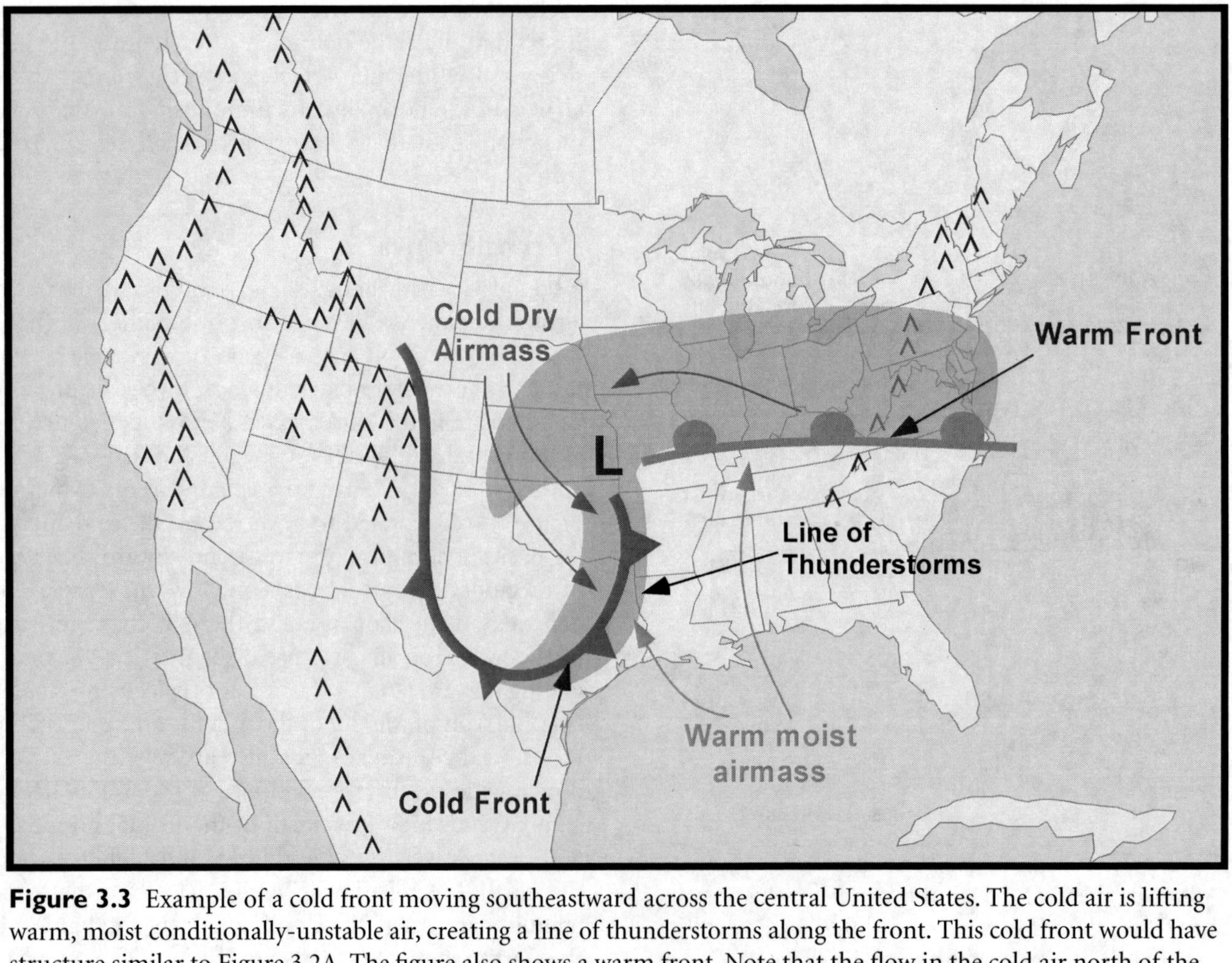

Figure 3.3 Example of a cold front moving southeastward across the central United States. The cold air is lifting warm, moist conditionally-unstable air, creating a line of thunderstorms along the front. This cold front would have structure similar to Figure 3.2A. The figure also shows a warm front. Note that the flow in the cold air north of the warm front has a component toward the north, so that the cold air is retreating northward with time. Gray shading denotes cloud cover.

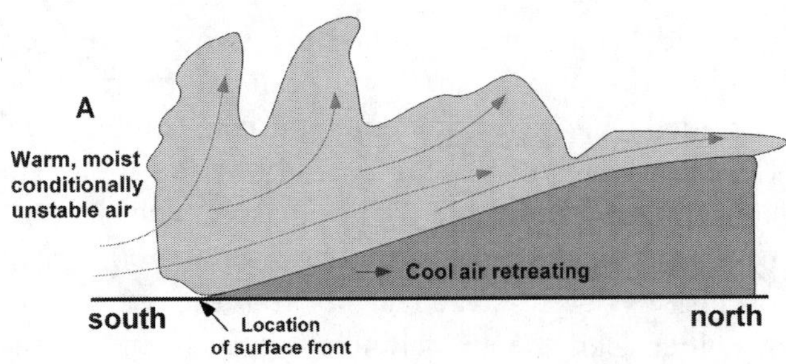

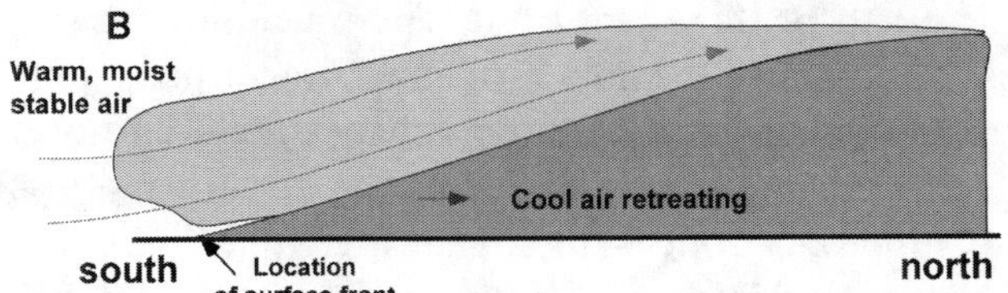

Figure 3.4 Cross section through two warm fronts. In A, the air south of the front is conditionally unstable and forms showers and thunderstorms as it rises over the cool air. In B, the moist air south of the front is stable. In this case, the clouds form a wide stratus layer that is deepest near the surface position of the front and thin farther north.

thunderstorms may develop over the warm front (Figure 3.4A). These are often embedded within, or emerge from, the widespread layered clouds. If the warm air is stable, the clouds will be layered (Figure 3.4B). If the temperature in the cold air is below freezing, snow, ice pellets, or freezing rain may occur. *Regardless of the cloud formations or precipitation, we say that a front is a warm front if the cold air is retreating and the warm air is advancing.*

Stationary Fronts

Airmass boundaries are sometimes stationary. Although the boundary is stationary, air on both sides of the boundary can be moving. With a ***stationary front,*** air on the cold side of the front will always be flowing parallel to the front (see Figures 3.5 and 3.6). If this is the case, the cold air is neither advancing nor retreating. The warm air normally flows toward the front. As the warm air encounters the cold air, it may be lifted along the boundary. If the air is conditionally unstable, a line of showers and thunderstorms may develop in the warm air over the front (Figures 3.5A and 3.6A), a situation that can lead to flash flooding (see Chapter 9) when the front's stationarity allows heavy rain to persist over a particular location. If the warm air is stable, widespread layered clouds may form over the front, with rain falling on the cold side of the front. *Regardless of the cloud formations or precipitation, we say that the front is a stationary front if the cold air is neither advancing nor retreating.*

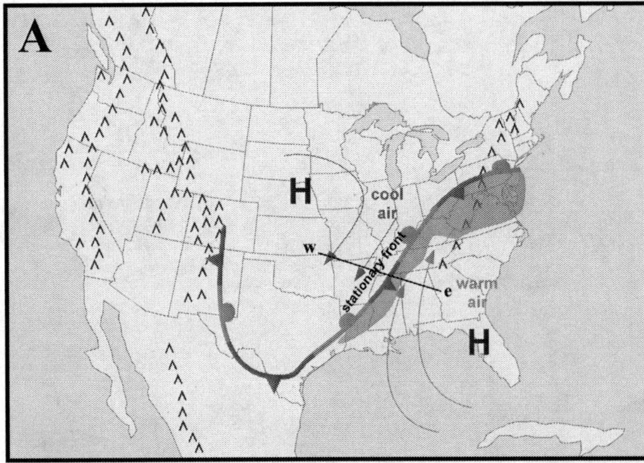

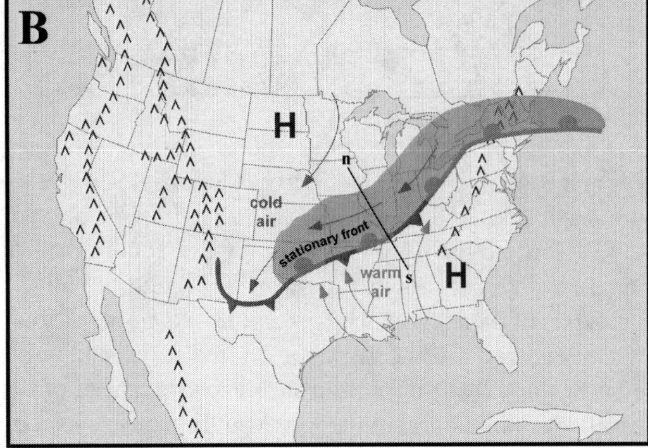

Figure 3.5 Maps showing two examples of stationary fronts and associated clouds (gray shading). Note that in both examples the cold air on the north side of the front is moving parallel to the front. In (A) clouds form on the warm side of the front and precipitation would fall in this region. In (B) clouds form on the cold side of the front and any precipitation would fall out on the cold side.

Occluded Fronts

As cyclones develop and go through their life cycle, the cold air to the west of the cyclone advances rapidly southward around the center of low pressure, while the air to the north of the warm front, which is also cold, retreats northward slowly. Because the cold front typically moves rapidly, it will progress around the south side of the low-pressure center. The cold air will then progress northeastward, approaching the warm front. Eventually, the cold front can actually catch up to the warm front. When this happens, the cold air comes in direct contact with the cold air north of the warm front, creating a new airmass boundary. This boundary,

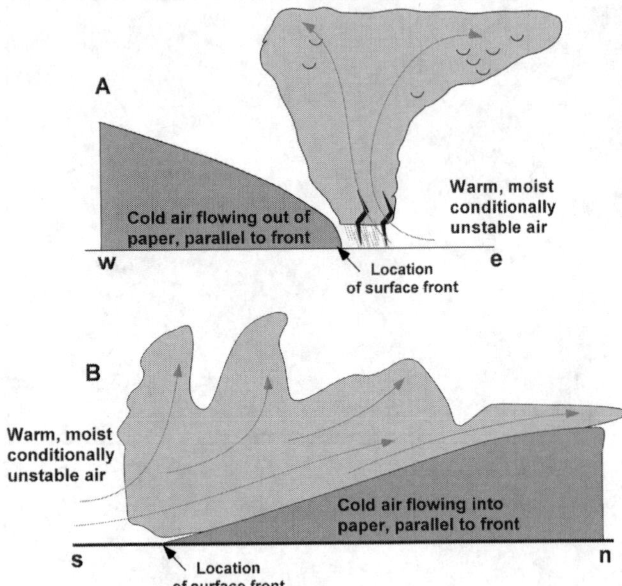

Figure 3.6 Two examples of cross sections through stationary fronts. In each case the cold air is flowing parallel to the front, so the front is neither retreating nor advancing. In both cases shown, the warm air is conditionally unstable. In panel A, which corresponds to cross section w-e in Figure 3.5A, the warm air is lifted at the leading edge of the cold air dome and showers erupt ahead of the front with rain falling in the warm air. In panel B, which corresponds to cross section s-n in Figure 3.5B, warm air flows up over the cold air dome so that the showers occur over the front, with the rain falling out on the cold-air side of the front.

between the cold air behind the cold front and the cold air north of the warm front, is called an ***occluded front.*** The process described above is depicted conceptually in Figure 3.7. We see the cold front progress southward (Figure 3.7A) where it eventually encounters the warm front (Figure 3.7B). The boundary between the two cold air regions becomes longer as the cold air behind the cold front continues to advance (Figure 3.7C). As the fronts meet, warm air is forced aloft over both the cold airmasses.

The three dimensional structure of an occluded front depends on the temperatures within the cold air behind the cold front and north of the warm front. Figure 3.7D shows two sets of cross sections through the fronts appearing in Figure 3.7C. The set on the left represents a ***cold occlusion.*** In this case, the air behind the cold front is colder than air north of the warm front. The lower cross section (u to v) is at a point where the cold front has not yet caught up to the warm front (see Figure 3.7C). The middle cross section (w to x) is located right at the point where the cold, warm, and occluded fronts meet. The top cross section (y to z) shows the occluded front. In the occluded region, cold air behind the cold front lifts the (less cold) air north of the warm front and the warm air riding on top of the cold airmasses. The right set of cross sections represent a ***warm occlusion.*** Warm occlusions develop when air north of the warm front is colder than the air behind the cold front. In this case, air behind the cold front ascends over the cold air north of the warm front. The warmest air again is found above the cold airmasses. Warm occlusions appear to be more common than cold occlusions. Occluded fronts develop during the mature and dissipating stages of cyclones. They are typically characterized by widespread cloudiness and rain or snowfall.

Dry Lines

The fronts discussed so far all separate airmasses with different thermal properties, one airmass cold and the other warm. In the south-central United States (the Texas, Oklahoma, Kansas region) and northern Mexico another type of airmass boundary develops that is primarily marked by a sharp moisture, rather than temperature difference between the two airmasses. A front characterized by a sharp moisture difference, but little temperature change, is called a ***dry line.*** Dry lines develop when air flowing eastward from the high desert plateau regions of Arizona, Colorado, New Mexico, and Mexico descends the Rockies into the southern plains and encounters moist air flowing northward from the Gulf of Mexico (Figure 3.8). The desert air typically has low moisture content because of its source region. When this air descends the east slope of the Rockies on its way to the Plains, the air compresses, warms, and dries even more, so by the time it reaches the High Plains, its relative humidity can be quite low (−20 to 30%). Air from the Gulf of Mexico, on the other hand, can be extremely humid. Moist air is less dense than dry air at the same temperature and pressure. This is true because the water molecule (H_2O, molecular weight 18) has less mass than an oxygen molecule (O_2, molecular weight 32), or a nitrogen molecule (N_2, molecular weight 28). As water molecules displace nitrogen and oxygen molecules in a volume of air, air becomes less dense. When the dry air descending the Rockies meets the moist air on the plains, the moist air will rise over the dry air. If the moist air is conditionally unstable, lifting over the dry air may trigger instability and produce thunderstorms. Often a line of thunderstorms will develop

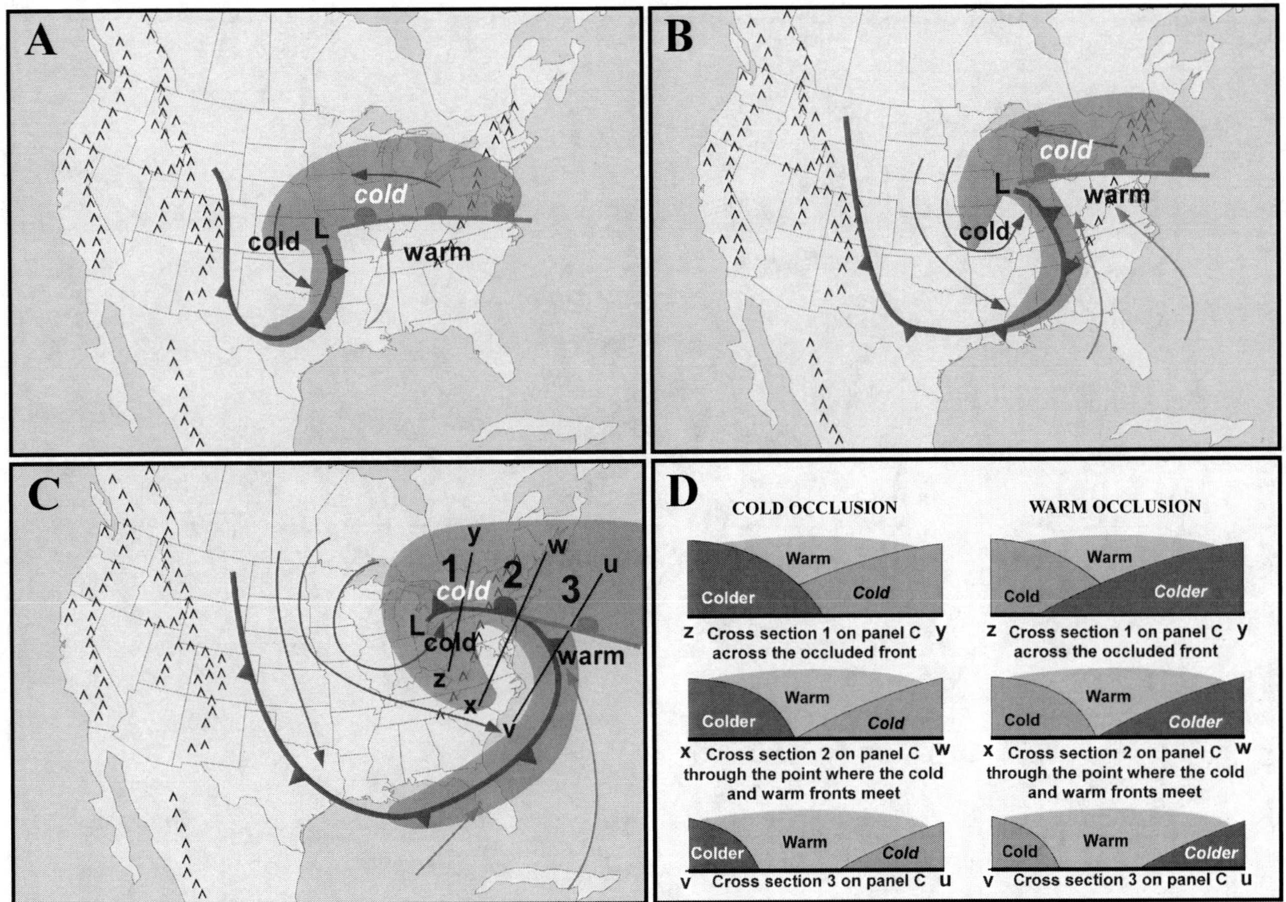

Figure 3.7 The development of an occluded front. (A) The cold front moves faster than the warm front because the winds in the cold air behind the cold front are moving rapidly toward the front, while the cold air north of the warm front is primarily moving westward, with only a small component of motion away from the front toward the north. (B) As a result, the cold front "catches up" to the warm front. (C) Cold air completely surrounds the low-pressure center, with the occluded front marking the boundary between air behind the cold front and ahead of the warm front. (D) The vertical structure of an occlusion. Each set of three cross sections correspond to the cross sections shown in (C). The set to the left show the alignment of airmasses when the coldest air is behind the cold front (a cold occlusion). The set to the right show the alignment of airmasses when the coldest air is behind the warm front (a warm occlusion). In all cases, the warm air in the "warm sector" of the storm is forced aloft over both fronts.

along a dry line. These thunderstorms can be severe if the moist air is sufficiently unstable. Thunderstorms tend to develop along dry lines in the mid-afternoon, when the moist air is warmest.

Upper-Level Fronts

Airmasses do not necessarily extend to the surface of the Earth. Often airmasses can be "stacked" in the vertical, so that an airmass boundary will be present aloft, but not at the surface. Meteorologists call this type of airmass boundary a ***cold front aloft*** or ***upper-level front*** (Figure 3.9). In this text, we will adopt the term "upper-level front" for this type of front to avoid confusion with surface cold fronts. Upper-level fronts are quite common features within cyclones that form east of the Rockies.

Upper-level fronts develop when two airmasses aloft meet. The first airmass originates in the convergent (west) side of a trough in the upper troposphere. This air, located near the top of the troposphere or even in the lower stratosphere, is very cold. However, as the air descends in response to the convergence aloft, it warms at the dry adiabatic lapse rate, dries, and is carried eastward by the jetstream winds. The airmass ahead of the upper-level front originates in the lower troposphere, east of the trough axis. This air, which

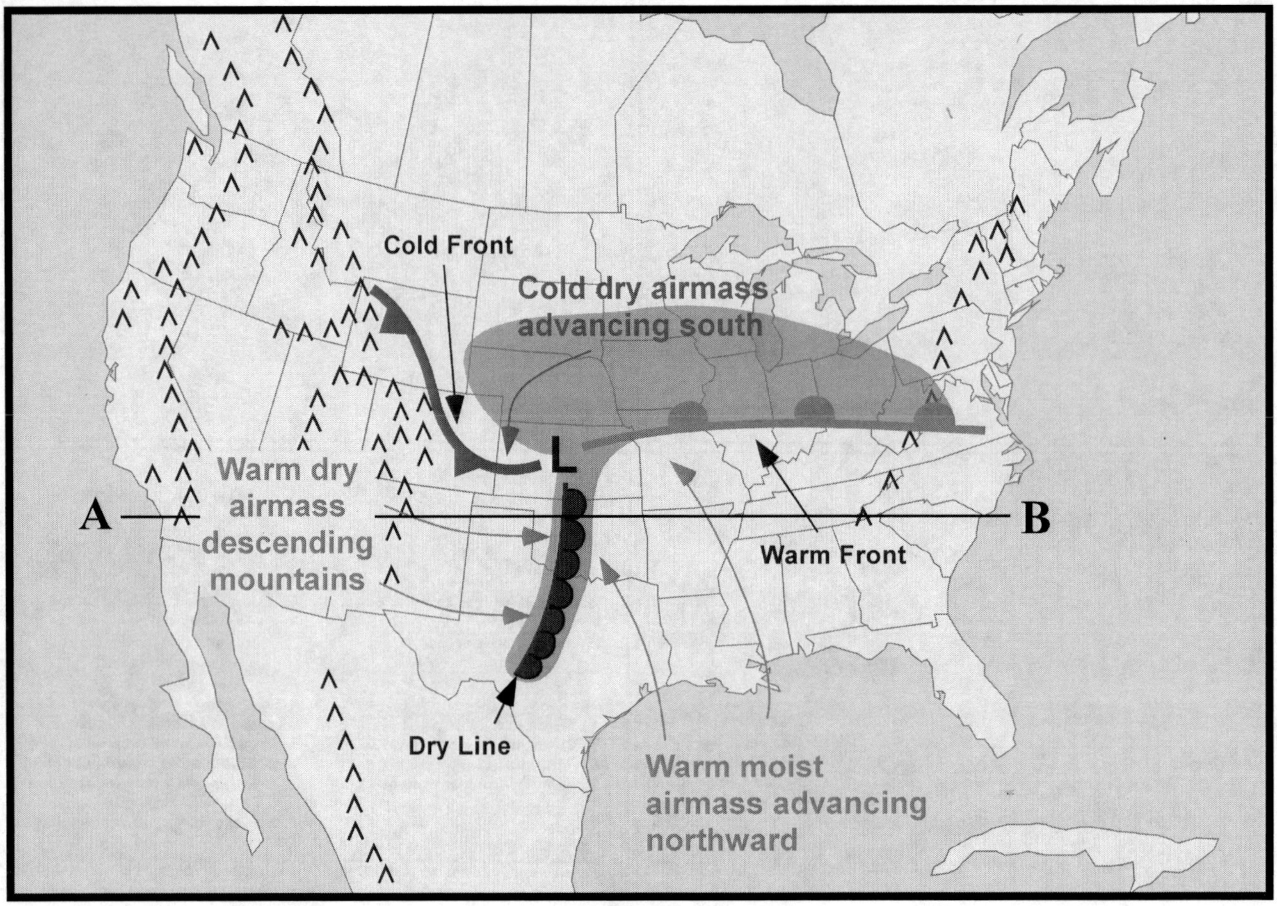

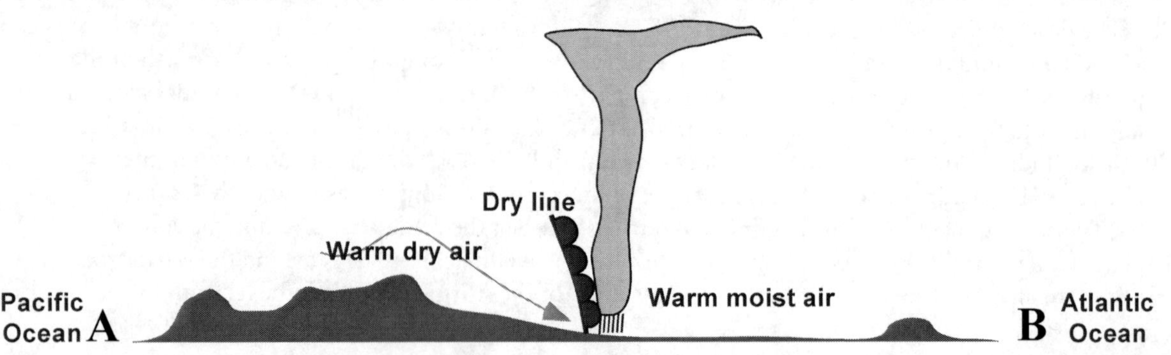

Figure 3.8 A dry line develops as warm dry air descends the east side of the Rocky Mountains. Ahead of the dry line, warm moist air, which originated over the Gulf of Mexico, is lifted. In this example, the warm moist air ahead of the front is conditionally unstable so that lifting at the dry line triggers a line of thunderstorms as illustrated in the cross section below the map.

initially is quite warm, rises and becomes saturated, cooling at the moist adiabatic lapse rate. The boundary where these two airstreams meet is characterized by a very sharp change in humidity and modest to little change in temperature. The reason there is often not a sharp temperature contrast across the upper-level front is that the descending airstream has warmed dry adiabatically, and the ascending airstream cooled moist adiabatically, to near the same temperature at the boundary where the airmasses meet. The upper-level front does *not* appear as a sharp boundary in *surface* temperature or moisture fields, since it does not extend to the surface. As the warm moist air east of the upper-level front is lifted by the dry air advancing from the west, strong thunderstorms can be triggered along the upper-level front.

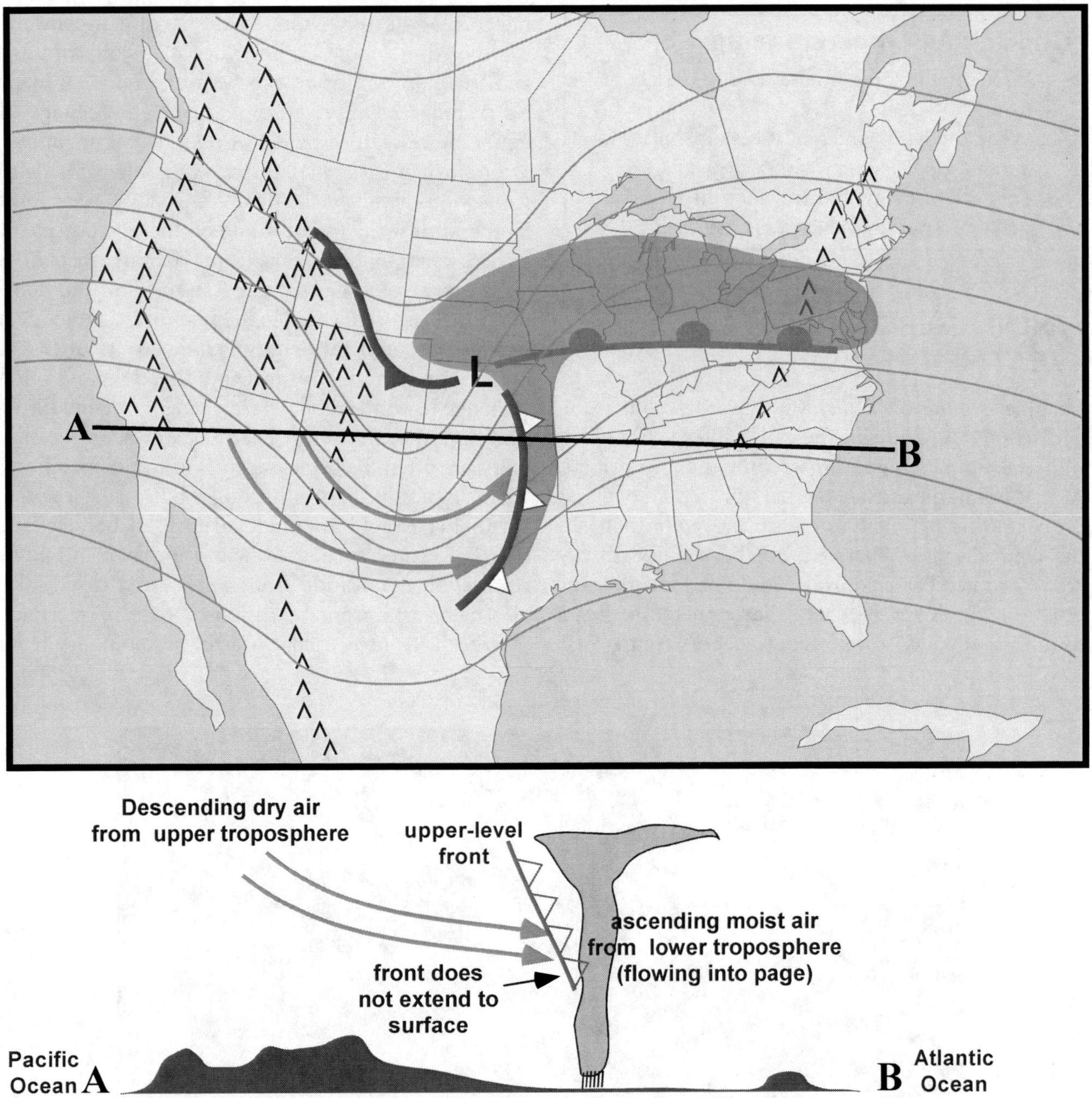

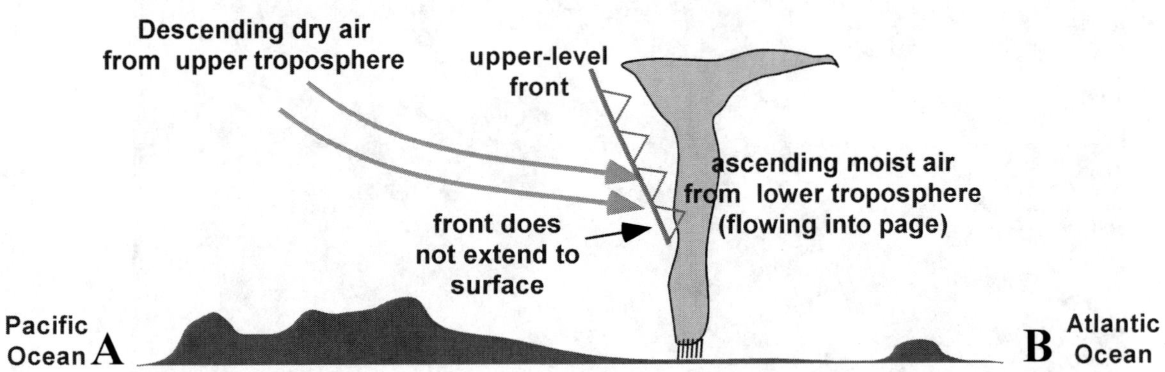

Figure 3.9 This figure illustrates both surface conditions and the upper tropospheric height pattern when an upper-level front is present. Cloud cover is depicted as gray shading. The solid lines denote height contours on the 500 mb surface. The lower panel of the figure shows the upper-level front in cross section AB.

In general, an upper-level front is likely to be present if (1) a sharp line of storms exists with clear air to the west of the line and (2) no significant change in the temperature or dewpoint temperature appears at the surface across the line of storms. Upper-level fronts develop in the same general region as dry lines. The primary distinction between these two fronts is that dry lines are surface based, while upper-level fronts are only found aloft. Air west of the dry line originates at low levels over the high plateau of the desert southwest. Air west of an upper-level front originates in the upper troposphere and lower stratosphere.

> **Check Your Understanding 3.2**
> 1. What are the three criteria used to classify fronts?
> 2. What are the six different types of fronts? How are they depicted on weather maps?
> 3. For each of the six fronts, which airmass is most dense and which airmass is lifted?

FINDING FRONTS ON WEATHER MAPS

Imagine driving on a highway toward a cold front. The temperature outside the car would remain warm until the moment the car crossed into the cold airmass. At that point, the outside temperature would begin to drop, continuing to fall as the car moved farther into the cold airmass. Where would the position of the cold front be? The cold front would be located at the point on the highway where the temperature *began* to fall rapidly. On surface maps such as Figure 3.10, meteorologists often plot contours of temperature. The position of the leading edge of a cold airmass, and therefore the front, can be found on such maps by examining temperature gradients (the change of temperature with distance). *A cold, warm, or stationary front will be located on the warm edge of a sharp temperature gradient.* In many cases, lower dewpoint temperatures will also be found on the cold air side of a cold, warm, or stationary front. For this reason, the leading edge of a sharp gradient in the dewpoint temperature can also be used to identify fronts. Other data can also be used to identify fronts. Fronts often are marked by a sharp shift in wind direction, and often a change in wind speed. Sharp changes in wind direction and speed between nearby stations on weather maps are often the best indicators of frontal positions. Fronts typically align with troughs in the surface pressure field (see cold front in Figure 3.10). Characteristic frontal weather, such as a line of showers or thunderstorms, or a transition from a clear to a cloudy sky, also help mark frontal locations. One can determine whether a front is a cold, warm, or stationary front

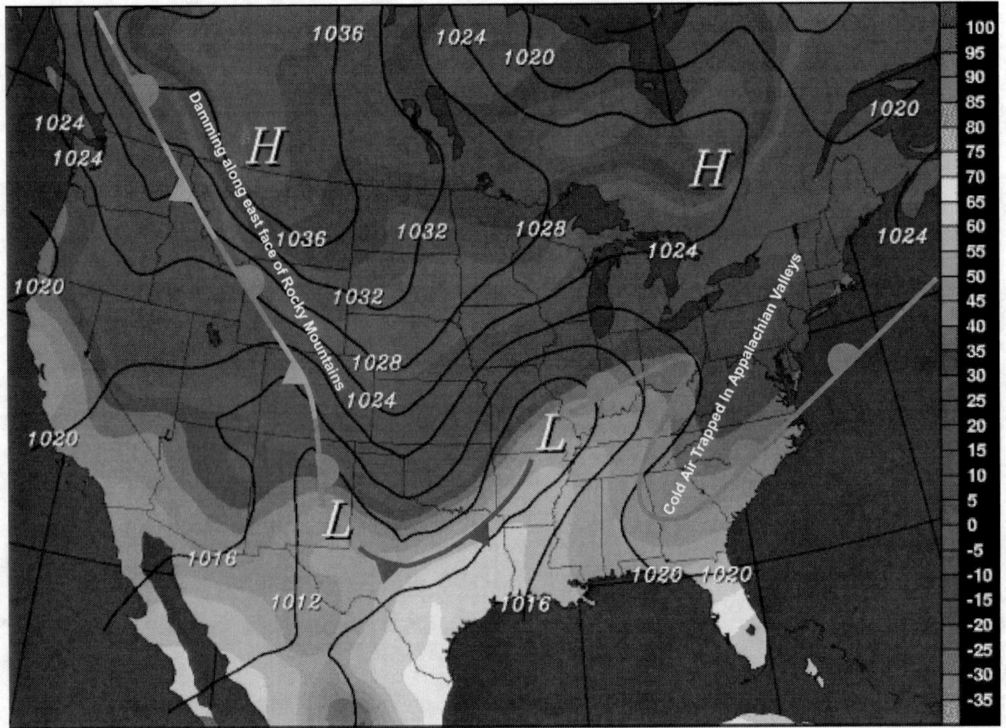

Figure 3.10 Analysis of sea-level pressure and surface temperature on a winter day in December. Note the effects of cold air trapping in the Appalachians and cold air damming on the east side of the Rocky Mountains.

by carefully examining the wind direction at stations near the front on its cold side. If the wind on the cold side blows toward the front, it is a cold front; away from the front, a warm front; and along the front, a stationary front. Occluded fronts develop late in the life of cyclones. Occluded fronts typically coincide with a sharp wind shift, with cold air on both sides of the boundary marked by the wind shift. Widespread clouds and light to moderate precipitation often accompany occluded fronts.

Dry lines appear as sharp gradients in dewpoint temperature, and are most common in the south-central United States east of the Rockies. Be careful not to confuse cold fronts with dry lines when looking at dewpoint temperature maps. Cold fronts have sharp surface temperature and dewpoint gradients day and night, while dry lines show up in daytime with strong surface dewpoint gradients but weak or no temperature gradients. At night, dry lines appear in surface data more like cold fronts. The reason for this diurnal change has to do with the difference between the daily cycle of heating and cooling on the west and east side of a dry line. The surface temperature on the dry side of a dry line undergoes rapid change from day to night because the skies are clear and dry. The moist side of a dry line is often hazy or cloudy and typically experiences small diurnal changes in surface temperature. Dry lines are typically marked by a wind shift, with southerly winds to the east, and westerly winds to the west of the boundary.

Upper-level fronts are only found aloft and are therefore difficult to identify on surface maps. An important signature of an upper-level front is a pressure trough in the surface data. This pressure trough may also have with it a slight wind shift. Upper-level fronts also coincide with lines of showers and precipitation. In general, if a line of showers moves over a region and surface conditions change little from before to after the passage of the line, there is a good chance that an upper-level front has passed. If it appears from surface data that an upper-level front has passed, the existence of the front aloft can be confirmed by examining the humidity and temperature on upper-level charts such as the 700 or 500 mb chart.

The Rocky Mountains in western North America extend from northern Canada into Mexico. Cold airmasses flowing southward from central Canada are often so shallow that they cannot flow westward over the Rockies, which act like a dam, trapping cold air on their east side. On surface weather maps, meteorologists draw stationary fronts to indicate the western edge of cold airmasses dammed along the mountains. These stationary fronts are not boundaries between airmasses, but rather boundaries between air and rock! (see Figure 3.10). Cold air damming also occurs on the east side of the Appalachians. When cold continental air arrives on the east side of the Appalachians, warm moist air moving westward off the Atlantic sometimes forces the cold air into a narrow wedge between the coastline and the Appalachian mountain chain.

Cold air damming and trapping also frequently occurs along and within the Appalachian Mountains. The Appalachians consist of parallel ridges and valleys that extend from Georgia and Alabama to Maine. Often after a cold airmass moves across the eastern United States, cold air will settle into the Appalachian valleys. When a new storm system approaches from the west, warm air will advance northward on both the west and east sides of the Appalachian chain, leaving the denser cold air trapped in the interior valleys. Meteorologists indicate cold air damming and trapping by drawing distorted warm fronts that wrap southward around the west side of the Appalachians and northward again on the east side. The effects of cold air damming by the Rocky Mountains and damming and trapping in the Appalachians both appear on the wintertime surface map shown in Figure 3.10. Figures 3.7 through 3.9 also imply damming of cold air by the Rocky Mountains.

Check Your Understanding 3.3

1. List at least five variables that can be used to identify the position of fronts on weather maps.
2. Where do cold air damming and cold air trapping typically occur?
3. How would you identify a dry line on a map of station reports?

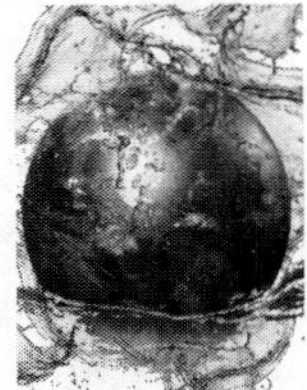

WATER PLANET EXERCISE 3

Name: ______________________________

Weather Maps and Humidity

1. Fill in the chart based on locations of fronts and pressure systems on this June weather map.

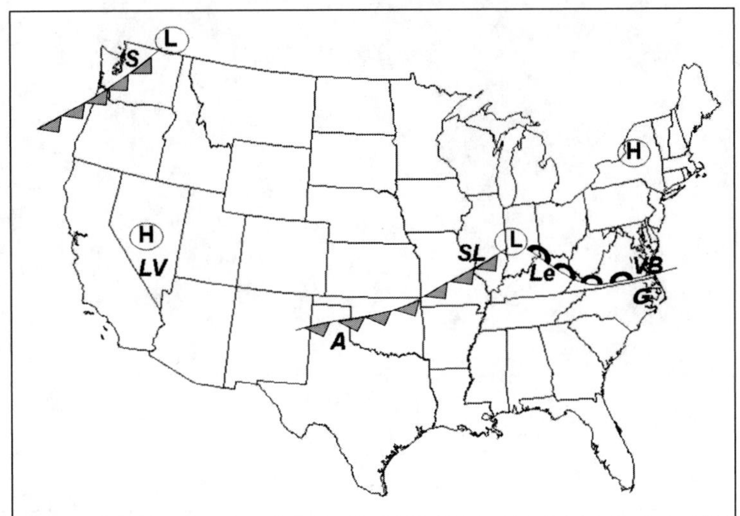

Location	Temperatures (cold, cool, warm, hot, or colder/warmer than normal)	Cloud presence (likely, unlikely) and Type if likely (cumulonimbus, nimbostratus)	Precipitation Type, if any (rain, snow)	Responsible lifting mechanism or pressure type for weather this day
Seattle, WA				
Las Vegas, NV				
Greenville, NC				
Amarillo, TX				

2. Of these locations, where would relative humidity likely be lowest? ______________________
Why? ______________________

3. On the map, draw arrows showing the direction of wind flows associated with each front.

4. Which direction do winds and frontal systems usually travel in the United States? ______________

Draw and name the two types of air rising methods (lifting mechanisms) that you are most likely to see in Eastern North Carolina in summer.

5. ______________________ 6. ______________________

Time	Air Temp (F)	Heat Index	Relative Humidity	Dew Point Temp. (F)
6:00 AM	78	82		78
10:00 AM	85	92	67%	72
12:00 PM	90	96	53%	66
4:00 PM	97	104	40%	61
10:00 PM	85	91	65%	72

Weather Data Interpretation: Use above chart of Greenville July weather for these questions:

7. The Relative Humidity at 6:00 AM should be ______________________.

8. As the day progresses from 10 AM to 4 PM, the air temperature normally __________, while the relative humidity ______________.

9. In order to exercise at the coolest part of the day **while it is still daylight**, a runner should go outdoors for a run at this time ______________.

10. What might you see when the Dew Point temperature and Air temperatures are the same? ______________
____

Chapter 4

TROPICAL CYCLONES

On November 12, 1970, a tropical cyclone moved northward across the Bay of Bengal toward the coast of what is now the country of Bangladesh. The storm's winds drove ocean water toward the shore, creating a surge that caused the sea to rise 15 to 20 feet (5 to 6 meters), flooding a densely populated low-lying region without warning in the early hours of the morning. The flood drowned over a half-million people, with 100,000 additional people never found. Twenty-one years later, a similar storm killed over 140,000 people in the same region. In October of 1998, Hurricane Mitch moved into the mountains of Honduras and Nicaragua in Central America causing floods and mudslides that left over 11,000 people dead and 8,000 missing. And most recently, in 2005, Hurricane Katrina devastated the Gulf Coast, destroyed much of the city of New Orleans, Louisiana, and left 1,836 people dead and over $80 billion in damage (2005 U.S. dollars) in its wake. In this chapter, we will learn why and how these storms form, why they cause so much devastation, and how forecasters use modern technology to warn those in harm's way as these great storms approach the coastlines.

Tropical cyclones are the most destructive storms on the planet. They always originate over tropical oceans, but their paths can take them into the middle latitudes and over land. The name ***hurricane*** is used to describe strong tropical cyclones that occur over the Atlantic and Eastern Pacific Oceans. The storms are called ***typhoons*** when they occur over the western Pacific and ***cyclones*** when they occur over the Indian Ocean. Since this chapter emphasizes tropical cyclones that affect North America, we will refer to tropical cyclones generically as hurricanes.

Meteorologists classify storms in the tropics based on their maximum sustained wind speeds. The maximum sustained wind in the United States is based on one-minute averages. Outside the United States, the maximum sustained wind is based on ten-minute averages. The technical definitions of tropical storm systems are given in Table 4.1. A ***tropical disturbance*** is a tropical weather system of apparently organized thunderstorms, generally about 250 to 600 km (~150–350 miles) in diameter, originating in the tropics or subtropics that maintains its identity for twenty-four hours or more. It may or may not be associated with a detectable perturbation of the wind field. When a cluster of thunderstorms has an identifiable surface pressure drop and a closed wind circulation, but its winds do not exceed 34 knots, it is classified as a ***tropical depression*** and is assigned a number, the first of the year called "tropical depression #1," the second "tropical depression #2" and so on. A storm is given a name when wind speeds increase to ***tropical storm*** strength (>34 knots). It keeps this same name through the rest of its life cycle.

There are name lists for all regions where tropical cyclones develop, including the Atlantic, eastern North Pacific, central North Pacific, Australia's oceanic areas, and the Indian Ocean. Hurricanes that affect North

Table 4.1 Classification of Tropical Weather Systems.

Organized thunderstorm cluster, no closed circulation	Tropical disturbance
Identifiable pressure drop and closed circulation	
Wind < 34 kts (39 MPH)	Tropical depression
34 kts ≤ wind < 64 kts (74 MPH)	Tropical storm
64 kts ≤ wind	Hurricane

America form in the tropical Atlantic Ocean and adjacent water bodies such as the Gulf of Mexico and Caribbean Sea, and in the eastern Pacific off the coast of Central America. Eastern Pacific hurricanes sometimes make landfall in Mexico, with the hurricane remnants moving over the deserts of the southwest United States and Mexico. Others of these hurricanes drift westward and strike Hawaii. The Atlantic name list for hurricanes from 2008 through 2013 is provided in Table 4.2. The list is alphabetical, skips letters that have few names (Q, U, X, Y, Z), alternates male and female names, and uses names from the English, Spanish, and French languages. Only once, in 2005, was the assigned list of names exhausted. When this

Table 4.2 Atlantic Hurricane Name List.

2008	2009	2010	2011	2012	2013*
Arthur	Ana	Alex	Arlene	Alberto	Andrea
Bertha	Bill	Bonnie	Bret	Beryl	Barry
Cristobal	Claudette	Colin	Cindy	Chris	Chantal
Dolly	Danny	Danielle	Don	Debby	Dean
Edouard	Erika	Earl	Emily	Ernesto	Erin
Fay	Fred	Fiona	Franklin	Florence	Felix
Gustav	Grace	Gaston	Gert	Gordon	Gabrielle
Hanna	Henri	Hermine	Harvey	Helene	Humberto
Ike	Ida	Igor	Irene	Isaac	Ingrid
Josephine	Jaoquin	Julia	Jose	Joyce	Jerry
Kyle	Kate	Karl	Katia	Kirk	Karen
Laura	Larry	Lisa	Lee	Leslie	Lorenzo
Marco	Mindy	Matthew	Maria	Michael	Melissa
Nana	Nicholas	Nicole	Nate	Nadine	Noel
Omar	Odette	Otto	Ophelia	Oscar	Olga
Paloma	Peter	Paula	Philippe	Patty	Pablo
Rene	Rose	Richard	Rina	Rafael	Rebekah
Sally	Sam	Shary	Sean	Sandy	Sebastien
Teddy	Teresa	Tomas	Tammy	Tony	Tanya
Vicky	Victor	Virginie	Vince	Valerie	Van
Wilfred	Wanda	Walter	Whitney	William	Wendy

*Hurricane names retired in 2007 will be replaced on the 2013 list.

happens, additional storms are given names from the Greek alphabet: Alpha, Beta, Gamma, Delta, and so on. Names of particularly devastating hurricanes have been "retired" from the list. Recent retired names include Katrina (2005), Wilma (2005), Rita (2005), Jeanne (2004), and Ivan (2004). With the exception of retired names, the list repeats itself after six years, so that the 2008 list will appear again in 2014.

Tropical cyclones reaching hurricane intensity (> 64 knots) are classified according to the ***Saffir-Simpson intensity scale***. The Saffir-Simpson scale, shown in Table 4.3, rates hurricanes from 1 to 5, with 5 being the strongest. The scale is based on sustained wind speeds and the minimum central pressure of the storms. Through early September of the 2007 season, only thirty-one Atlantic Basin hurricanes have been rated category 5, and only a fraction of those have made landfall with that intensity. Until 2007, no more than one hurricane has made landfall as a category 5 in a single year. That record was broken when Dean (2007) struck the Yucatan Peninsula of Mexico and Felix (2007) made landfall in central America within two weeks of each other in late August and early September of 2007. The last category 5 to make landfall in the United States (southern Florida) was Andrew (1992). In 2005, a record four hurricanes, Emily, Katrina, Rita, and Wilma, reached category 5 intensity, with Wilma setting new records for the Atlantic Basin. Wilma reached its peak sustained wind speed of 160 knots on October 19. During the strengthening episode, Air Force reconnaissance observations indicated that the eye of the hurricane contracted to a diameter of 4 km; the smallest eye yet recorded, and the estimated minimum central pressure fell to 882 mb, also a new record.

Worldwide, tropical cyclones cause extreme disaster and loss of life. The worst fatalities occur in Southern Asia, particularly at the North End of the Bay of

Table 4.3 Saffir-Simpson Scale.

Rating	Central Pressure (mb)	Winds mph (knots)	Storm surge ft. (m)	Typical Damage
1	≥ 980	74–95 (64–82)	4–5 (~1.5)	No real damage to building structures. Damage primarily to unanchored mobile homes, shrubbery, and trees. Some damage to poorly constructed signs. Also, some coastal road flooding and minor pier damage.
2	965–979	96–110 (83–95)	6–8 (~2.0–2.5)	Some roof, door, and window damage to buildings. Damage to shrubs and trees with some trees blown down. Considerable damage to mobile homes, poorly-constructed signs, and piers. Coastal and low-lying escape routes flood two to four hours before arrival of the hurricane center. Small craft in unprotected anchorages break moorings.
3	945–964	111–130 (96–113)	9–12 (~2.5–4.0)	Some structural damage to small residences and utility buildings. Large trees blown down. Mobile homes and poorly-constructed signs are destroyed. Low-lying escape routes are cut by rising water three to five hours before arrival of the hurricane center. Flooding near the coast destroys smaller structures, with larger structures damaged by battering from floating debris. Terrain continuously lower than 5 ft (1.5 m) above mean sea level may be flooded inland 8 miles (13 km) or more. Evacuation of low-lying residences within several blocks of the shoreline required.

(continued)

Table 4.3 Saffir-Simpson Scale (*Continued*)

Rating	Central Pressure (mb)	Winds mph (knots)	Storm surge ft. (m)	Typical Damage
4	920–944	131–155 (114–135)	13–18 (~4.0–5.5)	Complete roof structure failures on small residences. Shrubs, trees, and all signs are blown down. Complete destruction of mobile homes. Extensive damage to doors and windows. Low-lying escape routes may be cut by rising water three to five hours before arrival of the hurricane center. Major damage to lower floors of structures near the shore. Terrain lower than 10 ft (3 m) above sea level may be flooded requiring massive evacuation of residential areas as far inland as 6 miles (10 km).
5	< 920	> 155 (> 135)	> 18 (> 5.5)	Roof failure on many residences and industrial buildings. Some complete building failures with small utility buildings blown over or away. All shrubs, trees, and signs down. Complete destruction of mobile homes. Severe window and door damage. Low-lying escape routes cut by rising water three to five hours before arrival of hurricane center. Major damage to lower floors of all structures located less than 15 ft (4.5 m) above sea level and within 500 yards of the shoreline. Massive evacuation of residential areas on low ground within 5 to 10 miles (8 to 16 km) of the shoreline required.

Bengal in Bangladesh and India, as discussed in the introduction to this chapter. In the United States, loss of life has been greatly reduced due to new technological advances, such as satellites and computer forecast models, as well as excellent warnings, evacuation procedures, and public education. Yet in extremely vulnerable urban areas, these can all fail, as was clearly demonstrated when Hurricane Katrina devastated New Orleans and the Gulf Coast in 2005. In the early part of the previous century, when hurricane detection was still a problem and little was known about these storms, over 8,000 people died in Galveston, Texas—the worst number of fatalities in a hurricane in the United States. Loss of life continues to be a serious problem in poorer Caribbean nations despite the excellent warning systems. For example, Mitch in 1998 was the second most deadly hurricane in the Atlantic basin in history, leaving over 18,000 people dead or missing. The ten deadliest hurricanes in the Atlantic Basin through 2006 are listed in Table 4.4. Hurricane Katrina (2005), with 1836 deaths confirmed, currently ranks twenty-eighth on this list.

The costs inflicted by hurricanes have been increasing. This can be attributed almost entirely to the explosion in coastal population and real estate development in areas vulnerable to hurricanes. The ten costliest tropical cyclones in the United States through 2006 appear in Table 4.5. The costs in Table 4.5 are limited to damage in the United States. The total in many of these storms is higher due to damage in other countries, but information is not consistently available for these regions. Note that Agnes (1972) barely reached hurricane intensity. This storm did enormous damage in the Northeast United States due to inland flooding. Six of the ten storms on this list occurred in the 2004 and 2005 seasons, a fact that emphasizes both the large number of Atlantic tropical cyclones in these years and the increased property values as coastal populations have grown in this century and the latter part of the last century.

Table 4.4 Ten Deadliest Atlantic Hurricanes through 2006.

Hurricane	Year	Deaths[1]
1. Martinique, St. Eustatius, Barbadous, offshore	1780	>20,000
2. Mitch (Honduras, Nicaragua, Guatemala)	1998	>18,000[2]
3. Galveston, Texas	1900	>8000
4. Fifi (Honduras)	1974	>8000
5. Dominican Republic	1930	>8000
6. Flora (Haiti, Cuba)	1963	>7000
7. Guadeloupe	1776	>6000
8. Newfoundland	1775	>4000
9. Florida, Guadeloupe, Puerto Rico, Turk Islands, Martinique	1928	>4000
10. Puerto Rico, North and South Carolina	1899	>3000

[1]The number of deaths differ substantially in various data sources.
[2]Includes both confirmed deaths and missing persons.

Table 4.5 Ten Costliest Hurricanes in the United States (1900–2006) (Adjusted to 2005 dollars)

Hurricane	Year	Category (maximum intensity)	Category (landfall in U.S.)	Damage Costs (U.S. only)
1. Katrina (Louisiana, Gulf Coast, Florida)	2005	5	3	$81,200,000,000
2. Andrew (Florida and Louisiana)	1992	5	5	$44,900,000,000
3. Wilma (Florida)	2005	5	3	$20,600,000,000
4. Charley (Florida, S. Carolina)	2004	4	4	$15,400,000,000
5. Ivan (Alabama, Florida)	2004	5	3	$14,200,000,000
6. Hugo (South Carolina)	1989	5	4	$12,600,000,000
7. Agnes (Northeast United States)	1972	1	1	$11,600,000,000
8. Betsy (Florida and Louisiana)	1965	4	3	$11,100,000,000
9. Rita (Texas, Louisiana)	2005	5	3	$10,000,000,000
10. Frances (Florida)	2004	4	2	$ 9,100,000,000

FOCUS 4.1

Hurricane Katrina (2005)—A Warning Bell for Our Vulnerable Coastal Cities

Hurricane Katrina exposed fundamental flaws in hurricane preparedness in the United States. Studies by the Federal Emergency Management Agency and the Army Corps of Engineers, completed long before Katrina, clearly showed that a direct hurricane strike on New Orleans would lead to destructive flooding. *Scientific American* in 2001 published an article titled *Drowning New Orleans*, which detailed the destruction that occurred four years later! The *Houston Chronicle* published a story which predicted that a severe hurricane striking New Orleans "would strand 250,000 people or more, and probably kill one of ten left behind as the city drowned under twenty feet of water. Thousands of refugees could land in Houston." In fact, the previous edition of *Severe and Hazardous Weather*, published prior to Katrina, stated: *"New Orleans, protected by levees, lies below sea level. Should hurricane-driven floods top or break the protecting levees, the city would be inundated with seawater."* In short, the risk of catastrophic flooding in New Orleans was very well known. Despite many warnings and clear government and societal understanding of the threat, nothing was done to protect the city from the inevitable hurricane strike. Will this happen again?

Figure 4A Flooded neighborhood in New Orieans following Hurricane Katrina.

The threat of future destruction on the magnitude of Katrina is very real. All urban areas along the Atlantic and Caribbean coastlines and the entire Gulf of Mexico are threatened by storm surge and flooding when a major hurricane approaches, but several large urban areas, in addition to New Orleans, are particularly vulnerable. Tampa, Florida, for example, has no seawall or other storm protection and lies only feet above sea level. A major Gulf of Mexico hurricane moving eastward and making landfall just north of Tampa Bay could create a surge in the bay exceeding 5 m (16 ft) or more, putting much of the city under churning seawater. This nightmare scenario was almost realized in 2004, when Hurricane Charley approached Tampa from the south along the west coast of Florida. Charley, category 4 at landfall, made an unexpected turn inland south of Tampa, instead striking Punta Gorda and Ft. Myers, causing over $10 Billion in damage. The urban corridor on the Atlantic Coast between Miami and West Palm Beach, Florida is especially vulnerable to a major hurricane. Hurricane Andrew (1992), which struck south of this urban corridor, was the second most expensive hurricane on record. A direct hit by a hurricane of Andrew's strength on Miami or Ft. Lauderdale will dwarf the human and financial costs incurred in that storm.

Long Island, the large island east of New York City, currently has a population of 7.5 million. If the eye of a major hurricane would make landfall just west of the island, Long Island would experience major coastal flooding and destructive winds. The shoreline is very smooth and many parts of the island are only a few feet above sea level. Evacuation is a serious problem. Few highways cross to the mainland and traffic jams, which are common when there is not a hurricane, are a certainty. One of the greatest fears of emergency managers is that thousands of people trying to evacuate the island will be trapped in their cars in traffic jams as a hurricane strikes the coast. Manhattan Island in New York City is also vulnerable to coastal flooding associated with hurricanes. The financial and human costs of a catastrophic hurricane striking New York City are hard to imagine. Despite our understanding of the threats associated with hurricanes, preparation for the inevitable strike on an urban area continues to be a low priority for government and society.

FOCUS 4.2

The Record Setting Hurricane Season of 2005

The 2005 hurricane season was the most active season in recorded history and was remarkable for t he number of records that were broken. Twenty-seven named storms formed during 2005, the most named storms in a single season, breaking the record 21 set in 1933. Fourteen hurricanes formed during 2005, the most hurricanes in a single season, breaking the old record of 12 set in 1969. Seven major (category 3 or higher) hurricanes formed during 2005, tying the record set in 1950. Four category 5 hurricanes formed during 2005 (Emily, Katrina, Rita, and Wilma), the most ever recorded in a single season, breaking the old record of two set in 1960 and 1961. Seven named storms made United States landfall during 2005 (Arlene, Cindy, Dennis, Katrina, Rita, Tammy, and Wilma), a tie for second place behind the eight that occurred in 1916 and 2004.

The 2005 season was the most destructive for United States landfalling storms, largely due to Hurricane Katrina. Damage estimates for all hurricanes for 2005 exceeded $100 billion dollars. Five named storms (Cindy, Dennis, Emily, Franklin, and Gert), and two major hurricanes (Dennis and Emily) formed in July, the most on record in both categories for that month. Five named storms (Harvey, Irene, Jose, Katrina, and Lee) formed in August, surpassing

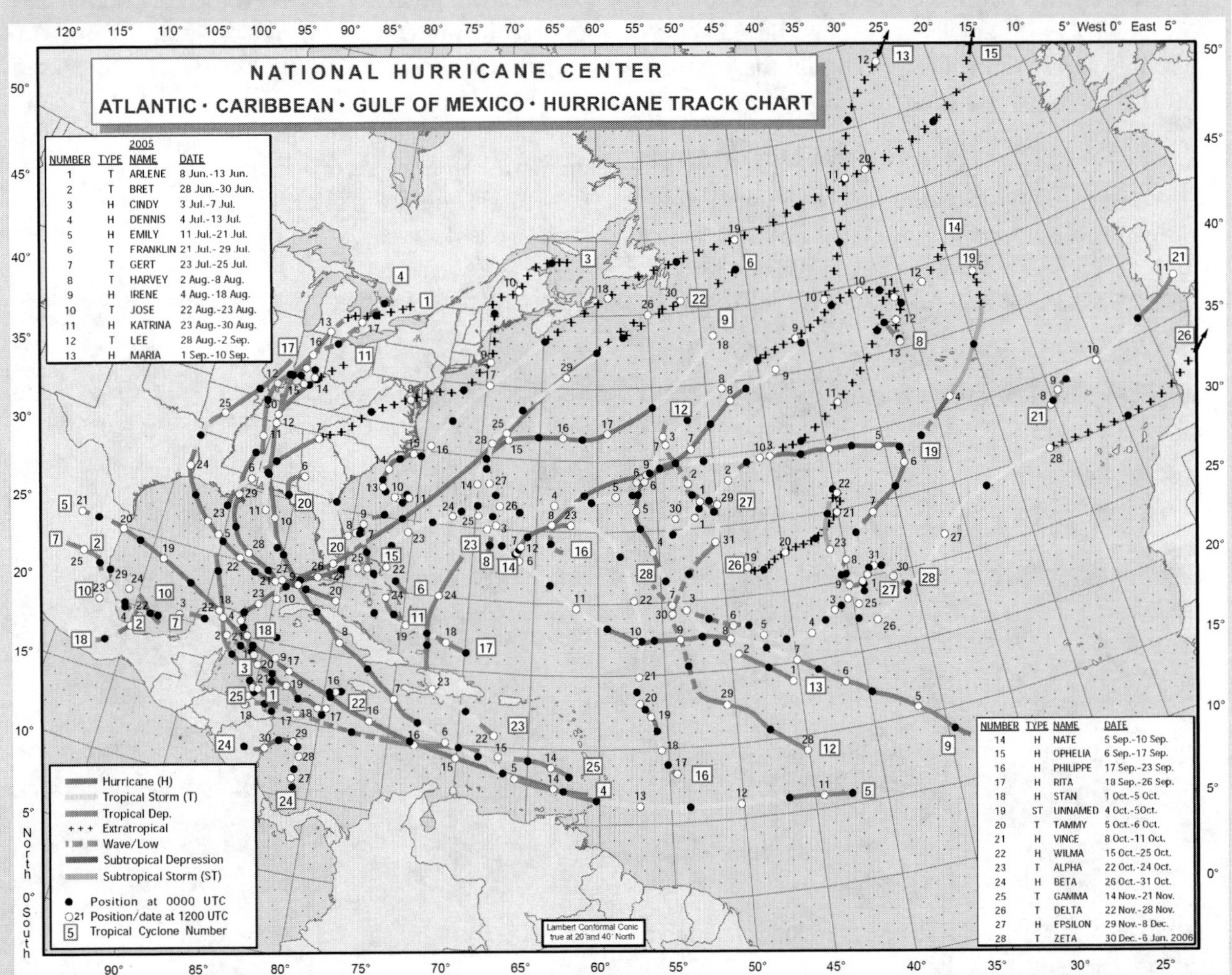

Figure 4B Map of tropical cyclone tracks during 2005.

(Continued)

FOCUS 4.2 (*Continued*)

the number of August storms in all years but 1990, 1995 and 2004. Five hurricanes (Maria, Nate, Ophelia, Philippe, and Rita) formed in September, tying 1955, 1969, 1981, 1998, and 2000 for the most hurricanes to form during that month. Six named storms (Stan, Tammy, Vince, Wilma, Alpha, and Beta) formed in October, tying 1950 for the most named storms forming during the month of October. Four hurricanes (Stan, Vince, Wilma, and Beta) formed in October, second only to 1950. Two intense hurricanes (Wilma and Beta) formed in October, tying 1950, 1961, 1964, and 1995 for the most intense hurricanes to form during that month. Finally, Epsilon was only the sixth hurricane to ever form in the month of December.

Individual hurricanes also set records or near records. Dennis became the most intense hurricane on record before August with a central pressure of 930 mb. Emily immediately eclipsed the record set by Dennis for lowest pressure in a pre-August hurricane with 929 mb. Emily was also the earliest category 5 storm on record. Katrina's central pressure dropped to 902 mb, at the time, the fourth lowest pressure ever measured in the Atlantic basin. Katrina became the most destructive storm on record with an estimated $81.2 billion dollars in damage, breaking the old record of approximately $44.9 billion dollars (normalized to 2005 dollars) set by Hurricane Andrew (1992). Rita's central pressure dropped to 897 mb, at the time, the third lowest pressure measured in the Atlantic basin.

Vince was the furthest north and east that a storm has ever developed in the Atlantic basin, and was the first tropical cyclone in recorded history to strike the Iberian Peninsula in Europe. Wilma's central pressure dropped to 882 mb, the lowest pressure ever measured in the Atlantic basin, eclipsing the record of 888 mb set by Hurricane Gilbert (1988). Zeta became the twenty-seventh named storm of the 2005 season, breaking the old record of twenty-one named storms set in 1933 and Epsilon became the fourteenth hurricane of the 2005 season, breaking the old record of twelve hurricanes set in 1969. Zeta also almost broke the record for the latest forming storm, missing the record set by Hurricane Alice in 1954 by six hours. Finally, the 2005 hurricane season itself broke the record—for breaking records!

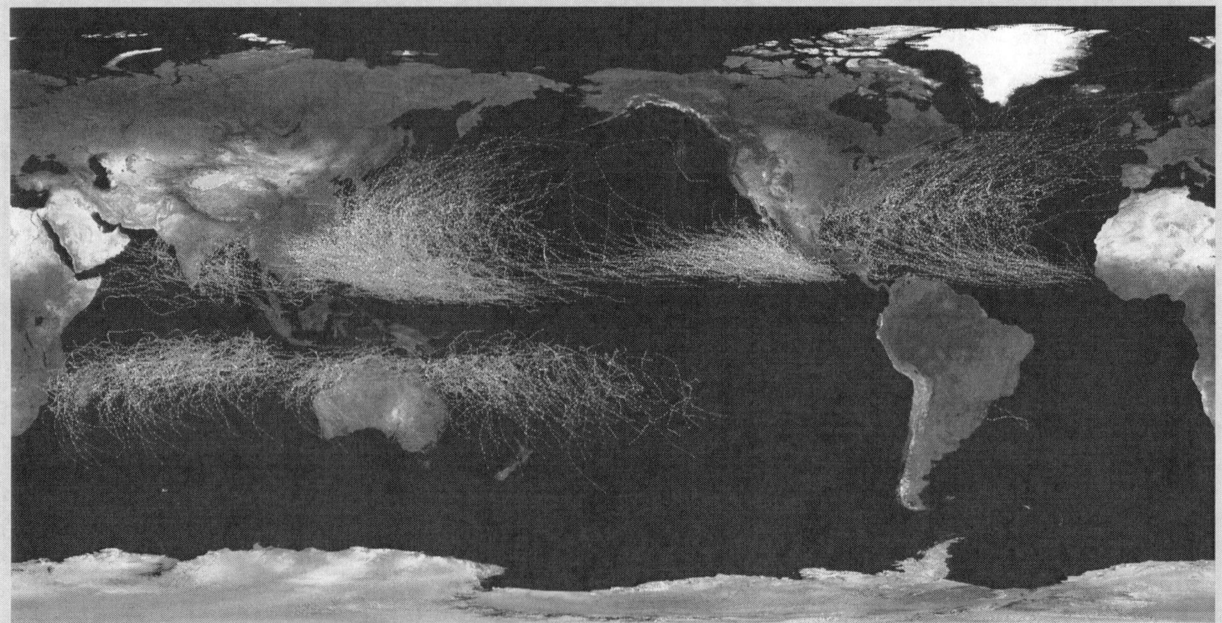

Figure 4.1 Tracks of all tropical cyclones that formed worldwide from 1985 to 2005.

WORLDWIDE HURRICANE OCCURRENCES

Figure 4.1 shows a map of tropical cyclone origins and tracks for a twenty-year period from 1985 through 2005. There are six important points related to this figure. (1) About 66 percent of all tropical cyclones occur in the Northern Hemisphere. All Atlantic and eastern Pacific, and most western Pacific and Indian Ocean tropical cyclones occur in the Northern Hemisphere summer and fall. Southern Hemisphere tropical cyclones develop in the Southern Hemisphere warm season. This prevalence of tropical cyclones in the Northern Hemisphere is because ocean temperatures in the Northern Hemisphere are generally warm over broader areas than in the Southern Hemisphere. (2) Hurricanes never originate within about 5 degrees of the equator, or cross the equator. The direction of air circulation about the low-pressure center of the hurricane is a result of both the pressure gradient and Coriolis forces. At the equator, the Coriolis force is zero, so the circulation of a hurricane could not persist. In fact, a hurricane would have to reverse direction to cross hemispheres. (3) Hurricanes rarely originate north (or south, in the Southern Hemisphere) of about 25 degrees latitude. The ocean water is generally too cold to provide the energy required for hurricane development. However, once formed, tropical cyclones often move to much higher latitudes before losing their tropical structure. (4) About 80 tropical storms develop annually around the globe. Between 50 to 70 percent of these develop into hurricanes. (5) The western Pacific in the Northern Hemisphere produces the largest number of tropical cyclones. The high frequency of tropical cyclones over the western Pacific is related to the high sea-surface temperatures in this region. 6) Hurricanes form over all tropical oceans except the south Atlantic and southeast Pacific. The surface water temperature is either too cold, or other atmospheric conditions are unfavorable to support hurricane development in the southeast Pacific and south Atlantic, with one very notable exception.

During the week of 22 to 28 March 2004, an extremely rare meteorological event took place in the southern Atlantic Ocean. A tropical cyclone developed from a cutoff extratropical system off the coast of Brazil. The system grew into a hurricane, with a clear eye and eyewall, as it moved toward the coast of Brazil (Figure 4.2). An unknown number of fishermen were lost at sea during the storm. Based on news reports, 35,000 homes were damaged or destroyed upon landfall, with damage to Santa Catarina estimated at $335 million. This storm, now referred to as Cyclone Catarina, became the first southern Atlantic hurricane in recorded history.

Figure 4.2 Cyclone Catarina off the coast of Brazil in the South Atlantic on 26 March 2004.

HURRICANE TRACKS

In summer in both hemispheres there are strong high-pressure centers located over the Atlantic and Pacific Oceans north of 30 degrees. Surface winds are normally easterly over the tropical oceans on the equator side of these high-pressure centers. This easterly wind flow is so persistent that early sailing ships depended on these winds to carry them westbound across the Pacific and Atlantic Oceans. Because of their early association with trade routes, the winds are called the ***trade winds*** or the ***easterly trades***. Hurricanes almost always form within the belt of trade winds, and normally move westward with these winds during their early lifetime. The Coriolis force also influences a hurricane's movement. A hurricane vortex is sufficiently large that the strength of the Coriolis force varies across the vortex from its equatorward to poleward side. This effect would cause a hurricane to drift westward and poleward, even if there was no background flow such as the trade winds. Eventually, hurricanes cross from the belt of easterly winds in the tropics into the belt of westerly winds in the mid-latitudes. Westerly winds steer a hurricane back toward the east around the north side of the high-pressure center.

Although many hurricane tracks will conform to the "normal" pattern described above, many take highly variable tracks that are anything but predictable. Panels A and B of Figure 4.3 show the paths of six different hurricanes. The three on Panel A had ordinary tracks, east to west, while drifting northward in tropical latitudes, and then west to east in middle latitudes. In contrast, the hurricane tracks shown on panel B are quite unusual.

Hurricane Kate (2003) began very far south in the trades and moved north-northwest, then turned northeastward toward Europe. It then abruptly turned westward after reaching the latitude of Georgia, and then finally turned northeast again after drifting westward. Olga (2001) formed at an unusually high latitude (30° N), and meandered over the Atlantic while drifting westward. The storm then took an abrupt turn to the southwest, approached the Bahamas, and then meandered again east of the Bahamas before dissipating. Perhaps the strangest track was Kyle (2002), which formed in the same area as Olga, drifted westward for weeks in the Atlantic while looping three times, then southwest to near the Florida coast, and finally northeast along the coastline to North Carolina. In general, hurricanes respond to the large-scale flows in which they are embedded, "drifting" within the background flows while interacting with them. Erratic tracks are most common when the background flow is weak.

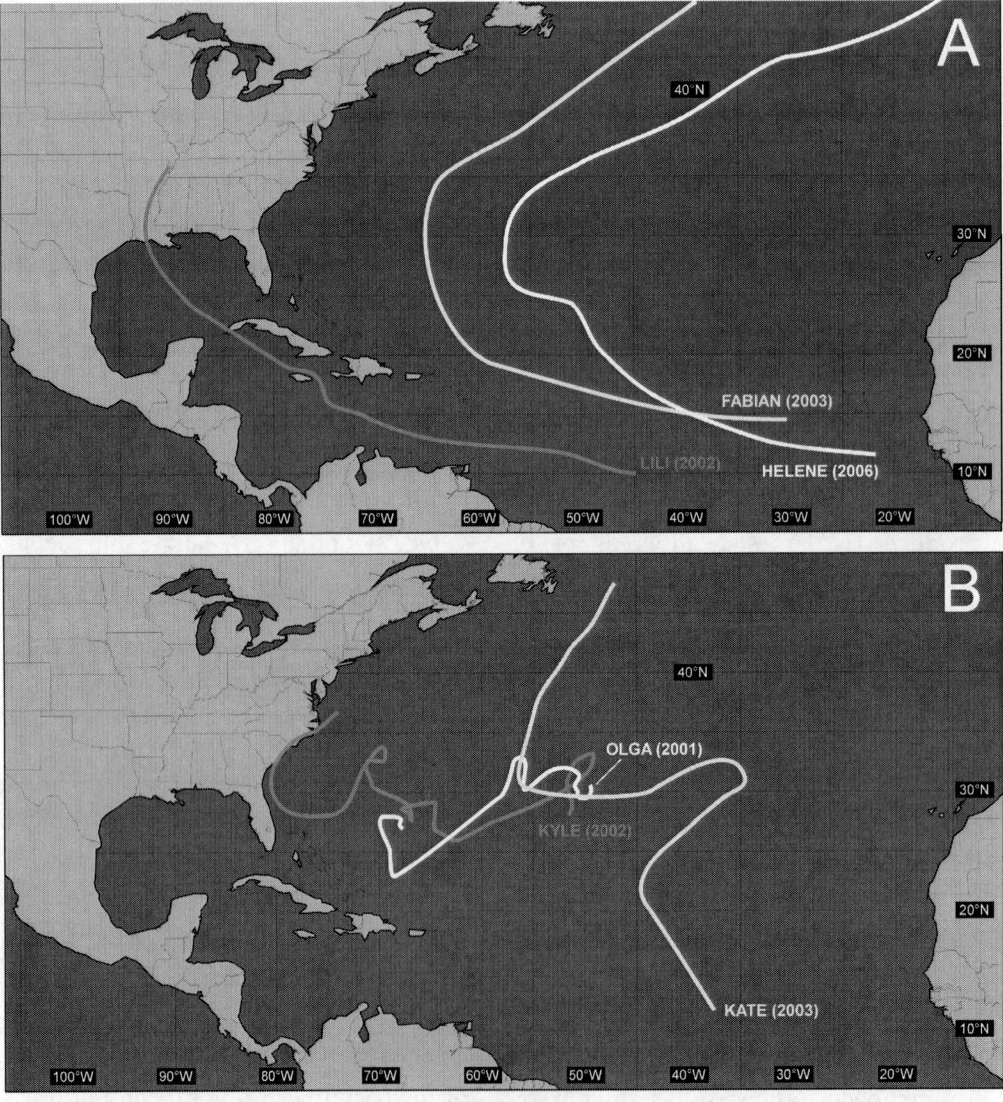

Figure 4.3 Typical (A) and unusual (B) tracks of some Atlantic hurricanes. The name and year of each hurricane are placed at the start of the track.

Check Your Understanding 4.1

1. By what weather variables are hurricanes and tropical storms ranked or categorized?
2. What is the Saffir-Simpson scale?
3. Describe the general trends in cost and fatalities associated with hurricanes.
4. Where do tropical cyclones form? Where do they not form?

HURRICANE STRUCTURE

In this section, we will examine the physical structure of a hurricane—its wind fields, air trajectories, pressure distribution, temperature distribution, cloud structure, rainband structure, the eyewall, and the eye. Figure 4.4 shows a satellite view of Hurricane Katrina (2005) while it was over the Gulf of Mexico. A hurricane typically appears as a large circular storm with spiral cloud bands extending away from its center. At the center of the hurricane is a prominent, nearly cloud-free area called the ***eye***.

The eye of a hurricane is one of the most spectacular locations in the Earth's atmosphere. The eye may be clear all the way to the ocean surface, but often has low-level clouds (referred to as ***scud clouds***) near its base. In strong hurricanes, such as Hurricane Isabel (2003) when it was category 5, these clouds are sometimes organized within small-scale vortices that rotate within the eye itself. Figure 4.5, for example, shows the "pinwheel" structure of the eye of Isabel (2003) at 1812 UTC on 13 September 2003.

Figure 4.4 Visible satellite image of Hurricane Katrina (2005). Important features of the hurricane are noted.

Figure 4.5 Visible satellite image showing four vortices within the eye of Hurricane Isabel at 1812 UTC on 13 September 2003.

ONLINE 4.1

The Eye of Isabel (2003)

The eye of Hurricane Isabel during the time the storm achieved category 5 intensity had four clearly identifiable small vortices rotating with it, giving the cloud pattern a pinwheel structure. The reason why these vortices form is still not well understood. Numerical models sometimes show transient features similar to these vortices. During Isabel, a NOAA research aircraft actually flew though these vortices and measured their structure, so we should be learning more about the vortices as research based on observations and modeling progresses. You can view these vortices in visible satellite imagery in the spectacular sequence of images of the eye of Isabel online.

ONLINE 4.2

Hurricane Katrina (2005)

Hurricane Katrina was the costliest and one of the deadliest hurricanes in the United States. The storm's evolution was captured by an array of satellites and radars as it made landfall in Florida, moved across the Gulf of Mexico, and made a second landfall in Louisiana. Online animations of radar reflectivity show Katrina from the perspective of the Miami and Key West, Florida radars as it moved across the state as a category 1 hurricane. These animations show the classic radar features of a hurricane—the eye, eyewall, and spiral rainbands. Animations of satellite data show the evolution of the hurricane from its formation east of Florida to its dissipation over the central United States, and its massive size as it became a category 5 storm over the Gulf of Mexico. Katrina's final landfall near New Orleans was documented by the New Orleans radar, until the radar itself succumbed to the storm's winds. Katrina's history and impacts are detailed online with the animations.

When viewed with radar, the hurricane's precipitation structure becomes more apparent. Surrounding the eye is a ring of deep convective clouds called the ***eyewall*** (see Figure 4.6), which extends from near the ocean surface to an altitude of about 15 km (9 miles). A ring of very heavy precipitation occurs within the eyewall, as can be seen from Figure 4.7, a radar image of the eyewall of Hurricane Andrew (1992) just before landfall in Florida. Air in the convective clouds that form the eyewall rises upward and radially outward, so that the convective clouds making up the eyewall form a shape like a funnel, with the storms violently rotating around

Figure 4.6 The eyewall of Hurricane Katrina at the time of maximum intensity. The clear eye, funnel shape, and sharp rotation are all evident from the cloud forms in the photograph that was taken from inside the eye.

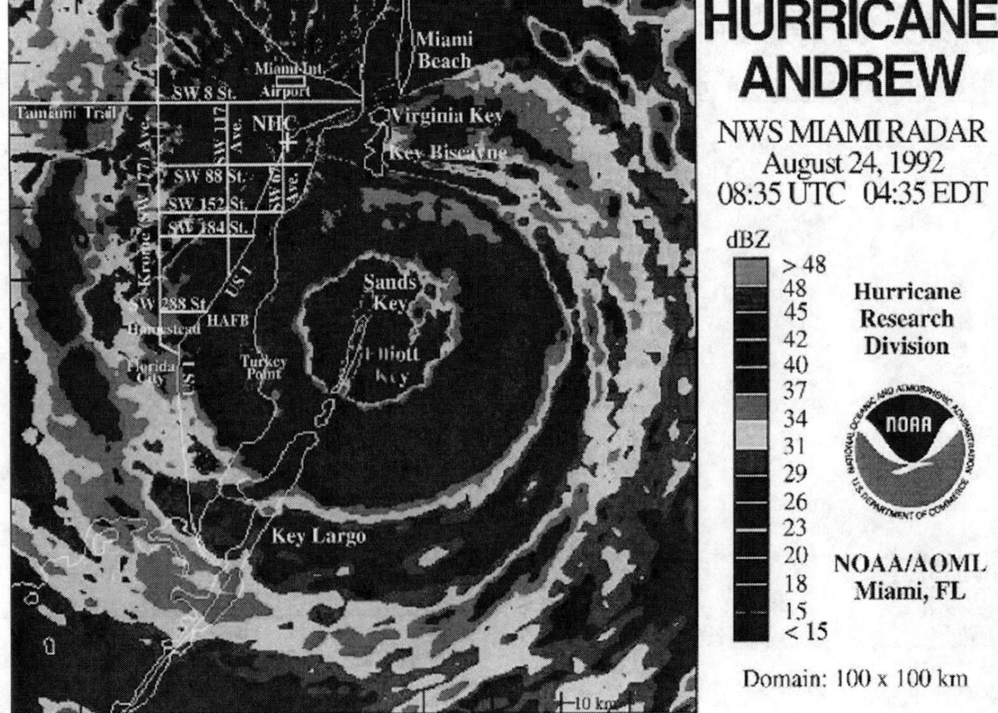

Figure 4.7 Radar reflectivity image of the eyewall of Hurricane Andrew as it made landfall on the coast of Florida as a category 5 storm.

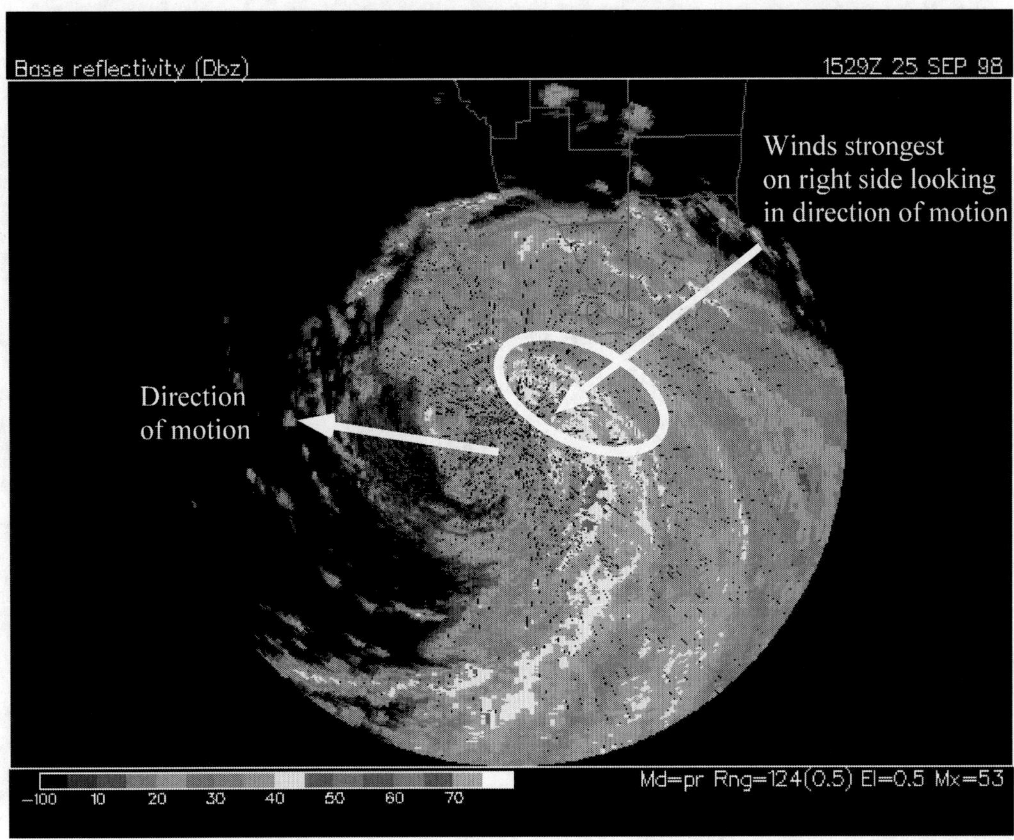

Figure 4.8 Hurricane Georges (1998) as viewed by Key West, Florida, radar. Note the asymmetry of the storm, and spiral rainbands extending outward from the center of the hurricane. The oval denotes the location of the strongest winds in Georges.

the eye. Outside the eyewall, precipitation can be quite light, although the winds are still moderately strong.

Heavier rain also occurs in ***spiral rainbands*** that extend outward from the eyewall. These bands are evident in the satellite image in Figure 4.4 and in the radar data from Hurricane Georges (1998) as it crossed Key West (Figure 4.8). Hurricanes are not necessarily as symmetric as implied by the eyewall of Andrew in Figure 4.7. In Georges, for example, almost all the rain was on the east side of the storm.

An oversimplified description of the airflow in a hurricane would be that the air spirals in at the surface, rises from the surface to the tropopause in the eyewall, and then spirals outward from the eyewall at the tropopause level. This description actually captures much of the process—as is demonstrated by the three-dimensional trajectories in Figure 4.9. Hurricanes also have ***secondary circulations*** associated with the eye, the spiral rainbands, and the regions between the spiral rainbands and the eyewall. These circulations, and other important features of hurricane structure, are shown in Figure 4.10, a cross section through a hurricane.

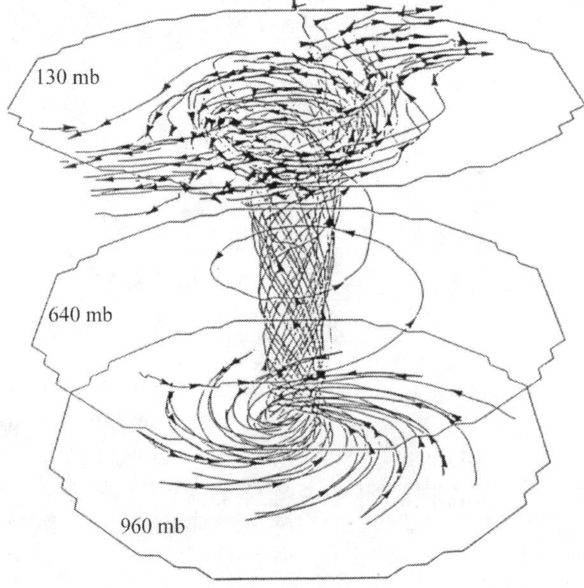

Figure 4.9 Trajectories of air parcels as they move through a numerically modeled hurricane. A full trajectory covers a period of eight days and each arrow head along a trajectory denotes a nine-hour interval.

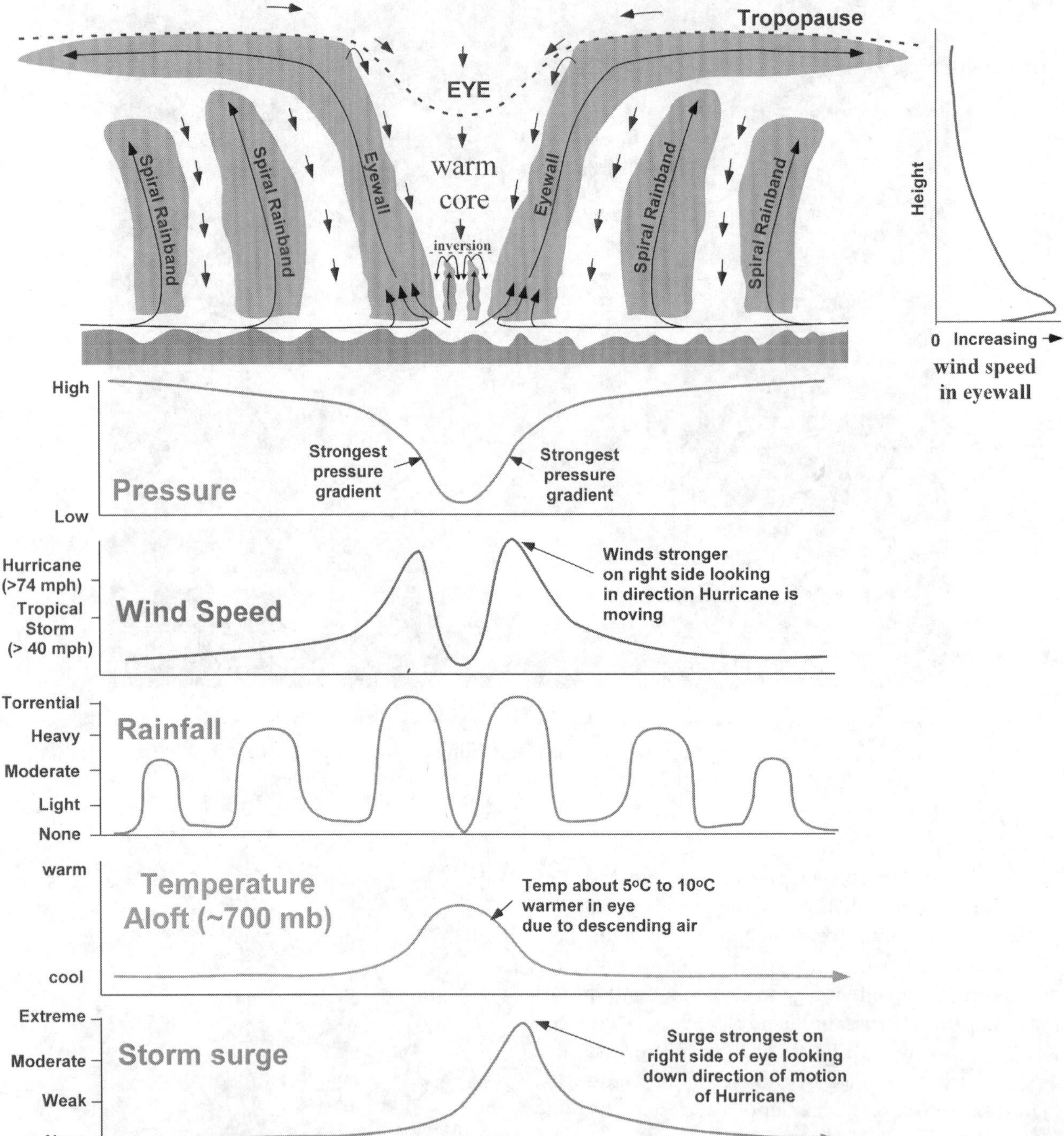

Figure 4.10 Top: A cross section through a hurricane showing the clouds (gray) and circulation (arrows). The remaining panels, from top to bottom, show the distribution of surface pressure, wind speed, rainfall, temperature at 700 mb, and the sea-level height (storm surge) across a hurricane. The cross section is drawn such that the hurricane is moving into the paper. The winds are strongest on the right side looking in the direction of hurricane motion. The rightmost top panel shows the variation of wind speed with altitude at the radius of maximum surface winds in the eyewall.

The top portion of the figure shows the location of the eye, eyewall, spiral rainbands, and vertical air motion within a hurricane. Below this diagram are five diagrams showing how the pressure, wind speed, rainfall, temperature, and storm surge vary across a hurricane. The diagram to the right of the top panel shows how the wind speed varies with height within the eyewall.

Air in the upper and middle troposphere is descending within the eye of a hurricane. Air descends into the eye from the stratosphere at the top of the eye (note the descent of the tropopause on Figure 4.10). Most of the air in the eye descends very slowly, taking days to traverse the eye's depth. However, air within the eye that is immediately adjacent to the eyewall descends more rapidly. In this region, mixing of dry air in the eye with cloudy air in the eyewall leads to evaporative cooling, which makes the air denser and prone to sinking. Air sinking in the eye warms at the dry adiabatic lapse rate, and is much warmer than in any other region of the storm. A reasonable question to ask is 'Why, if the air is so warm in the eye, does it sink? Shouldn't this air be buoyant?' Indeed the air *is* buoyant and would rise immediately except that another force is acting to prevent the air from rising. The extreme low pressure at the base of the eye of a hurricane significantly reduces the magnitude of the upward directed pressure gradient force. This causes the downward force of gravity to exceed the upward pressure gradient force, so much so that the downward acceleration of air by gravity slightly exceeds the upward acceleration of air due to the air's buoyancy. The net effect: air gradually descends in the eye, despite its warmth.

Air within the upper part of the eye does not descend completely to the ocean surface, but rather to about the 1.5 to 2.0 km (0.8 to 1.2 mile) level. The base of the descending air is marked by an ***inversion***. Within the layer between the inversion and the ocean surface, weak convection typically occurs, producing the scud clouds visible at the base of the eye in some hurricanes.

In the eyewall air ascends from the surface to the tropopause. Most air enters the base of the eyewall after spiraling inward over the ocean surface toward the eye. A small amount of air also enters the eyewall from the eye side (Figure 4.10). When air rises in the eyewall, it eventually encounters the tropopause and can no longer rise farther. Most of the air exhausts outward away from the center, creating the large shield of clouds visible on satellite images (e.g. Figures 4.2, 4.4 and 4.5). Some air exhausts inward, cools as the cloud evaporates, and then descends along edge of the eyewall. The strongest winds in a hurricane are found in the eyewall about 0.5 to 1.0 km (0.3 to 0.6 miles) above the ocean surface (Figure 4.10 top right diagram). Friction with the ocean surface keeps the strongest winds from extending to the surface.

Other secondary circulations in hurricanes involve the spiral rainbands. Some of the air converging toward the center of the hurricane rises along preferred regions of ***convergence*** in the flow. These convergence zones spiral out from the center and are the locations of the spiral rainbands. Except for the spiral rainbands, the air outside of the eyewall slowly descends to compensate for the ascent in the eyewall and spiral rainbands.

Moving toward the center of a hurricane from the clear region around its perimeter, the pressure drops slowly at first, but then drops very rapidly from the outer radius of the eyewall to the inner radius. This strong pressure gradient within the eyewall creates the powerful winds of the hurricane. Hurricane Andrew had an extremely strong pressure gradient compared to the location of its eyewall during landfall (Figure 4.7). Although the most violent winds are confined to the eyewall, strong winds can exist well over 100 km (~60 miles) from the center of the storm. Atmospheric pressure is lowest in the eye—the center of the hurricane. Inside the eye, the winds are nearly calm.

Note from Figure 4.10 that the wind speeds are higher on the right side of the eye, when looking in the direction the storm is moving. For example, if a storm were moving northward, the "right side" would be the east side. To understand why this is so, examine Figure 4.11. Winds in a hurricane circulate counterclockwise in the Northern Hemisphere. We can think of a hurricane as having "rotational velocity," the speed it is rotating, and a "translational velocity," the forward speed of the hurricane itself.

Let us assume that a hurricane is moving due north at 20 knots and rotating at 100 knots. Taking into account these two velocity components, the wind to the right of the eye at point B will have a translational component directed north and a rotational component also directed north. We therefore add 100 + 20 to obtain 120 knots. However, on the left side of the eye at point A, winds will have a northward translational velocity but a southward rotational velocity. We must subtract 100 − 20 = 80 knots to determine the wind speed on the left side. *Winds are always strongest to the right of the storm's direction of motion in the Northern*

FOCUS 4.3

RAINEX, Eyewall Replacement Cycles, and the Double Eyewall

Intense hurricanes such as Katrina (2005) and Rita (2005) often develop a *double eyewall*. The outer eyewall forms as outer rainbands contract into a closed ring about the inner eyewall. A wind maximum appears within each eyewall. Both the outer and inner eyewalls contract with time. Hurricanes typically reach peak intensity during the inner eyewall contraction period. The inner eyewall eventually weakens and dissipates, as the outer eyewall continues to contract and intensify. Once the inner eyewall disappears, the intensity of a hurricane will often decrease. This *eyewall replacement cycle* may occur more than once during a storm's lifetime.

The dynamics of hurricane intensification, particularly the eyewall replacement cycle, remain poorly understood. In 2005, hurricane researchers undertook an ambitious project to close this gap in our knowledge about hurricanes. The project, called the *Hurricane Rainband and Intensity Change Experiment, (RAINEX)*, was carried out in the heart of the record 2005 hurricane season, and involved three large aircraft (two NOAA P-3 hurricane hunter aircraft and the Naval Research Laboratory P-3). Scientists flew these aircraft, each equipped with dropwindsondes and dual-Doppler radar capability, across the eye and eyewalls of hurricanes to measure winds and reflectivity, as well as the storms' thermal, wind and moisture structure. One of their ambitions was to document the eyewall replacement cycle as it happens. On the afternoon of 22 September, the scientists hit the meteorological jackpot over the Gulf of Mexico—they flew the aircraft through the eye and double eyewall of Hurricane Rita while category 5 and while undergoing an eyewall replacement cycle (Figure 4C). They documented a clear double peak in the wind profile across the hurricane (Figure 4D), and obtained detailed data about the wind structure throughout the eyewalls. With the help of complementary hurricane numerical modeling studies they are pursuing, these unprecedented data will shed new light on how hurricanes reach category 5 intensities.

Over the course of RAINEX, scientists flew thirteen multi-aircraft missions through three hurricanes, Katrina, Ophelia, and Rita, sampling both Katrina and Rita while category 5. In addition to their many records, these storms are now the best documented in the history of hurricane research. Teams of scientists are now analyzing the RAINEX datasets to develop a better understanding of the eyewall replacement cycle and the process of hurricane intensification.

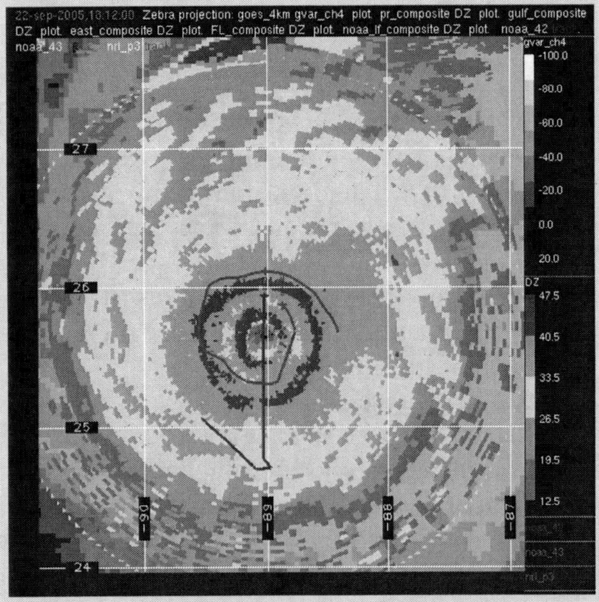

Figure 4C Overlay of radar (color) and satellite (gray) data collected during RAINEX during aircraft penetrations of the double eyewall of Hurricane Rita (2005) in its category 5 stage. The track of the Navy Research Laboratory aircraft is blue, and the NOAA aircraft is red.

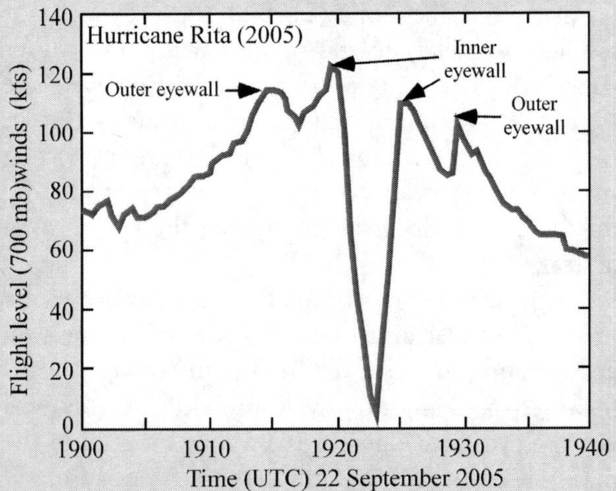

Figure 4D Flight-level winds measured aboard a NOAA aircraft on 22 September 2005 while crossing concentric eyewalls in Hurricane Rita.

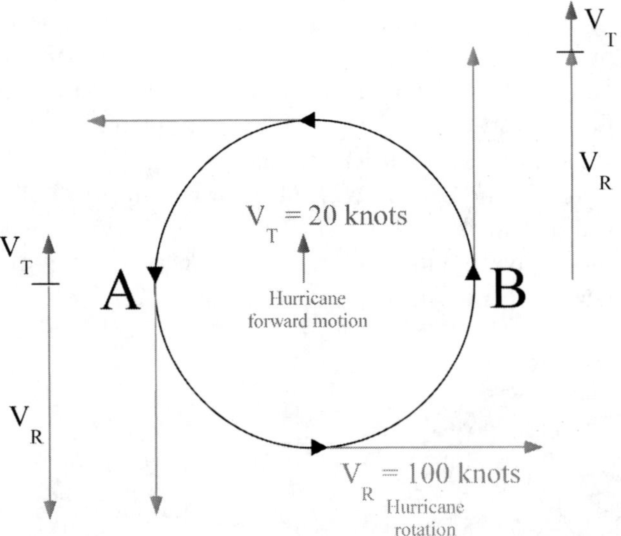

Figure 4.11 Illustration showing why winds are strongest on the right side of a hurricane looking in the direction of storm motion. In this figure, the hurricane has a rotational velocity (Vr) of 100 knots, while moving with a translational velocity (Vt) of 20 knots. At Point A, the wind = rotation − translation = 100 knots − 20 knots = 80 knots. At Point B, the wind = rotation + translation = 100 knots + 20 knots = 120 knots.

Hemisphere. Figure 4.8 outlines where the strongest winds were in Hurricane Georges as it crossed the Florida Keys.

Returning to Figure 4.10, we see that rainfall intensity varies substantially across a hurricane. No rain falls in the eye. The most violent rainfall occurs under the eyewall. Rain is light, if it is raining at all, about 80 to 120 km (50 to 75 miles) outside the eyewall, except in the spiral rainbands. Moderate to heavy rainfall can fall within these rainbands, with heavier rain typically occurring in the innermost spiral bands and lighter rain in the outer bands.

Descending air within the eye contributes to sharp warming of the core of a hurricane. Temperatures are significantly higher in the eye, with aircraft measurements of temperature showing increases as large as 11° C (20° F). Hurricanes are often referred to as ***warm core systems,*** in contrast to extratropical cyclones, which are ***cold core systems,*** having cold air aloft above the surface low during their most intense stages.

Storm surge is an abnormal rise in sea level associated with the movement of a hurricane over a coastal region. Notice in Figure 4.10 that storm surge is greatest to the right of the eye of the hurricane, again looking in the direction the storm is moving. The strong surge on the right side is directly related to the strength and direction of the wind. When a hurricane nears land, winds to the right of the eye are blowing onshore causing water to "pile up" along the coastline and the sea level to rise, while winds to the left of the eye are blowing offshore. Low pressure at the center of the eye also causes sea level to rise, enhancing the surge to the right of the eye, and compensating for decreases in sea level due to offshore winds to the left of the eye. Storm surge will be discussed in more detail later in the chapter.

Check Your Understanding 4.2

1. What path would an air parcel have if it were injected into a hurricane at the surface?
2. Why are wind speeds across a forward-moving hurricane not symmetric?
3. Where would you expect to find the heaviest rainfall rates in a hurricane?
4. Does the center of a hurricane have a warm or cold core? Why?

TROPICAL CYCLONE DEVELOPMENT

A cluster of thunderstorms must exist for a tropical cyclone to develop. In the tropics, thunderstorms seldom form unless convergence is occurring in the low-level flow to force air upward far enough to become unstable. Even when these thunderstorms form, the environmental conditions must be right for the thunderstorms to organize themselves into a tropical cyclone. In this section, we consider how tropical thunderstorms form, the environmental conditions that support the organization of the thunderstorms into a tropical cyclone, and the mechanism by which that organization occurs.

Trigger Mechanisms for Thunderstorms in the Tropics

Low-level convergence is required in the tropics to lift air sufficiently to trigger tropical thunderstorms. These local areas of convergence develop in three primary ways. To understand the first of these mechanisms, we must step back and examine the basic general circulation in the tropics. The top diagram of Figure 4.12 shows average horizontal and vertical circulations in the tropics. The most prominent features of the general circulation of the atmosphere in the tropics are the ***Hadley Cells***. These cells, one in each hemisphere, consist of rising motion along a belt near the equator, a poleward flow of air in the upper troposphere, descending motion centered around 25° north and south latitudes, and return flow near the surface toward the equator. This flow occurs in direct response to solar heating, which is maximum near the equator, and is a persistent feature of the tropics. Because of the Coriolis force, the poleward upper tropospheric branch of the flow turns eastward (westerly winds), and the lower equatorward branch of the circulation flows westward (easterly winds). The easterly trade winds discussed earlier are one branch of the Hadley circulation. The two Hadley Cells shift north and south with the seasons so that the point where they meet approximately follows the sun on its annual journey north and south.

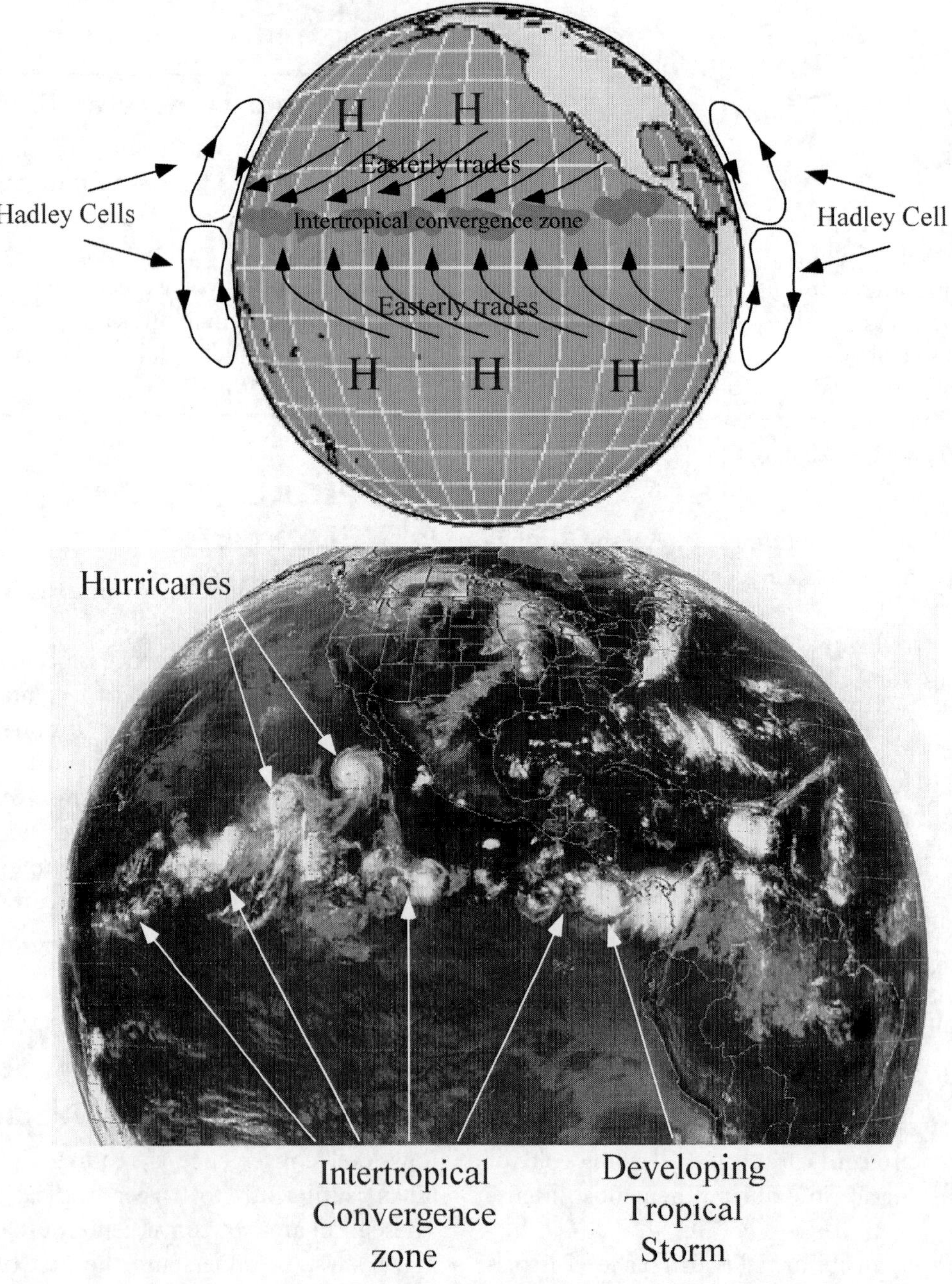

Figure 4.12 Top: Schematic showing the Hadley Cells, easterly trade winds, and the intertropical convergence zone. Bottom: An infrared satellite image from 26 July 1990 showing the ITCZ over the Pacific and several tropical storms in different stages of development.

Figure 4.12 shows the location of the Hadley Cells in late July, the middle of the Northern Hemisphere summer. At the surface, the flows in the north and south Hadley Cells collide in a zone of convergence called the ***Intertropical Convergence Zone (ITCZ)***. The ITCZ is a preferred location for thunderstorm formation (see bottom of Figure 4.12). When the ITCZ is far enough north (or south) of the equator so that the Coriolis force is sufficiently strong, a cluster of thunderstorms forming along it may sometimes organize into a hurricane, as illustrated in the lower panel of Figure 4.12. Worldwide, the ITCZ is the greatest source of hurricanes.

The second mechanism forcing convergence in the tropics is provided by "waves" in the easterly flow. These ***easterly waves*** are similar to the waves in midlatitude flow, except that they are in the low-level trade wind air. Figure 4.13 shows a schematic diagram illustrating several easterly waves moving across the Atlantic Ocean, and the position of cloud clusters relative to the waves. Examples of these cloud clusters, including one that intensified to become Hurricane Erika (1997), are shown in the satellite image of the Atlantic Basin in Figure 4.14. To understand how easterly waves create low-level convergence, we must turn to principles concerning changes in flow curvature and their effect on air acceleration.

Figure 4.15A shows a schematic of an easterly wave. Easterly waves are most apparent near the surface in the low-level airflow. Within the Hadley Cell in the Northern Hemisphere tropics, the highest pressure lies to the north at the oceanic subtropical high and the lowest pressure to the south at the ITCZ. In an easterly wave, *high-pressure ridges bulge southward, while low-pressure troughs extend northward,* the exact opposite of what appears in upper atmosphere midlatitude flow.

Air flows clockwise around ridges in the Northern Hemisphere at a velocity that exceeds the geostrophic value. Flow around a trough will be counterclockwise in the Northern Hemisphere and have a velocity that is less than its geostrophic value. As shown in Figure 4.15A, air flowing from the crest of the ridge to the base of the trough will decelerate and undergo convergence. Air in this region must rise to compensate for the convergence (Figure 4.15B), since the convergence occurs in the low-level flow. It is this rising motion that can trigger thunderstorm formation. In contrast, air accelerates on the west side of the trough, leading to low-level divergence, downward air motion, and clearing skies.

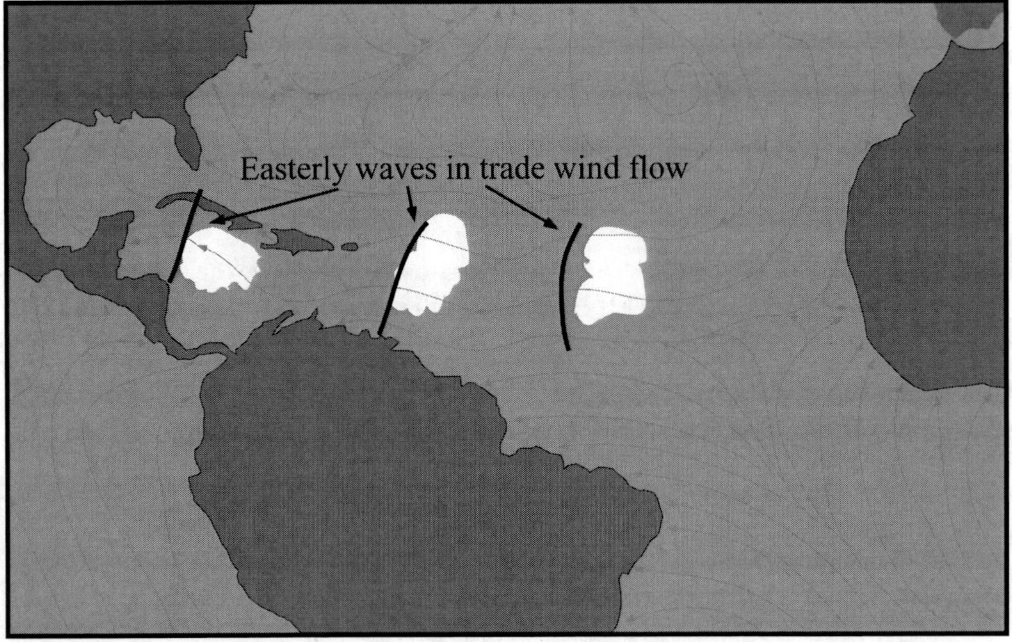

Figure 4.13 Schematic of the typical summertime wind pattern over the Atlantic Ocean. Note the three easterly waves and associated cloud patterns. Thunderstorms forming on the convergent (east) side of these waves have the potential to organize into hurricanes.

Figure 4.14 Satellite image of the Atlantic Ocean showing several easterly waves and Hurricane Erika (1997), a tropical storm that developed from an easterly wave.

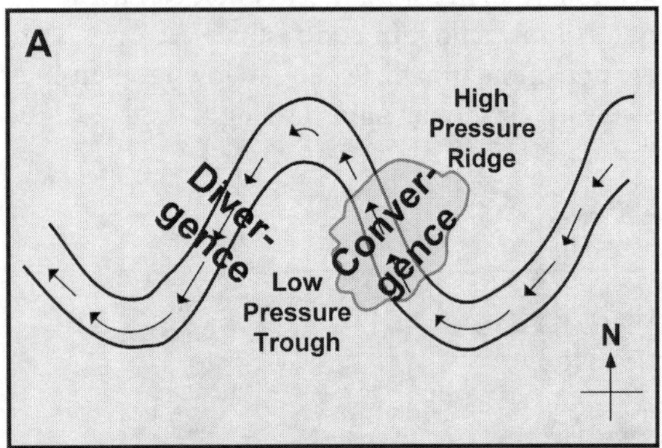

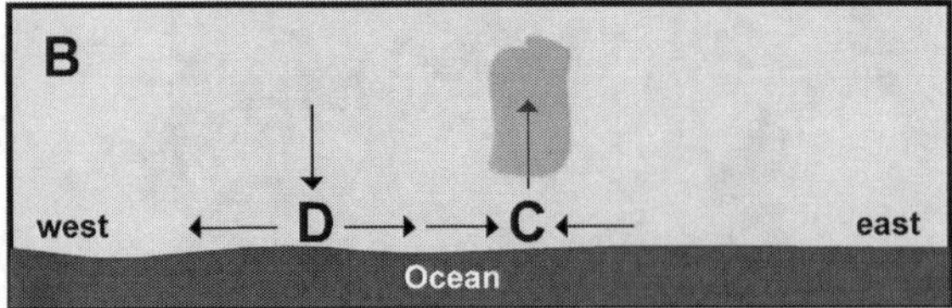

Figure 4.15 (A) Schematic of a lower tropospheric easterly wave embedded in the trade winds. Convergence, clouds, and precipitation occur on the east side of the trough. (B) Vertical cross section through the easterly wave in panel A showing convergence (C), divergence (D), circulations relative to the wave, and clouds associated with these circulations.

Thunderstorms will erupt in the convergent region if the convergence is sufficiently strong. Easterly waves generally originate over continents as air moves across mountains and/or deserts, particularly the Sahara of Africa. Storms develop as the waves propagate over the ocean. Clusters of thunderstorms within these waves will sometimes organize into hurricanes. Easterly waves moving off of the continent of Africa are the main source of tropical thunderstorm clusters over the North Atlantic Ocean.

The final source of tropical thunderstorms actually has mid-latitude origins. Occasionally cold fronts from the mid-latitudes will progress far enough south that they will intrude into tropical latitudes. Thunderstorms will frequently occur on the warm side of these fronts, triggered by lifting over the cooler air to the north. This process of tropical thunderstorm formation is most common in the fall, when cold fronts are stronger than in summer, and have the energy to make it far enough south into the Gulf of Mexico or over the Atlantic near the Bahamas. Thunderstorms along a cold front will occasionally organize into a hurricane as illustrated in Figure 4.16, the weather pattern near the time of development of Hurricane Kyle in 2002. Cold fronts are particularly important for triggering thunderstorms that develop into late-season Gulf of Mexico hurricanes.

The Environment Required for Tropical Cyclones to Form from Thunderstorm Clusters

Tropical cyclones form from thunderstorm clusters in environments that have four specific characteristics. If these environmental conditions are not met,

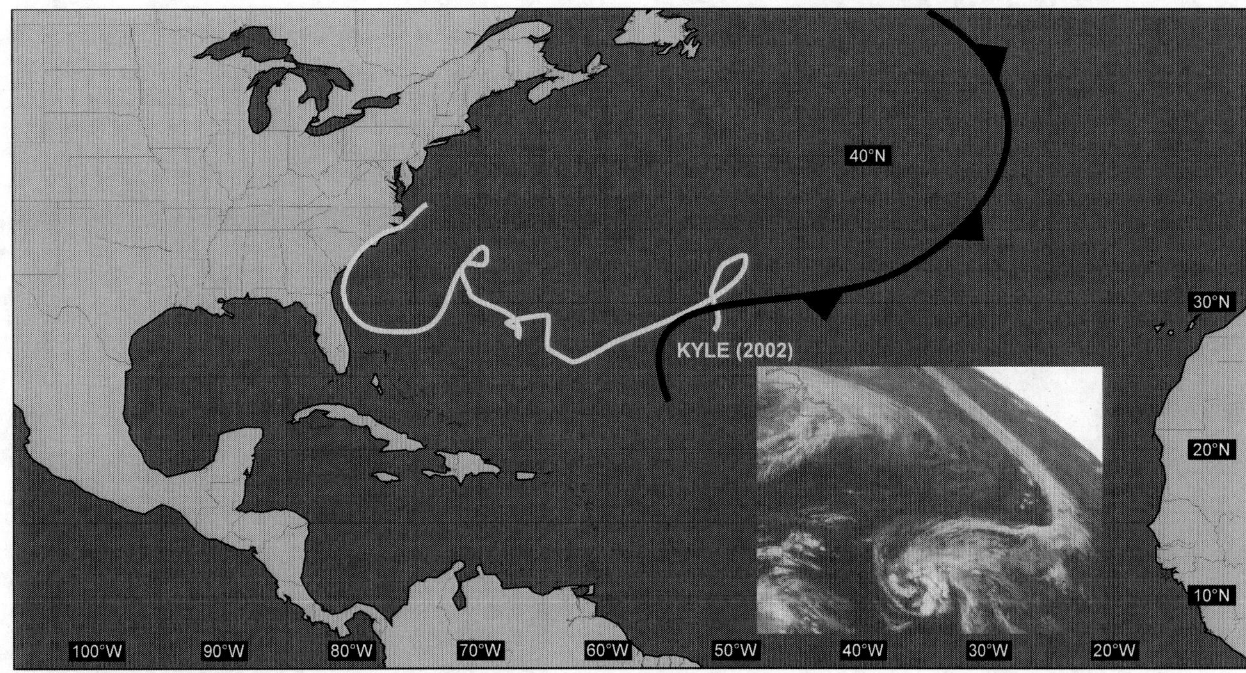

Figure 4.16 Hurricane Kyle (2002) is an example of a hurricane that formed from thunderstorms developing in the vicinity of a weak cold front that intruded into tropical latitudes. The satellite inset shows the cloud pattern associated with the cold front extending to the position where Kyle was forming on 21 September 2002.

tropical thunderstorm clusters, regardless of their trigger mechanism, cannot develop into hurricanes. The required conditions are:

1. the sea-surface temperature must exceed about 80° F (26.5° C);
2. the surface layer of warm water in the ocean must be sufficiently deep, typically about 60 meters (– 200 ft.) or more;
3. the winds in the atmosphere must not change substantially with height (weak vertical wind shear); and
4. the location must be at least 5 degrees north or south of the equator.

Sea-Surface Temperature

The energy for a hurricane comes from heat and moisture supplied by the ocean that is released into the atmosphere as latent heat during condensation. The higher the temperature of the uppermost layers of the ocean, the more energy can be supplied to the atmosphere. There is a direct relationship between the central pressure of the most intense hurricanes and the temperature of the sea surface over which the storms are moving. When the sea-surface temperature falls below about 80° F (26.5° C), the ocean cannot supply sufficient moisture and heat to support hurricane formation. The North Atlantic and northeast Pacific Oceans generally only achieve sufficiently warm temperatures in late July to early November. In the Western Pacific, the ocean is above 80° F (26.5° C) for much of the year, so typhoons can occur in both the Northern Hemisphere summer and winter. This oceanic region is unique in this regard.

Pressure readings from exceptionally strong typhoons in the Western Pacific Basin and hurricanes in the Atlantic Basin are listed in Table 4.6. Western Pacific storms have not been routinely sampled using aircraft since 1987 when the Air Force disbanded its Pacific Typhoon Chasers squadrons. Maximum winds are now estimated from satellite data, and the central pressure determined from an equation relating central surface pressure and wind speed. The five storms listed in Table 4.6 occurred prior to 1987.

Comparing Atlantic and Pacific storms, note that the lowest pressures recorded all occurred in the western Pacific where the ocean temperatures are warmest. A theory that predicts the lowest possible central pressure of a hurricane based on sea-surface temperature is remarkably accurate (Figure 4.17). The colors

Table 4.6 Low-Pressure Readings in Exceptionally Strong Tropical Cyclones.

Western Pacific Basin

Tropical Cyclone	Season	Central Pressure (mb)
1. Typhoon Tip	1979	870
2. Typhoon June	1975	876
3. Typhoon Nora	1973	877
4. Typhoon Ida	1958`	877
5. Typhoon Rita	1978	878
Atlantic Basin		
1. Hurricane Wilma	2005	882
2. Hurricane Gilbert	1988	888
3. Labor Day Hurricane	1935	892
4. Hurricane Rita	2005	895
5. Hurricane Allen	1980	899

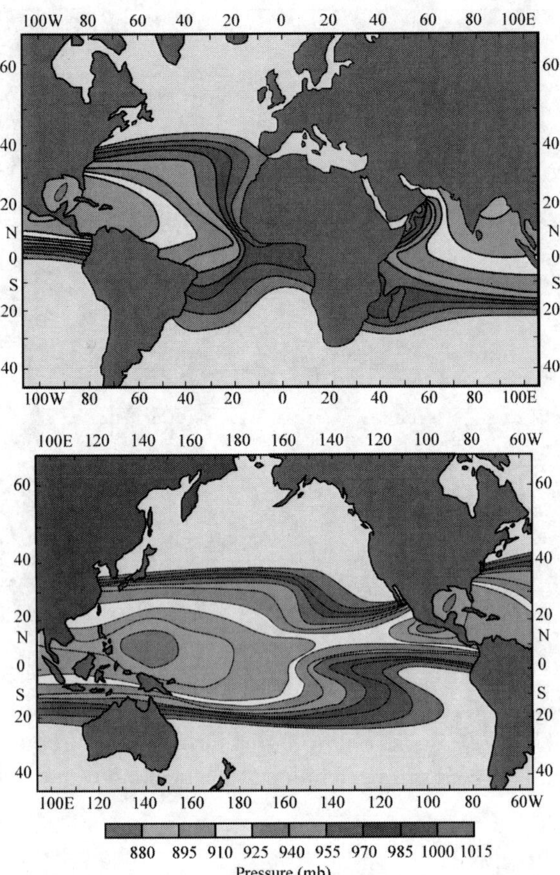

Figure 4.17 Predicted maximum intensity of a hurricane based on average ocean surface temperatures in the Atlantic (upper) and Pacific (lower) regions. The agreement between the predicted values shown here and observed values from Table 4.6 is excellent, showing the importance of a warm ocean for hurricane formation.

on this figure show the predicted extreme minimum pressures possible in hurricanes. The values closely correspond to observations of the minimum pressure in strong hurricanes (Table 4.6).

Depth of Warm Water

A deep layer of warm water is required for hurricane development because a hurricane "stirs" the ocean water much like water in a teacup. This leads to ***upwelling*** of water in the vicinity of the eye and eyewall. If the warm layer is shallow, colder water will rise to the surface, and the developing storm will no longer have its warm water energy source. This is one reason why hurricane season typically does not start in the Atlantic until late summer, peaking in September. The summer's heat is required to warm the water to the depth necessary to support hurricane formation.

Weak Wind Shear

Hurricanes derive their energy from the release of latent heat in the eyewall. For a hurricane to develop, this energy must be locally concentrated. The clouds cannot be carried downstream by high winds in the upper atmosphere. It is also difficult for a vortex of wind to form in the presence of strong flow in the upper atmosphere. The vortex is simply torn apart by the strong winds aloft, which tilt the circulation and carry it downstream. Hurricanes form best in an atmosphere where the background winds are very weak aloft.

ONLINE 4.4

Wind Shear

How do meteorologists determine whether the wind shear profile is favorable over the oceans for tropical storm development when there are no stations to collect upper atmosphere data? Animation of satellite data permits meteorologists to observe the movement of cloud features, and features in the water vapor field. The approximate altitudes of these features are estimated from the intensity of the radiation received by the satellite, and the speed of the features is measured from changes between successive frames in the animation. Pattern recognition programs are used to track features and convert the data to wind measurements. Online you can see an animation of infrared satellite data over the Atlantic taken during Hurricane Isaac (2000). The category 4 hurricane is drifting northward toward a jetstream that originated at higher latitudes. The jetstream, which is characterized by strong wind shear, quickly tears at the hurricane, disrupting its circulation and causing its central pressure to rise.

Away from the Equator

The Coriolis force is important for storm rotation. At the equator the Coriolis force is zero. About 5 degrees north and south of the equator, the Coriolis force becomes significant enough that rotation can occur within developing thunderstorm clusters.

How Thunderstorms Organize into a Hurricane

Most clusters of thunderstorms in the tropics do not organize into a tropical cyclone. If the environment (the four conditions described above) is right, however, the individual thunderstorms can

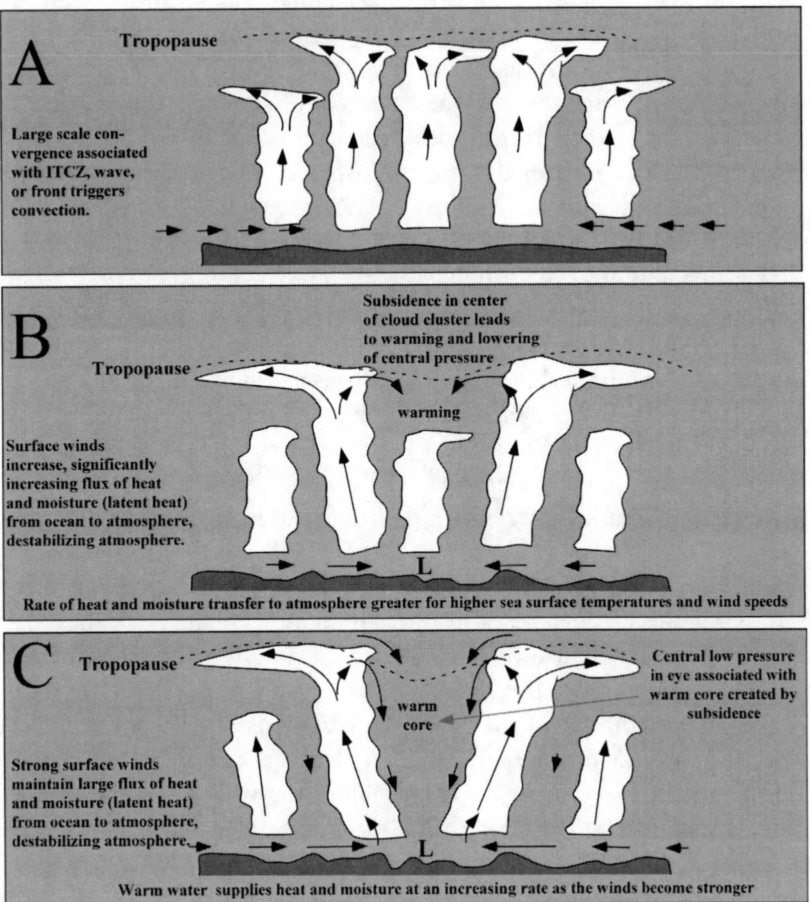

Figure 4.18 Illustration of Wind Induced Surface Heat Exchange (WISHE), a mechanism for tropical cyclone intensification. Tropical cyclone intensification occurs as sensible and latent heat and moisture are extracted from the ocean surface by the action of the wind, and carried into the core of the tropical depression. Subsidence in the center of the cloud cluster leads to adiabatic warming and the lowering of surface pressure, intensifying the surface winds, and significantly increasing the rate of transfer of heat from the ocean to the atmosphere. The heat is transferred upward to the tropopause within the developing eyewall.

quickly organize into a ***vortex***, and rapidly develop into the eyewall surrounding a newly-formed eye. How does this happen? Scientists are still studying this process. The most promising theory about how this happens, called ***Wind Induced Surface Heat Exchange (WISHE)***, considers the feedback that occurs between the heat and moisture transfer from the ocean surface and the development of the vortex (Figure 4.18).

We know that there is a close association between the sea-surface temperature and hurricane strength. The sea provides the energy for the hurricane. The transfer of energy from the ocean to the lower atmosphere occurs in two ways. The first, less important way is through direct transfer of ***sensible heat*** when the ocean is warmer than the atmosphere. The more important way is through evaporation and the transfer of ***latent heat***. Evaporation of water from the ocean surface requires energy, which comes directly from the ocean. As water evaporates, heat is extracted from the water, cooling the ocean surface. This heat, called latent heat, reappears when condensation occurs in tropical thunderstorms. Enormous quantities of latent heat are released as condensation occurs and precipitation falls out of the clouds.

The rate at which water evaporates from the ocean surface is a strong function of wind speed. At high wind speeds the spray generated by the rough ocean surface significantly enhances the evaporation rate so that the moisture (energy) transfer from the ocean to the atmosphere can be 100 to 1,000 times greater than when the winds are weak.

Figure 4.18A shows a cloud cluster over a tropical ocean in the absence of wind shear. As air rises in a thunderstorm cluster, most of the air exhausts outward away from the cluster, but a small amount exhausts inward (Figure 4.18B). The inward branch of the flow causes weak descent in the center of the cluster. Air in this weakly descending branch of the flow warms adiabatically, raising the temperature at the center of the cluster. Recall that any time heating occurs in the atmosphere, divergence will occur in the heated column. This divergence induces the formation of a weak surface low-pressure center within the cluster.

As the newly-formed low increases the low-level pressure gradient, the winds increase at the surface, agitating the ocean, and increasing the evaporation rate. More moisture and heat can now be supplied to the clouds in the cluster, causing the updrafts to intensify. The system also begins to rotate under the combined influence of the pressure gradient and Coriolis forces as the central low pressure develops. Rotation has a centrifugal effect, which acts with heating to reduce the central pressure further.

Outflow from the convection near the tropopause now becomes more focused in two directions, most outward away from the center, but some inward toward the center of rotation (Figure 4.18B). The inward branch descends within the developing eye as the low-pressure center develops near the surface, and the descending air further increases the core temperature through adiabatic warming. The pressure at the surface lowers in response to this warming, centrifuging of the rotating air is enhanced, and the cycle of pressure lowering continues. The lower central pressure also increases the downward-directed pressure gradient force within the eye, further enhancing the descending motion within the eye and the associated adiabatic warming. Stronger wind, more heat transfer into the convection, stronger updrafts, and stronger descent of air in the developing eye all rapidly transform a cluster of storms into a hurricane.

As the whole system of thunderstorms rotates, the updrafts organize to form the eyewall. The descending air, which initially covered much of the eye region, becomes preferentially concentrated just inside the eyewall with slower descent across the remainder of the eye (Figure 4.18C). The system becomes a very efficient simple heat engine, the fuel being the moisture (latent heat) supplied to the storm from the ocean through evaporation, the "combustion" being the release of latent heat in the eyewall, the exhaust being the outflow at the tropopause (which cools as it radiates heat to space), and the overall maintenance of the circulation enhanced by the adiabatic compression and warm core in the descending air in the eye. The storm will roar along as long as the environment—*warm ocean, weak or no shear in the environment*—supports it. Tropical cyclones have maintained hurricane force winds for over twenty days while moving thousands of kilometers over tropical oceans.

The primary limiting factor in the process is how much energy can be transferred to the atmosphere at the sea-surface, and that is related to the-sea-surface temperature. The other limiting factor is the vertical wind shear. With strong winds aloft, the vortex circulation, particularly the warm core of air in the eye, cannot be protected and will be dispersed downstream, weakening the surface low-pressure center and weakening the surface winds. Cold water, land with its increased friction and lack of moisture, or strong environmental wind shear shut down the engine and quickly destroy the circulation. Ultimately, one or more of these factors destroy a hurricane.

The Source of Strong Rotating Winds

The strong rotating winds in the core of a hurricane can be understood by examining a simple physical principle called the ***conservation of angular momentum***. As we learned in previous chapters, the angular momentum for an object rotating around a point is defined as:

$$\text{Angular momentum} = \text{mass} \times \text{radius} \times \text{rotational velocity}$$

where the mass is the mass of the object, the rotational velocity is its velocity along the path of rotation, and the radius is its distance from the axis of rotation. Consider a simple experiment. Let's suppose we have a ball on a long string and we are whirling the ball slowly around in a circle. While we are whirling the ball, let's rapidly pull the string into the center of rotation so that the string is now one fourth of its original size. What happens to the rotation rate of the ball? The common experience we have as kids playing this game is that the ball rotates faster. Skaters apply the same principle by drawing their arms and legs into the center of rotation, speeding up their rotational velocity. A simple law, called the conservation of angular momentum, governs this process. The law states that in the absence of a torque (an external force that would act to change the rotation rate of an object), the angular momentum of an object will remain constant. In Figure 4.19, we examine this law for a hurricane.

Our "object" will be a parcel of air spiraling into a hurricane. Let's assume for the moment that our parcel is not subject to torque forces. Since its mass does not change, conservation of angular momentum depends only on its radius and rotational velocity. Let's suppose, when the air is 100 nautical miles from a hurricane, it is moving 20 knots. Our "constant" is rotational velocity × distance from center = 20 × 100 = 2000 nautical miles^2/hour. When air spirals inward to a radius of 60 nautical miles, its velocity will be 2000/60 = 33.3 knots. When air spirals in to 20 nautical miles from the center of rotation, its speed will be 2000/20 = 100 knots. Like the ball on the string, the rotational velocity of the air increases as it approaches the axis of rotation. In real hurricanes, friction with the ocean surface acts as a torque force that reduces the rotation rate of air. The magnitude of the force of friction increases with wind speed because of ocean roughness. Although conservation of angular momentum cannot be strictly applied in this situation, it illustrates the basic principle explaining why air speeds up considerably as it approaches the center of rotation in a hurricane.

Figure 4.20 summarizes all the conditions and processes associated with hurricane formation. Tropical thunderstorms must be present. These thunderstorms form in three preferred locations: along the ITCZ, within easterly waves, and along cold fronts. The tropical environment, both atmosphere and ocean, must meet four critical conditions for these thunderstorms to organize into a hurricane. These include a very warm and sufficiently deep layer of water in the tropical ocean; little vertical wind shear in the atmosphere; and a location far enough from the equator for the Coriolis force to influence storm rotation. If all environmental conditions are met and thunderstorms are present, latent heat release in the storms, combined with the transfer of energy from the ocean surface to the atmosphere through the action of the wind, will lead to a lowering of the central pressure within the thunderstorm cluster. As air is drawn into the circulation, conservation of angular momentum will then lead to rapid spin-up of the winds.

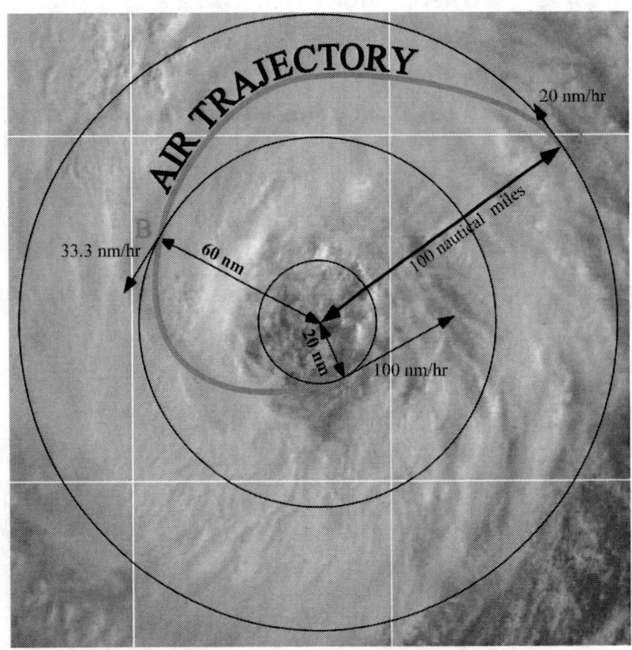

Figure 4.19 llustration of the principle of conservation of angular momentum: the rotational speed × distance = constant. At Point A 20 nm/hr × 100 nm = 2000 nm^2/hr. At Point B: 33.3 nm/hr × 60 nm = 2000 nm^2/hr. At Point C:

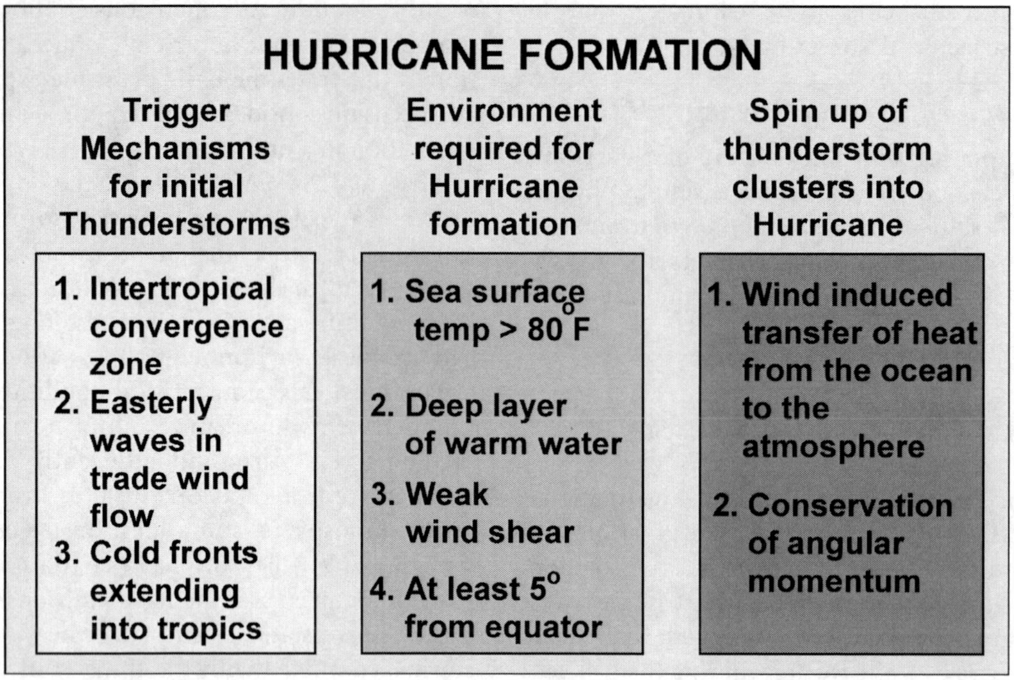

HURRICANE FORMATION

Trigger Mechanisms for initial Thunderstorms	Environment required for Hurricane formation	Spin up of thunderstorm clusters into Hurricane
1. Intertropical convergence zone 2. Easterly waves in trade wind flow 3. Cold fronts extending into tropics	1. Sea surface temp > 80°F 2. Deep layer of warm water 3. Weak wind shear 4. At least 5° from equator	1. Wind induced transfer of heat from the ocean to the atmosphere 2. Conservation of angular momentum

Figure 4.20 Summary of trigger mechanisms for tropical thunderstorms, the environmental conditions required for these storms to organize into a hurricane, and the mechanisms by which the thunderstorms organize into hurricanes.

Check Your Understanding 4.3

1. What are three trigger mechanisms for tropical thunderstorms?
2. What are the four characteristics of the hurricane environment?
3. How does wind shear work against hurricane development?
4. Why don't hurricanes form on the equator?

DESTRUCTIVE FORCES IN A HURRICANE

Storm Surge

Storm surge is an abnormal rise in sea level associated with the movement of a hurricane over a coastal region. Storm surge is one of the greatest concerns to coastal communities as it is responsible for a large percentage of structural damage and coastal flooding. Figure 4.21 illustrates the factors that contribute to the height of storm surge. There are two primary causes of storm surge, and three factors that enhance its destructiveness.

As a hurricane makes landfall, winds to the right of the eye are blowing onshore. The first cause of storm surge is the wind, which pushes ocean water toward shore, raising sea level (Figure 4.21A). The stronger the winds, the deeper the ocean water piles up along the shoreline. The second cause of storm surge is the air pressure difference between the eye and areas surrounding the hurricane. Low pressure in the eye of the hurricane causes the ocean to rise, much like water in a straw rises when air is removed from the straw. This ***barometric effect*** causes the sea level along the coast to rise as this raised region of seawater approaches land (Figure 4.21B).

The factors that can enhance storm surge are natural tides, waves, and shoreline shape. If the hurricane makes landfall during high tide, the problem of storm surge is exacerbated because sea level is higher already. Particularly high tides occur during a new or full moon (Figure 4.21C). Strong winds within the eyewall of the hurricane cause surface waves, which are normally small, to become extraordinarily large, sometimes as high as 10 m (32 ft) or more. These large waves are moving on top of the already raised sea (Figure 4.21C). Finally, the shape of the coastline influences the intensity of the storm surge. Inland bays, especially with relatively flat shorelines, enhance the sea-level rise, much like waves grow in height as they move toward shore into shallower water (Figure 4.21E).

The Galveston hurricane of 1900 came ashore during high tide, was enhanced by the shallowness of

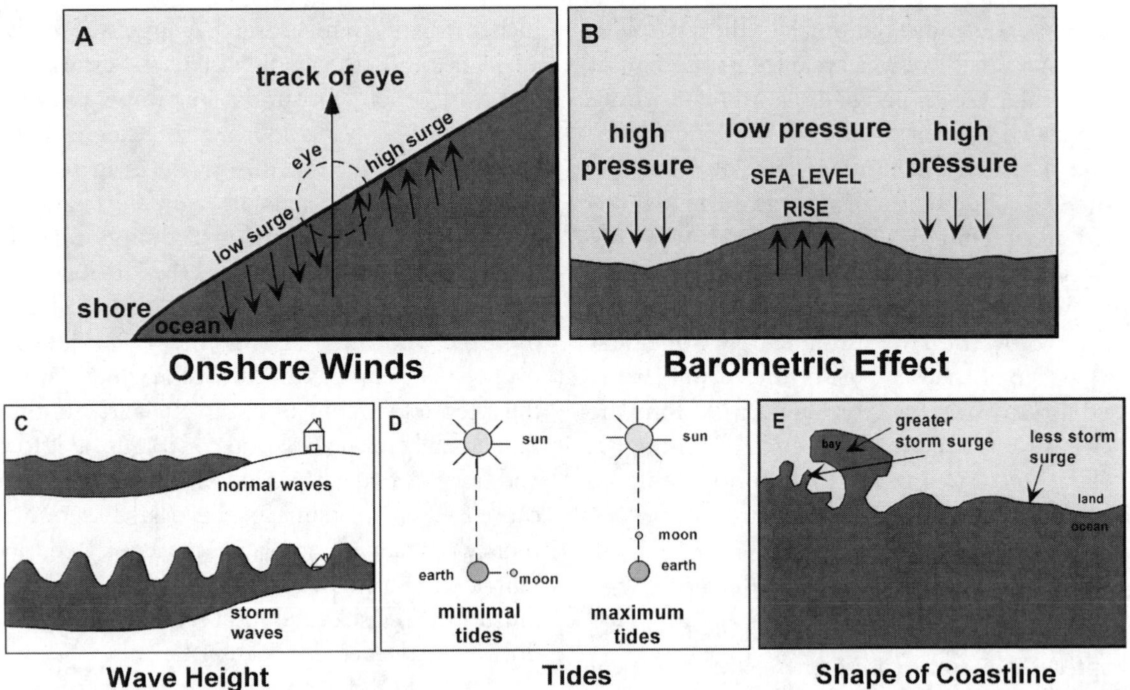

Figure 4.21 The two primary causes of storm surge (A and B) are onshore winds and the barometric effect, a rise in sea level associated with low-pressure. Factors that enhance storm surge (C, D, and E) include wave heights, tides, and the shape of the coastline.

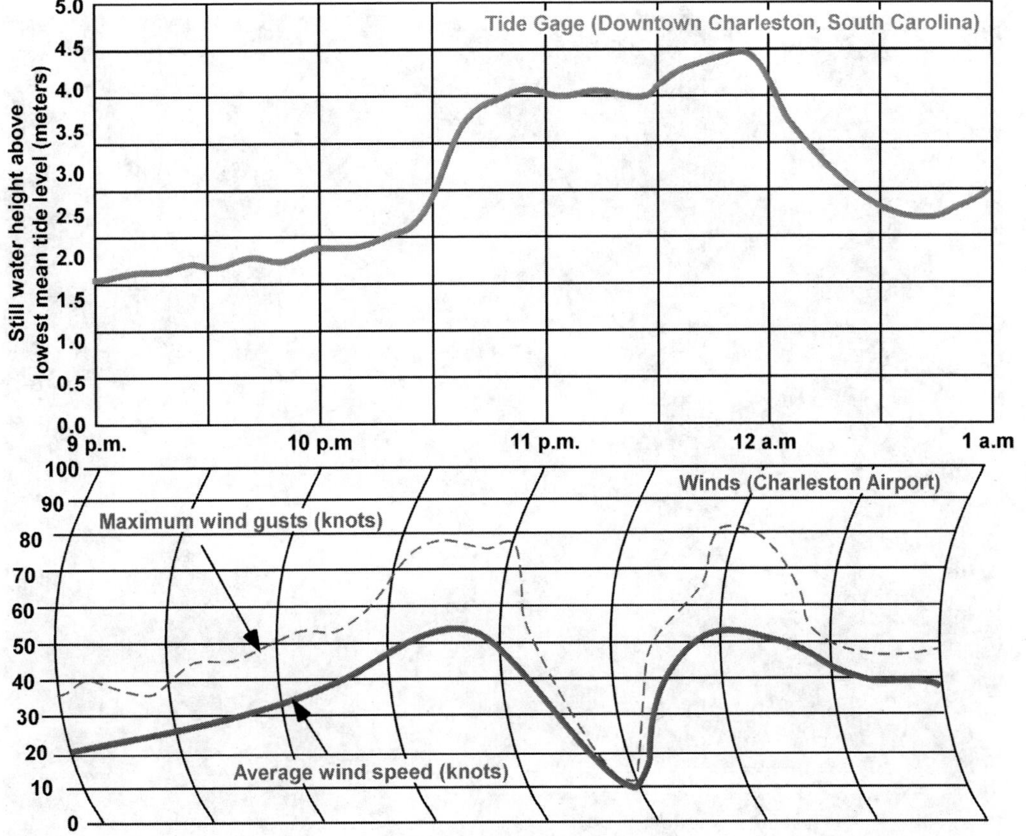

Figure 4.22 Top: Variation in the tide level in the Charleston, South Carolina, harbor during the landfall of Hurricane Hugo on 21 to 22 September 1989. Bottom: Winds measured at the Charleston airport.

Galveston Bay, and submerged much of the city under several feet of water. Tropical cyclones in the Bay of Bengal, particularly near Bangladesh, inundate entire islands populated by poor people who have no chance to evacuate. These disasters often claim over 100,000 lives. Figure 4.22 shows the storm surge during Hurricane Hugo in September 1989 as recorded by the gage in the Charleston, South Carolina, harbor. The tide in the harbor was 3 m (~ 10 ft) above normal and 4.5 m (~ 15 ft) above low tide level, with the peak coincident with the passage of the east part of the eyewall as the eye passed directly over the city. Many cities along the East and Gulf Coasts of North America lie on the flat coastal plain, so a 3 to 4 m (10 to 13 foot) rise in sea level can flood areas far inland (see Focus 4.1).

Other Disastrous Forces in Hurricanes

Hurricanes produce heavy rains as they move over land (see Chapter 9). In some cases, where the movement is slow, 30 to 40 inches of rain have been recorded in two days. For example, Figure 4.23 shows the radar-estimated rainfall from Hurricane Georges during landfall on the Gulf of Mexico Coast. Local values as high as 24 inches (61 cm) were recorded. A large area received over 12 inches (30 cm). In July 2001, Tropical Storm Allison, which never became a hurricane, produced over 30 inches of rain in southeastern Texas and Louisiana. Heavy rainfall such as this produces incredible floods along rivers and streams. In many hurricanes, it is the ***inland flooding***, rather than the surge-caused coastal flooding, that leads to most of the fatalities. The worst case of inland flooding in the Western Hemisphere occurred with Hurricane Mitch in 1998. Flooding killed over 18,000 people as the hurricane winds slammed into the steep topography of Nicaragua and Honduras. The rain actually filled a volcano cone, causing it to collapse and bury several villages in mud. Although storm surge caused extensive damage, the deaths were attributed mostly to inland flooding and the associated mudslides. Hurricane Katrina (2005) was the most recent, grim illustration of the devastation caused by inland flooding during hurricanes (see Focus 4.1).

High winds have the potential to cause great damage, but generally not as significant as the damage caused by flooding. There are exceptions where high winds cause most of the destruction, as was the case

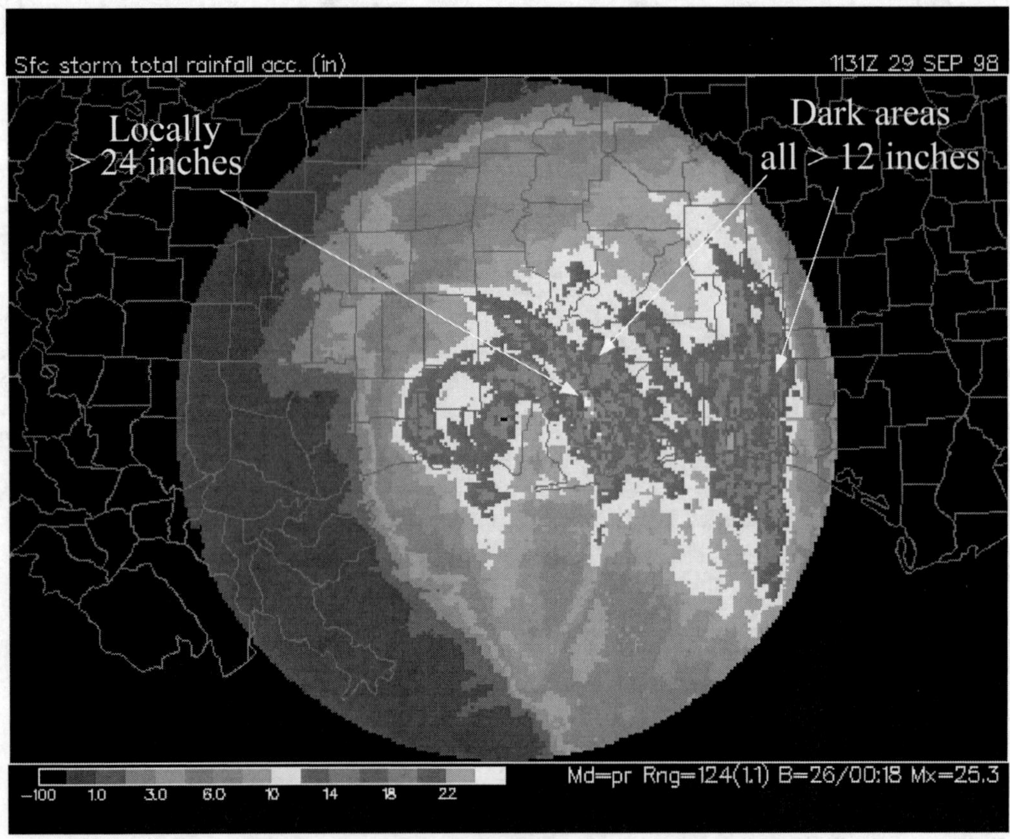

Figure 4.23 Radar estimated rainfall from Hurricane Georges (1998) as it moved on the Gulf Coast near Mobile, Alabama.

of Hurricane Andrew (1992) as it moved over Florida. Hurricanes often also have ***tornadoes*** embedded within the storms in the spiral bands and occasionally within the eyewall. These tornadoes are generally in the EF0 to EF2 range, but are hard to see because of the heavy rain. The manner in which they form is still under study. The damage caused by Gilbert (1988) in the United States was mostly attributed to tornadoes spawned by the storm. Hurricane Opal (1995) also produced a large number of tornadoes as it made landfall along Florida's Gulf Coast.

FORECASTING HURRICANE TRACKS AND INTENSITY

The National Hurricane Center (NHC), one of the National Centers for Environmental Prediction of the U.S. National Weather Service is responsible for issuing watches, warnings, forecasts, and analyses of hazardous weather conditions in the tropics. The National Hurricane Center maintains a continuous watch on tropical cyclones over the Atlantic, Caribbean, Gulf of Mexico, and the Eastern Pacific from 15 May through 30 November or longer. Forecasting hurricane movement and intensity begins with data collection. Over the oceans, this is not an easy task—it must be accomplished with reconnaissance aircraft and satellites. The three types of aircraft currently used in reconnaissance are a fleet of 10 U.S. Air Force C-130 Hercules aircraft, two National Oceanic and Atmospheric Administration (NOAA) Lockheed P-3 aircraft, and a NOAA Gulfstream-4 jet aircraft.

The C-130 and P-3 aircraft fly directly into the eye of hurricanes, measuring the storm's location and intensity by dropping ***dropwindsondes*** into the storm. Dropwindsondes are rawinsondes that fall from an aircraft rather than rise with a balloon (Figure 4.24). The P-3 aircraft also carry a suite of advanced instruments, such as scanning Doppler radar, that collect data used for scientific investigations of hurricanes. The G-4 has a long range and can fly at high altitude. This aircraft flies in the environment around the hurricane, also dropping dropwindsondes.

The data from these aircraft and from satellites are used at the NHC to initialize numerical models that calculate the future evolution of a storm. Several models are used. Because of uncertainty in the initial state of the atmosphere, differences in the ways models incorporate physical processes, such as evaporation of moisture from the ocean surface, and different ways the models are constructed, a range of predictions for the future behavior of the hurricane is obtained. These predictions are assessed from a statistical point of view, and strike probability maps are developed. These maps

Figure 4.24 Photograph of a NOAA P-3 aircraft (foreground) and an Air Force C-130 (background). The inset photograph shows the dropwindsonde station on the NOAA P-3.

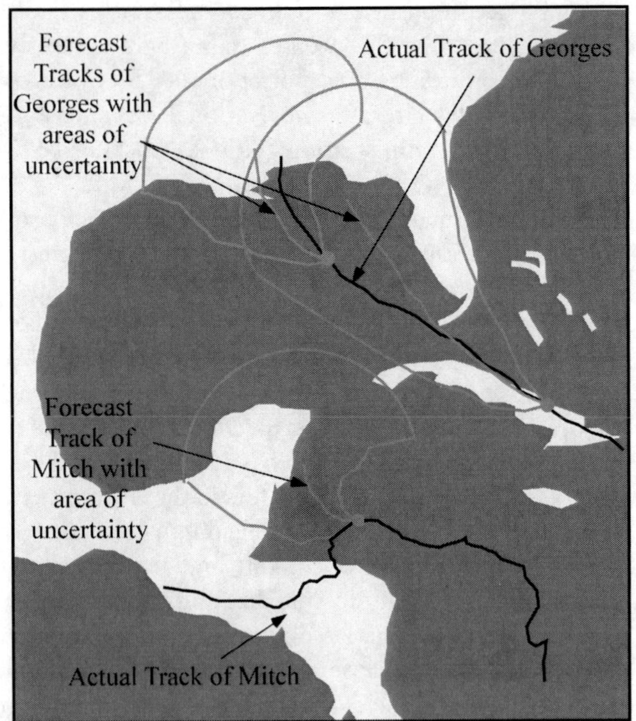

Figure 4.25 The tracks (black lines) of Hurricanes Georges (1998) and Mitch (1998). The National Hurricane Center forecast tracks and areas of uncertainty are shown at select positions along the tracks.

estimate the probability that the storm will strike a particular region within a specific time.

Nevertheless, the paths hurricanes take are always somewhat uncertain and sometimes defy predictions. For example, Figure 4.25 shows the predicted and actual tracks of Hurricanes Georges and Mitch in 1998. As shown in the figure, the location of landfall for Hurricane Georges, both in Florida and Mississippi, was very close to model predictions. Hurricane Mitch, on the other hand, took an unexpected southwestward turn, moving not only off track, but completely outside the area of uncertainty in its predicted path. The primary reason for unpredicted behavior is poor initialization of the models due to the lack of observations available throughout the tropics.

The NHC issues watches and warnings based on probabilities from prediction models, but always warns the public outside the area of low-strike probability to stay alert for the unexpected changes hurricanes often display. ***Hurricane watches*** are issued for tropical storms or hurricanes that pose a potential threat within thirty-six hours. ***Hurricane warnings*** are issued for these storms when hurricane conditions or tropical storm conditions will be present in an area within twenty-four hours. ***Coastal flood watches*** and ***warnings*** are also issued if significant flooding is a possibility with landfalling storms. ***Heavy surf advisories*** are issued for coastal areas not expected to be impacted directly from the landfalling storm but that can expect high surf that may threaten life or property.

In the past, the NHC issued forecasts out to three days, but since 2003, they have extended their forecasts to five days. This extension is both a reflection of improvements in forecast models and the need to plan evacuations farther in advance due to increased coastal populations. Public attention and response to these storms remain key to saving lives and protecting property. This is particularly true as the population along coastlines increases, and the length of time and expense of full coastal evacuations grow. It is extremely important that residents on the coastlines heed evacuation orders, move to inland shelters, and remain indoors during hurricanes. Timely evacuations today remain the best way to prevent loss of life in hurricanes, the most dangerous storms on Earth.

GLOBAL WARMING: POTENTIAL EFFECTS ON HURRICANES

Concerns about the catastrophic effects tropical cyclones have on society have motivated scientists to undertake many investigations in the last two decades to determine if global warming is affecting tropical cyclone frequency, duration, and intensity. The record 2005 season in the Atlantic Basin, and the large number of intense landfalling hurricanes in the United States in 2004 and 2005, has raised public awareness of the hurricane threat and led to heightened interest into questions concerning global warming and its influence on hurricanes. This increased threat is particularly important in light of the observation that global ice sheets and glaciers are rapidly melting and that sea level is expected to continue to rise through the 21st century (see Chapter 5).

We know from very accurate measurements that the average sea-surface temperature of the tropical oceans has been increasing over the last several decades. For example, the solid curves in Figure 4.26 shows the September sea-surface temperature change since 1930 for the prime hurricane genesis region over the Atlantic Basin (Panel A), the July–November sea-surface temperature change since 1930 in the genesis region of the west Pacific Basin (Panel B), and annual mean sea-surface temperature change since 1930 averaged over all tropical oceans between 30 degrees north and south of the equator (Panel C). In each of these panels,

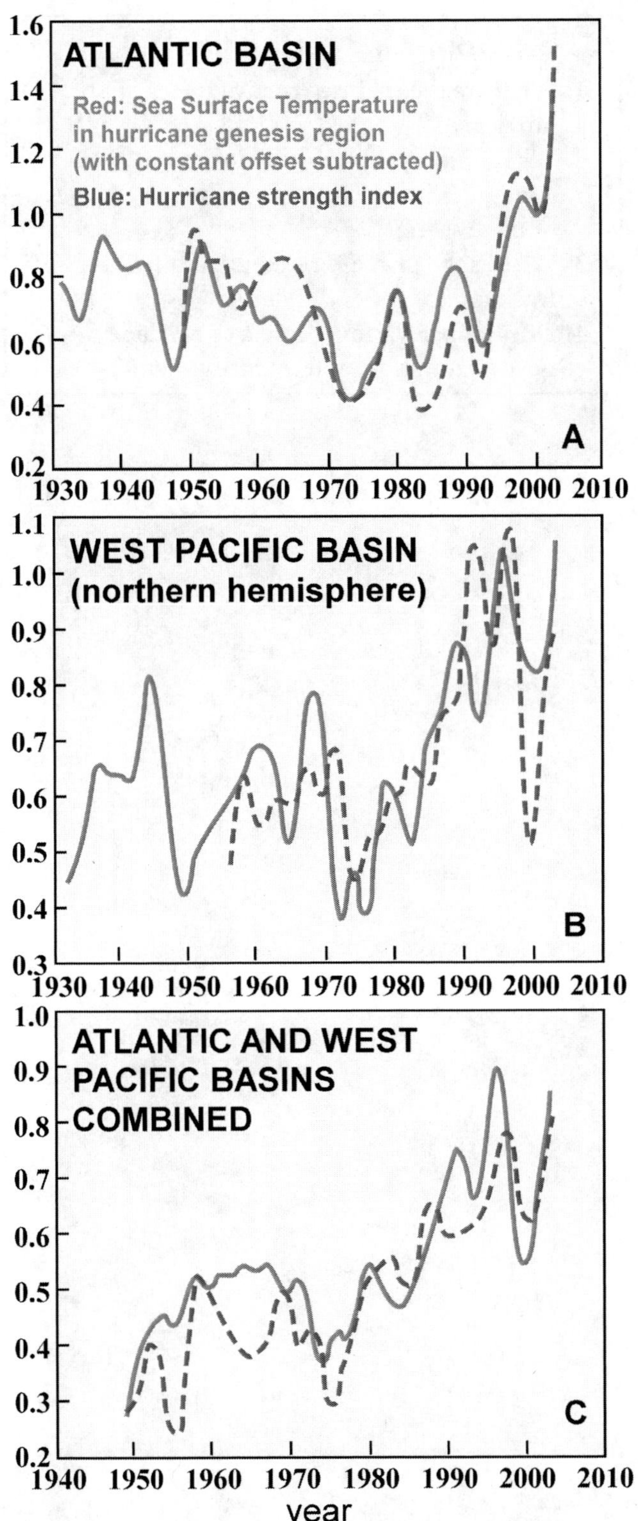

Figure 4.26 The sea-surface temperature data and hurricane strength index of hurricane regions of the (A) Atlantic Basin, (B) west Pacific Basin, and (C) Atlantic and West Pacific Basins combined. Solid lines show departures from the average of the measured sea-surface temperature. Darker dashed lines show the hurricane strength index.

an upward trend in sea-surface temperature is obvious. There are also smaller time-scale cycles associated with phenomena such as El Niño and other oceanic circulations. Theory, modeling studies, and worldwide observations of hurricanes all show a close relationship between maximum hurricane intensity and sea-surface temperature. It is therefore relevant and important that we ask the question "Does global warming cause more hurricanes, stronger hurricanes, and/or longer duration hurricanes?" Scientific evidence collected to date indicates that the answer to the first question is no, and to the second and third questions is yes.

According to several studies, the global annual frequency of tropical cyclones has shown no trend over the period of reliable record (1949–present). There *has* been a distinct increase in North Atlantic tropical cyclone frequency that corresponds with an increase in sea-surface temperature in that basin. However, North Atlantic tropical cyclones account for only 11 percent of all tropical cyclones. Worldwide, the number of tropical cyclones continues to range between 80 and 100 per year, with no clear trend over the period of record.

In contrast to cyclone frequency, there have been clear and discernable upward trends in both the maximum wind speed and duration of hurricanes. We know from past studies that damage due to wind increases approximately as the cube of the wind speed (V^3, the wind speed times itself three times). A potential way to estimate the total destructive effects of a hurricane is to simply add together the cube of the maximum wind speed at equal time intervals for all tropical cyclones in a given year. Fortunately, this type of calculation is possible because positions and maximum sustained surface winds for all tropical cyclones since 1949 are available at six hour intervals from the National Hurricane Center for the Atlantic, eastern and central Pacific basins, and by the United States Navy Joint Typhoon Warning Center for the western Pacific, Indian Ocean, and the Southern Hemisphere basins.

The dashed curves in Figure 4.26 show this ***hurricane strength index*** for the Atlantic (Panel A), western Pacific (panel B), and all tropical oceans (panel C). In each panel, a clear discernable upward trend in tropical cyclone destructive power is evident. Furthermore, this trend closely corresponds to the increase observed in sea-surface temperature. These data are clear evidence that the destructive power of hurricanes worldwide is increasing as the tropical sea-surface temperatures increase. The trends in Figure 4.26 are due to both increases in hurricane intensity and duration.

Sea-surface temperatures in the tropics over the last several thousand years have been estimated from geologic evidence derived from cores taken from the sea floor. Studies of these cores suggest that the increases in sea-surface temperature observed in the recent decades are unprecedented in the historical record. Such rapid change is so unusual that it is compelling evidence that the increase in sea-surface temperature is a direct consequence of global warming. The close connection between global warming and human production of greenhouse gases suggest that human activities may indeed be behind the trend toward stronger and longer duration hurricanes over our tropical oceans.

Check Your Understanding 4.4

1. What are the four destructive forces of a hurricane?
2. What unique information do aircraft provide about hurricanes as they fly through the eyes of these storms?
3. What is the primary reason that hurricane track forecasting is difficult?
4. Does global warming impact hurricane frequency, duration, and intensity?

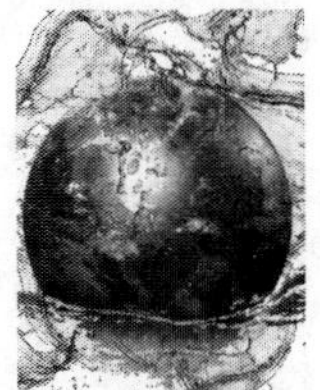

WATER PLANET EXERCISE 4

Name: ______________________________

Storms and Severe Weather

Severe storms often do not occur alone. For instance, tornadoes are associated with thunderstorms, but they can also be generated within hurricanes, again frequently associated with thunderstorms. Some events allow for warning because they take time to form (hurricanes, for example), while others, especially tornadoes, can occur rather quickly, leaving little time for warning. Sometimes the weather would not be categorized as severe, but the event that results from it is. Flooding is an example of this. Precipitation and snow melt can contribute to flooding, as soils become saturated and rain that falls on the ground can only run off into streams. This can occur slowly as rainfall continues over time, resulting in slow-rise but perhaps widespread flooding. Or it can occur rapidly with very intense precipitation over a short period of time, leading to a quick rise in streams and rivers.

Thunderstorms

The data in the table below show statistics on severe thunderstorms and tornadoes.

	2008			2009			2010		
	# Thunder-storm days	# tornadoes	# tornado fatalities	# Thunder-storm days	# tornadoes	# tornado fatalities	# Thunder-storm days	# tornadoes	# tornado fatalities
Jan	4	84	7	1	6	0	4	30	0
Feb	8	147	59	5	36	9	1	1	0
Mar	14	129	4	9	115	0	5	33	1
Apr	17	189	0	15	226	6	16	139	11
May	22	462	44	14	201	5	24	304	7
Jun	29	292	7	26	270	0	30	324	12
Jul	22	95	1	24	118	0	25	146	2
Aug	12	101	0	11	60	0	9	55	1
Sep	5	111	2	2	8	0	9	57	2
Oct	3	21	0	4	65	1	6	108	0
Nov	2	15	2	0	3	0	6	53	0
Dec	6	46	0	5	48	0	3	32	9

1. Using the three graphs provided, plot the data for 2008, 2009, and 2010 using a different color for each year. Note that the data on thunderstorms refer to the number of days that severe thunderstorms were recorded, not the number of thunderstorms.

Number of Thunderstorm Days

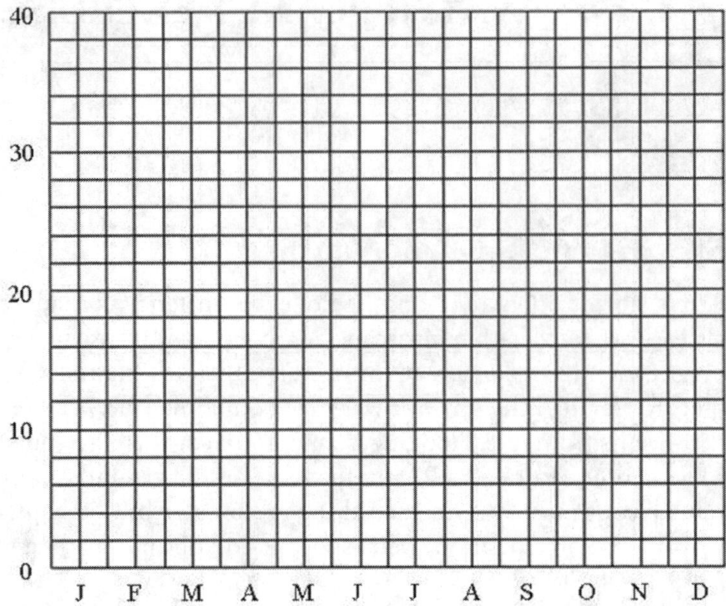

Number of Tornadoes

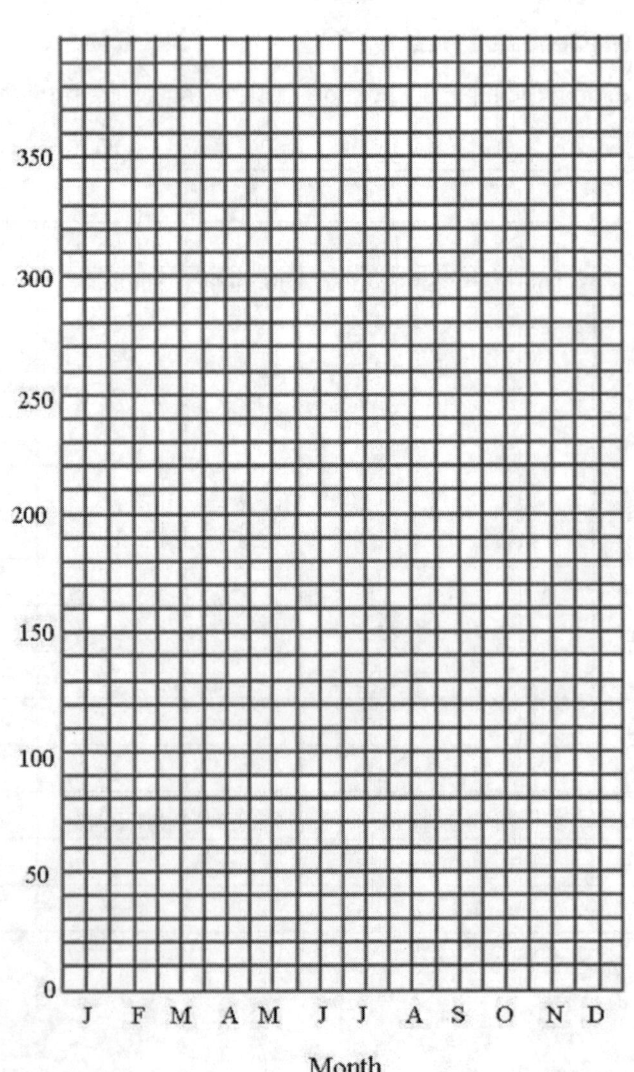

Number of Tornado Fatalities

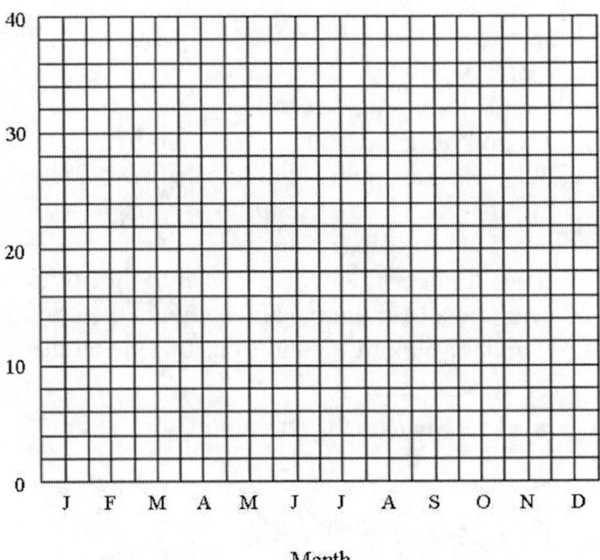

2. Describe in detail the monthly pattern for:
   a. the number of days with severe thunderstorms

   b. the number of tornadoes

   c. the number of tornado related fatalities

3. Describe the similarities between the three graphs focusing on both the monthly patterns and the trends in numbers.

4. Describe the differences between the three graphs focusing on the same factors.

5. Explain why we see the patterns that we see on the graphs, being sure to include consideration of air masses and fronts.

Now, to look at events that have a relatively long period of development—hurricanes. Typically, but not always, these originate as tropical cyclones, but are not associated with fronts. Instead, these events start as tropical depressions and, depending on conditions that are described very well in the textbook, can intensify to become tropical storms and hurricanes (or cyclones in the Indian Ocean and typhoons in the western North Pacific). The map below shows the number of events that were tracked during the 2005 hurricane season (June through November) for the Atlantic. This was an unusual year, given the number of storms. The 27 named events shown here compare to 15 in 2004 and 10 in 2006.

1. The numbers in the squares refer to the number of the storm. Look at those that occur early in the season (numbers 1 through 6) and compare them to those from later in the season (number 18 and higher). Thinking about the conditions that are required to create a hurricane, are there differences in their points of origin? ________

   a. If so, what are the differences?

   b. If not, why do you think that is the case?

2. Use the hurricane track map to explain why it can be very difficult to forecast the path of a hurricane. Include information about both surface and atmospheric conditions.

3. Using the same information, explain why it is so difficult to predict where landfall will occur much sooner than 24 hours prior to landfall.

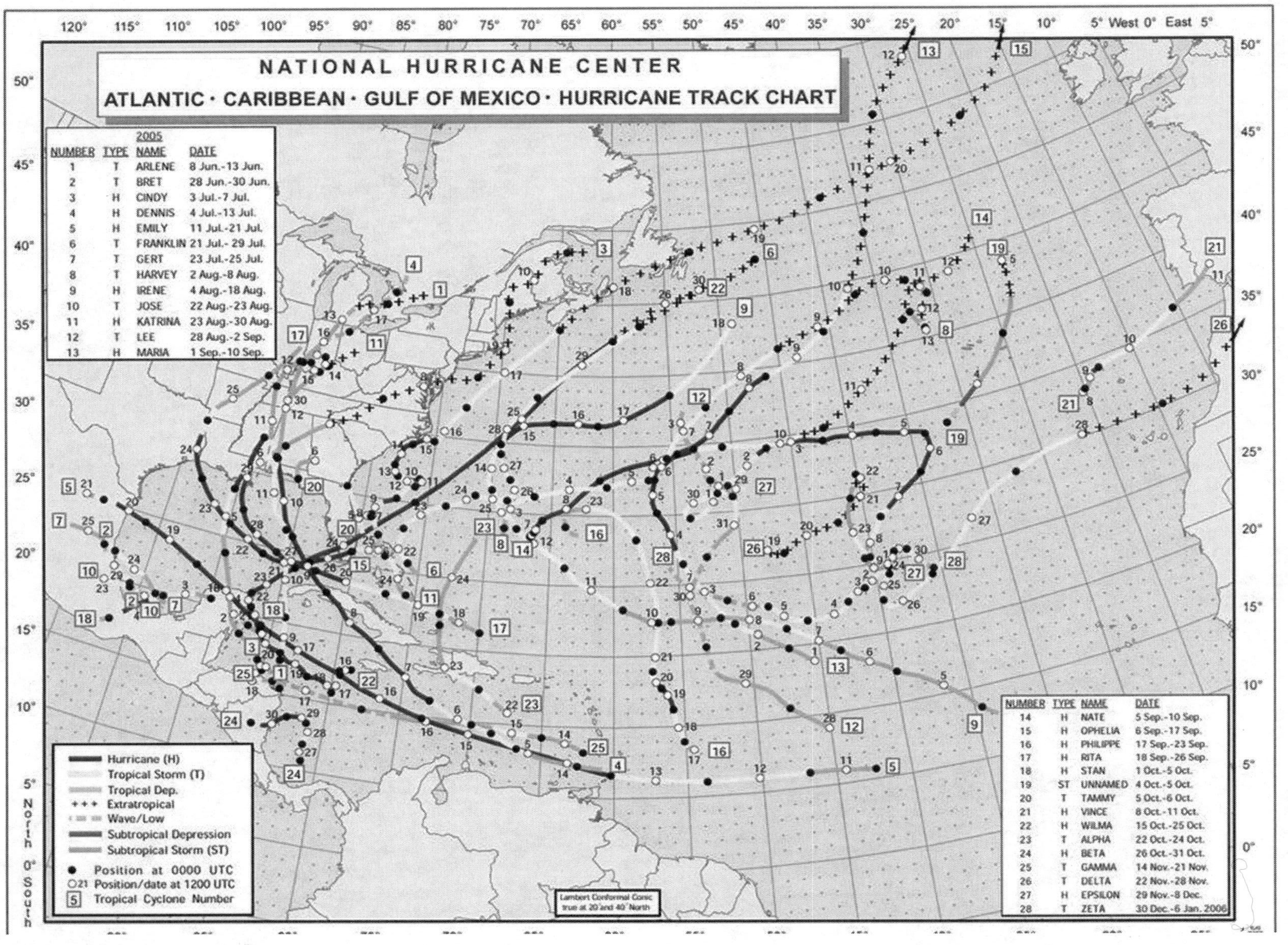
NATIONAL HURRICANE CENTER
ATLANTIC · CARIBBEAN · GULF OF MEXICO · HURRICANE TRACK CHART
2005
NUMBER TYPE NAME DATE
1 T ARLENE 8 Jun.-13 Jun.
2 T BRET 28 Jun.-30 Jun.
3 H CINDY 3 Jul.-7 Jul.
4 H DENNIS 4 Jul.-13 Jul.
5 H EMILY 11 Jul.-21 Jul.
6 T FRANKLIN 21 Jul.- 29 Jul.
7 T GERT 23 Jul.-25 Jul.
8 T HARVEY 2 Aug.-8 Aug.
9 H IRENE 4 Aug.-18 Aug.
10 T JOSE 22 Aug.-23 Aug.
11 H KATRINA 23 Aug.-30 Aug.
12 T LEE 28 Aug.-2 Sep.
13 H MARIA 1 Sep.-10 Sep.
NUMBER TYPE NAME DATE
14 H NATE 5 Sep.-10 Sep.
15 H OPHELIA 6 Sep.-17 Sep.
16 H PHILIPPE 17 Sep.-23 Sep.
17 H RITA 18 Sep.-26 Sep.
18 H STAN 1 Oct.-5 Oct.
19 ST UNNAMED 4 Oct.-5 Oct.
20 T TAMMY 5 Oct.-6 Oct.
21 H VINCE 8 Oct.-11 Oct.
22 H WILMA 15 Oct.-25 Oct.
23 T ALPHA 22 Oct.-24 Oct.
24 H BETA 26 Oct.-31 Oct.
25 T GAMMA 14 Nov.-21 Nov.
26 T DELTA 22 Nov.-28 Nov.
27 H EPSILON 29 Nov.-8 Dec.
28 T ZETA 30 Dec.-6 Jan. 2006
Hurricane (H)
Tropical Storm (T)
Tropical Dep.
+++ Extratropical
Wave/Low
Subtropical Depression
Subtropical Storm (ST)
Position at 0000 UTC
21 Position/date at 1200 UTC
5 Tropical Cyclone Number
Lambert Conformal Conic true at 20 and 40 North
5° West 0° East 5°
North
South

Chapter 5

GLOBAL WARMING

"We simply must do everything we can in our power to slow down global warming before it is too late. The science is clear. The global warming debate is over."

Governor Arnold Schwarzenegger

"The whole (global warming) thing is created to destroy America's free enterprise system and our economic stability."

Reverend Jerry Falwell

When my son Liam was four years old, his favorite story was a glow-in-the-dark book about space. We read it before bed at least once a week, constantly turning the lights on and off, watching as the Milky Way, constellations, moon, and planets revealed their glowing forms. It was mesmerizing stuff. I remember one night, as we were reading this book, I happened to mention that Venus, a planet approximately the same size and at the same distance from the Sun as Earth, is a very warm place (the surface temperature is 464 °C, or 867 °F). I told him that was hot enough to melt my car! He seemed impressed and followed immediately with the inevitable question "Why is Venus so hot, Dad?" Well, I had never had to explain the greenhouse effect to a four-year-old before, and I remember fumbling through a tale that involved covering him with additional blankets to keep him warm on a cold night. He did not seem to buy that, but I didn't quite know how to tell him that the thick Venus atmosphere, composed of 96% carbon dioxide (CO_2), compared to Earth's 0.038%, is what really drives the hot surface temperatures. In effect, the planet has a very strong greenhouse effect.

The greenhouse effect lies at the heart of the global warming debate, so that is where we begin. Many people think that the terms greenhouse effect and global warming are synonymous. They are not. Indeed, many misconceptions relating to global warming exist, and hopefully by the end of this chapter, we'll have addressed most of them. However, a word of caution: of all the topics in this book, global warming is the most controversial and complex. Intense political passions surround any discussion of global warming. For example, the Kyoto Protocol, the international treaty on climate change designed to get signatory nations to commit to reduce their emissions of greenhouse gases, was never ratified by the United States. This is often portrayed as being divided strictly along political party lines, with the blue states being perceived as pro-environment, favoring immediate action, and the red states perceived as wanting to drag their heels for fear of hurting the economy (even though in 1997 the U.S. Senate voted 95–0 during a Democratic administration against ratification). President George W. Bush never supported ratification, primarily because of the strain he believed the treaty would put on the economy. And although world leaders agreed in Copenhagen in December 2009 that global warming is significant and should be limited, they failed to deliver a legally-binding climate deal.

In this chapter I will present current scientific understanding agreed on by the majority of climate scientists on what global warming is, how it could impact our world, and what is currently being done politically and socially to prepare for the effects of it. However, it would be remiss of me not to address the issue of political polarization, and I will try to do so in an unbiased manner.

CO_2 AND THE GREENHOUSE EFFECT

We begin our discussion of global warming at an elevation of 11,000 ft on the northern slopes of Mauna Loa, the spectacular volcano on the big Island of Hawaii. It is here that you will find the Mauna Loa Observatory (MLO), a research station where scientists have been monitoring our atmosphere since the 1950s. They record changing levels of atmospheric gases, including CO_2.

MLO measurements were started by Charles David Keeling, a scientist who developed the first instrument capable of measuring CO_2 in air samples. In 1961 Keeling produced data showing that CO_2 levels were rising steadily in what has became known as the "Keeling Curve" (Figure 5.1). This data (which continues to be recorded at MLO today) is the longest continuous record of atmospheric CO_2 in the world. Despite early skepticism, it is considered an extremely reliable indicator of current trends in CO_2 levels. The data show that the atmospheric concentration of carbon dioxide has increased from approximately 315 ppm in 1958 to 388 ppm in 2009.

The CO_2 record shown in Figure 5.1 raises several important questions. First, is this trend in increasing CO_2 levels significant? That is, is there some driving force or, in climatological terms, forcing mechanism, behind this increase, or is it just part of a longer-term (say several hundred years) natural variation in CO_2 levels? Second, are the levels themselves noteworthy—that is, what does a concentration of 388 ppm really mean? Third, why should we be focused on CO_2 as opposed to other atmospheric gases that are potentially more harmful? And finally, what does this all have to do with a warming global climate?

In order to address the first question, we have to put the last 50 years of CO_2 data in a much wider context. In Figure 5.2, for example, the MLO record is shown with CO_2 concentrations measured from ice cores obtained from drilling expeditions in Antarctica. These cores provide an important means for determining atmospheric gas concentrations thousands of years ago. The principle is really very simple: as annual snowfall settles and is compacted under subsequent snow layers, tiny bubbles of air become trapped within the ice; these bubbles actually contain samples of what the atmosphere was like at different times in Earth's history. By extracting the air trapped inside these bubbles, we can measure, for example, what CO_2 concentrations used to be in our atmosphere. How neat!

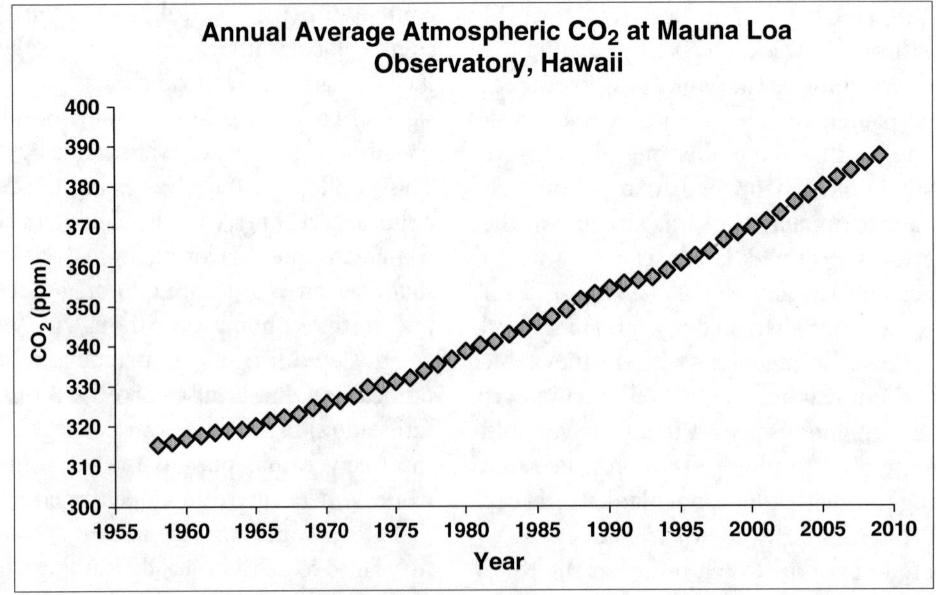

Figure 5.1 Instrumental record of atmospheric CO_2 at the Mauna Loa Observatory, Hawaii (Source: National Oceanic and Atmospheric Administration—**http://www.esrl.noaa.gov/gmd/ccgg/trends/**).

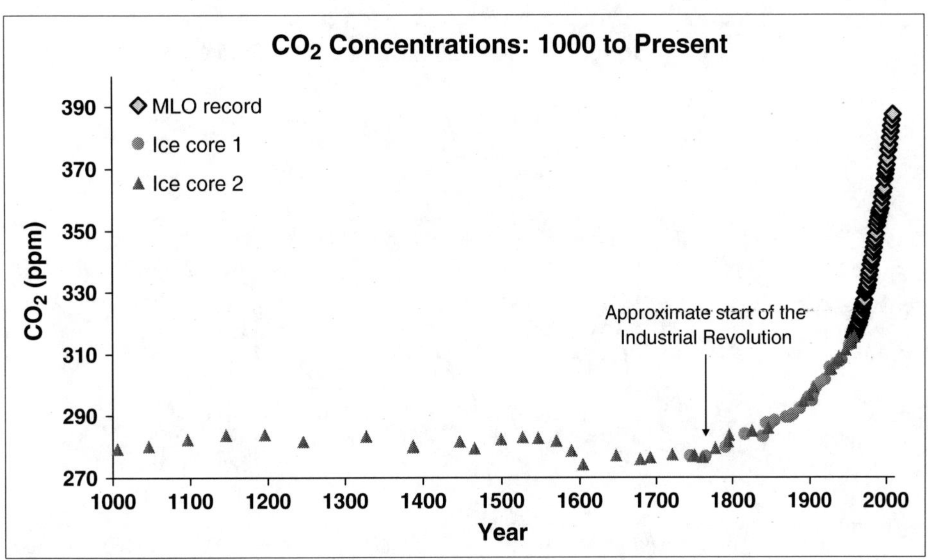

Figure 5.2 Carbon dioxide concentration in the atmosphere over the last 1000 years based on both direct measurements on Mauna Loa, Hawaii (diamonds, as shown in Figure 5.1) and sampling of gases trapped in ice cores from Antarctica (circles and triangles) taken during two scientific expeditions (Source: Carbon Dioxide Information Analysis Center—http://cdiac.ornl.gov/).).

As you can see in Figure 5.2, CO_2 concentrations are approximately 270–275 ppm for the 750 years or so preceding the Industrial Revolution. Levels then begin to rise throughout the 19th and 20th centuries, and then accelerate dramatically during the last 50 years, the period of the MLO record. Overall, CO_2 in the atmosphere has risen by almost 40 percent since the Industrial Revolution. Visually and, more importantly, statistically, the increase in CO_2 shown in Figure 5.2 is both significant and compelling.

However, the secrets from the ice cores do not stop there. Scientists have now sampled ice from the Greenland and Antarctic ice caps, and have been able to extend the record back several hundreds of thousands of years (Figure 5.3). The results show atmospheric CO_2 concentrations of approximately 200 ppm during ice ages, increasing to approximately 280 ppm during warmer periods, known as the interglacials (those periods in between glaciations). During the Holocene, a geologic period stretching back 10,000 years, CO_2 levels fluctuated between about 260 ppm and 280 ppm, a very narrow range. The dramatic rise during the latter half of the 20th century clearly lies outside anything previously recorded. It seems highly improbable, therefore, that the recent increase in CO_2 from 280 ppm to 388 ppm is part of some natural background variability. The consensus among the scientific community is that it is driven by the release of carbon during the combustion of fossil fuels, such as coal and petroleum. Emissions from such sources are constantly adding carbon to the atmosphere at rates far in excess of those supplied by natural sources, such as volcanic activity. Most of this CO_2 has been released since 1945.

Carbon dioxide levels of almost 390 ppm look and sound impressive, but at this concentration it only represents 0.039% of the atmosphere (Table 5.1). Nitrogen and oxygen completely outweigh all other gases in the atmosphere; they are literally the heavyweights of the atmosphere. Why then is CO_2 the focus of such attention? Surely at such low concentrations, adding just a few more parts per million of a particular gas, even during a relatively short time period like 50 years, won't have much effect, right? The simple truth is that CO_2 plays a disproportionate role in our atmosphere relative to its concentration. It is a greenhouse gas (GHG), a term I am sure many of you have encountered. But what does that really mean? Well, greenhouse gases such as CO_2, methane, and water vapor occur naturally in our atmosphere and regulate the atmospheric thermostat—that is, they keep our planetary temperatures livable. To understand how these gases operate, and how temperature may respond to increased GHG concentrations in the 21st century, it's important to first understand how energy enters and exits our atmosphere.

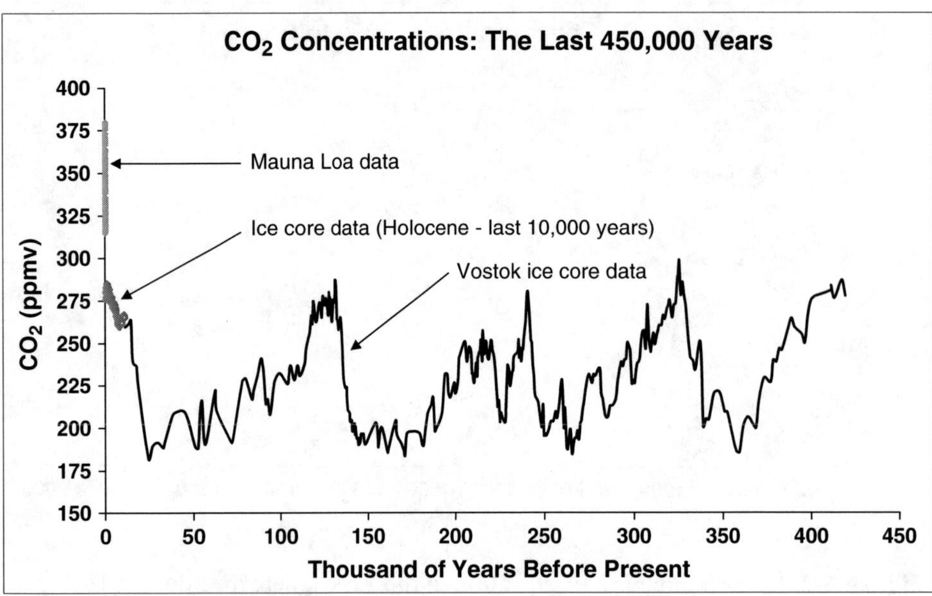

Figure 5.3 Carbon dioxide concentration in the atmosphere over the last 450,000 years based on both direct measurement, sampling of gases trapped in ice cores and other proxy data, such as tree rings and sediments (Source: National Oceanic and Atm[illegible]spheric Administration and National Climatic Data Center —www.ncdc.n[illegible]a.gov).

Table 5.1 Composit[illegible] of the Atmosphere (When Dry).

Gas	ppm	%
Nitrogen (N_2)	780,840	78.084
Oxygen ([illegible]	209,460	20.946
Argon (A[illegible]	9,340	0.934
Carbon [illegible] (CO_2)	387	0.0387

Not inclu[illegible]n above dry atmosphere: water vapor (~0.25 percent over full atmosphere; typically 1 to 4 percent near surface).

The Electromagnetic Spectrum

Most of you are familiar with UV light, which describes the type of energy, or radiation, that is emitted by the sun. It comes to Earth in the form of waves (similar to ocean waves). UV light is an example of shortwave radiation, and it can be graphed on a spectrum of other different types of radiation, known as the electromagnetic (EM) spectrum (Figure 5.4). This is a very important diagram, and it illustrates several key concepts about radiation.

Most of the waves that arrive from the sun have very short wavelengths, defined as the distance between the crest of two waves. Gamma rays, ultraviolet rays, and visible light are all classified as shortwave radiation and constitute about 90 percent of the radiation coming from the Sun. It is also important to appreciate that the shorter the wavelength, the higher the intensity of the radiation.

Now the Sun isn't the only body that emits radiation. Everything on Earth emits radiation. As you read this book, you, the book, the chair in which you're sitting, everything around you is constantly emitting radiation. This is known as longwave radiation, or infrared radiation, and is much less intense than the incoming solar shortwave radiation. On the electromagnetic spectrum, these waves all lie to the right of the 0.4 μm point (Figure 5.4). The radiation emitted by Earth lies wholly within the middle infrared bands. An important point to note about the electromagnetic spectrum is that Earth's radiation curve has been

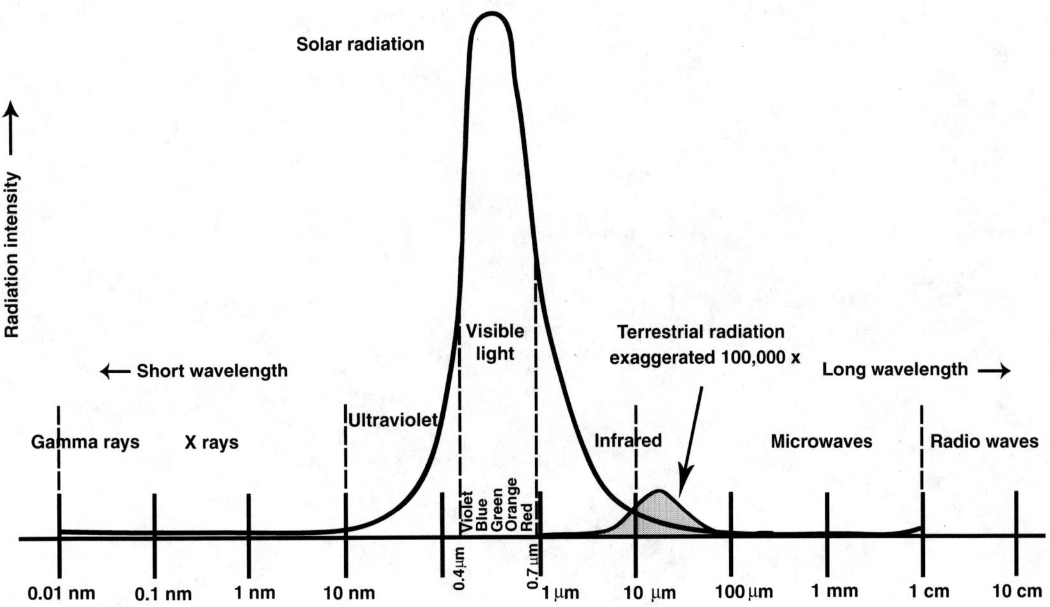

Figure 5.4 Electro-magnetic spectrum.

greatly exaggerated. If we didn't do this, and plotted the curves on the same y-axis at the same scale, you simply wouldn't see it.

The type of radiation emitted from an object is also based on temperature. As you increase the temperature of an object, the wavelength decreases. For example, Earth as an object has an average temperature of about 59°F whereas the Sun's average temperature is almost 10,000 °F! This enormous thermal difference accounts for the difference in wavelengths emitted by each object.

The Earth-Energy Balance and the Greenhouse Effect

Now, Earth is located approximately 93 million miles from the Sun, although this distance varies slightly because Earth's orbit around the Sun is elliptical. Still, the amount of solar radiation that reaches Earth annually remains relatively constant. This consistent amount of radiation being supplied to Earth's atmosphere in any given year is balanced by an amount of radiation given off by our Earth-atmosphere system into outer space. This is called the energy balance. It can be written simply as:

$$I - O = \Delta S \quad (1)$$

where I = energy input, O = energy output, and ΔS = the change (delta) in storage within the system (in this context, the change in global temperatures).

We can quantify the energy balance a little more by studying what happens to UV radiation when it hits Earth's atmosphere. As solar radiation passes through the atmosphere toward Earth's surface, some is reflected off clouds and Earth's surface itself (~30 percent, which is known as the albedo, or reflectivity), some is absorbed by the atmosphere (~19 percent), while the rest (~51 percent) strikes Earth's surface and warms it (Figure 5.5). This is probably a bit surprising, since it's hard to believe that only half of the sun's radiation actually hits the ground. However, once it does, Earth's surface heats up and begins emitting radiation in the form of long waves back up into the atmosphere.

The atmosphere now plays a critical part in the energy balance story, and it's not necessarily what the atmosphere is, but what is <u>in</u> the atmosphere—that is, the greenhouse gases. These gases are known as selective absorbers of radiation, and here is how they work. CO_2 is transparent to the incoming shortwave radiation from the Sun. It simply doesn't "see" it. Water vapor behaves much the same way. However, CO_2 (and the other greenhouse gas molecules) are able to "see" longwave radiation, easily absorb it, and subsequently reemit that radiation back to Earth's surface. This effect, which reduces the amount of longwave radiation emitted directly back into space, warms the Earth's surface and lower atmosphere, and is called the greenhouse effect. Put another way, we get our heat from two sources: the Sun, which is obviously pretty important, but also the atmosphere.

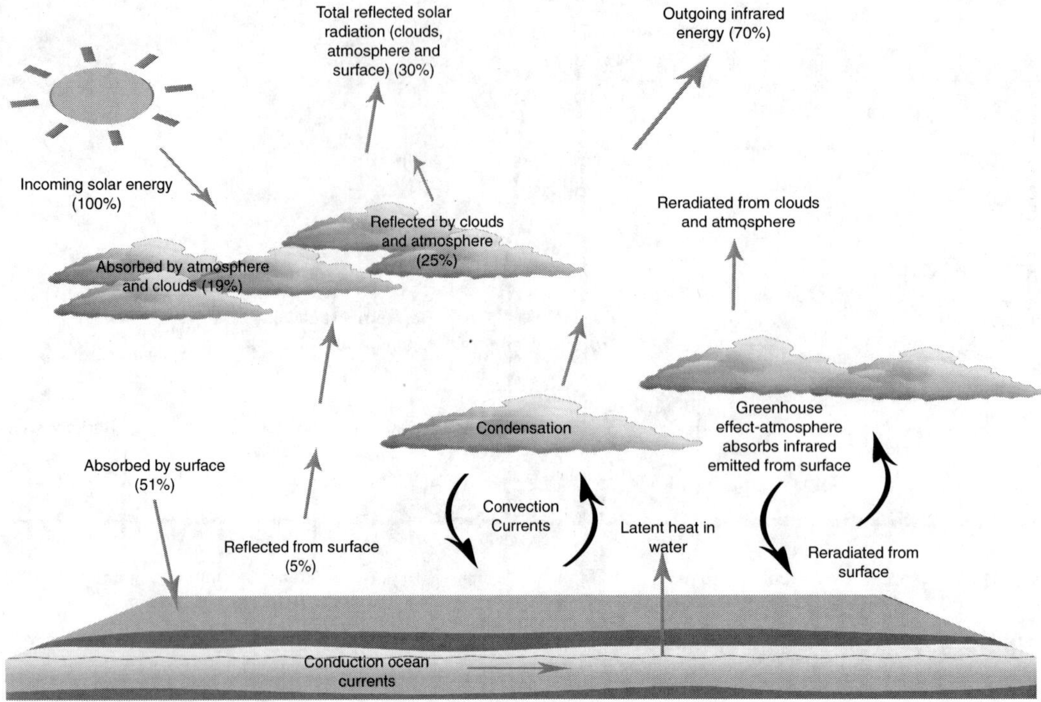

Figure 5.5 Schematic illustration showing Earth's energy (or heat) budget and the processes involved in the re-distribution of that heat.

Just to illustrate how important this effect is in regulating Earth's temperatures, let's pretend for a moment that we didn't have an atmosphere surrounding our planet. What would the average temperature of Earth be? The answer will surprise you: −0.7°F, or about −18°C. In other words, Earth would be a frozen ball! Because we have an atmosphere and greenhouse gases within it, our Earth is a much more comfortable 59°F, or 15°C. That's a difference of 33°C!

Given the importance of greenhouse gases, adding CO_2 to the atmosphere at rates never before measured (which seems apparent given the trends observed from the MLO) means that we are, in effect, tampering with our planet's thermostat. Bringing this back in terms of the energy balance in equation 1, we are reducing the output (O) on an annual time frame which, with a constant input of solar radiation (I), means that the change in storage (ΔS) must become more positive. This means greater amounts of radiation will remain in our atmosphere, increasing global temperatures. This is the definition of global warming: a human-caused acceleration of the greenhouse effect.

It's a little unfortunate that we use the term *greenhouse effect* in the context of the atmosphere. The term is actually a misnomer, because the process described above is not how actual greenhouses work. Greenhouses do let in lots of light, but the resulting warmer temperatures inside are due to reducing air currents and turbulence in the greenhouse, rather than "trapping" longwave radiation. The atmosphere does not act like a greenhouse or blanket; this is just a popular way of portraying the phenomenon in literature and media. It's a small point, yet worth noting.

IS GLOBAL WARMING REAL?

This question has fueled a debate that often pits the scientific community and the environmental movement against industry, specifically large energy companies. Global warming is no longer only a scientific question; it carries political and social connotations. For example, here are two views on the same issue from two high profile politicians:

> *I believe that climate change is the most important long-term issue we face as a global community. It is an issue that will require sustained action over the coming decades. A sound understanding of the science must be the basis for this action.*
>
> Tony Blair, UK Prime Minister, 3 November 2004

Much of the debate over global warming is predicated on fear, rather than science. I called the threat of catastrophic global warming the greatest hoax ever perpetrated on the American people. Everything on which they [the environmentalists] based their story, in terms of the facts, has been refuted scientifically.

James M. Inhofe, U.S. Senator & Chairman of Environment and Public Works Committee, 4 Jan 2005; 2006 interview with *Tulsa World*

In the United States this issue is most frequently split along party lines, with blue states being perceived as pro-environment, favoring immediate action and red states perceived as wanting to drag their heels for fear of hurting the economy. In *An Inconvenient Truth*, now the third highest grossing documentary film, former vice president Al Gore lays blame squarely on the Bush administration for not signing up to the Kyoto protocol. He asks: "Are we going to be left behind as the rest of the world moves forward? There are only two advanced nations in the world that have not ratified Kyoto and we are one of them." Celebrities are also getting in on the debate. Actor Leonardo DiCaprio co-wrote, produced, and narrated a feature-length documentary film about global warming, and his official website[1] is focused solely on environmental issues. In Roland Emmerich's blockbuster *The Day After Tomorrow*, global warming triggers an Ice Age, tornadoes flatten Los Angeles, and a tidal wave engulfs New York City while the entire Northern Hemisphere begins to freeze solid! Unfortunately, a lot of what is portrayed in the film is scientifically ludicrous, because when scientists refer to abrupt changes in Earth's climate, they are generally referring to changes that occur over decades, not a week to ten days. It is highly unlikely that we will be chased by glaciers down the halls of New York's Public Library!

How, then, is the general public supposed to respond to an issue such as global warming with any sense of objectivity? How do we make an informed decision about what our course of action should be without the confusion of political and media bias? As always, we should turn first to the scientific data.

Figure 5.6 shows a record of global average temperatures over the last 125 years and it is a critical diagram in this debate. The data, taken from sensors around the world, show that the planet's average near-surface

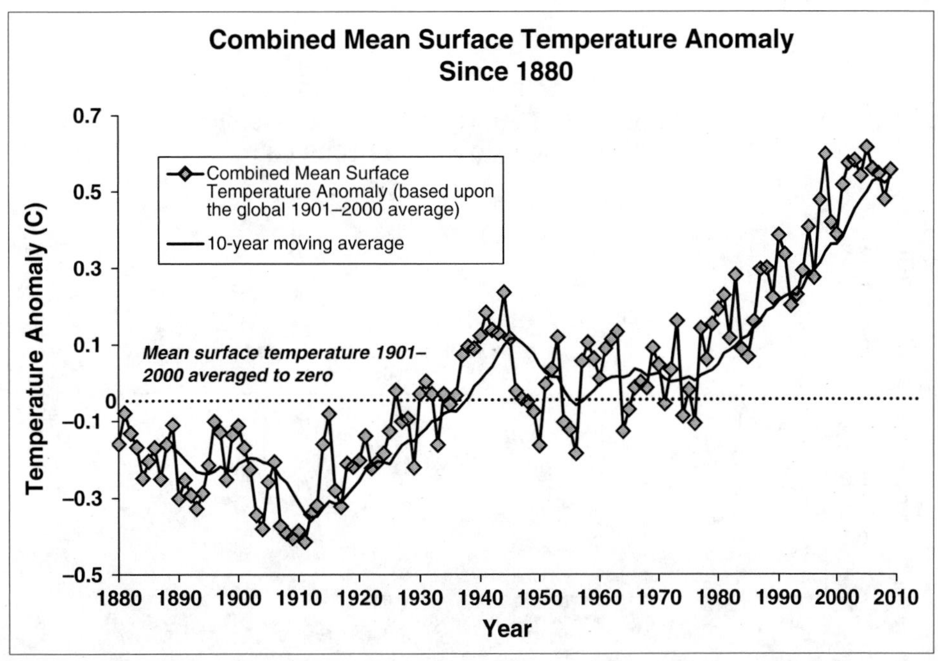

Figure 5.6 Surface temperature anomalies (i.e., departures from the long-term mean) since 1880 (Source: National Oceanic and Atmospheric Administration and National Climatic Data Center—www.ncdc.noaa.gov).

[1] (http://www.leonardodicaprio.org)

atmospheric temperature has risen approximately 0.9°C (1.5°F) in the 20th century. It is important to stress here that this is the instrumental temperature record, where temperature is measured by ground-based thermometers. The accuracy and geographic coverage of the record decreases as you move back through time, but the data is nonetheless remarkable in its extent and the trend seems unequivocal. The warming occurs during two periods: 1910 to 1945 and 1976 to the present day. The early twentieth century warming has been explained by a combination of factors, including greenhouse gases and natural forcing. Scientists also agree that in the second half of the century, the warming is largely caused by increased concentrations of greenhouse gases, specifically carbon dioxide. The fact that the 10 hottest years on record all occurred in the last 12 years, with 2005 the hottest of all, supports the prevailing scientific opinion that most of the warming observed over the last 50 years is attributable to human activities. It appears to be the only logical conclusion.

If we then accept that Earth has warmed over the last century, the next question relates to the significance of the warming in the context of the longer-term climatic record. Just like the 50-year CO_2 record shown earlier, the 20th century temperature record must be set within a broader context. The problem, of course, is that there are no instrumental data going back hundreds, let alone thousands, of years. Our only course of action is to turn to proxies—variables that, themselves, may not be of any enormous interest, but from which a variable of interest, in this case temperature, can be obtained. Tree ring widths are a well documented example of such a temperature proxy. Dendrochronologists (tree ring scientists) use the width and other characteristics of tree rings to infer temperature. Generally, the ring pattern reflects the climatic conditions in which a tree grew, with wide rings reflective of wet years with a long growing season and vice versa. Figure 5.7 shows the reconstruction of temperature for the last 1000 years using a number of proxies, including tree rings and historical records, and includes the late-19th and 20th century instrumental record. Again, the data appear unequivocal: the rate of temperature increase during the 20th century, as well as the magnitude of the temperatures in the latter half of the century, are the highest in the climatic record. And with a little less certainty, we can keep going back farther and farther into geologic time, in order to set the 20th century record into an even longer temporal context. Detailed palaeoclimatology is beyond the scope of this book, but let's look briefly at the last 0.5 million years where, once again, the ice cores and their trapped bubbles of atmosphere, have proven invaluable. Figure 5.8

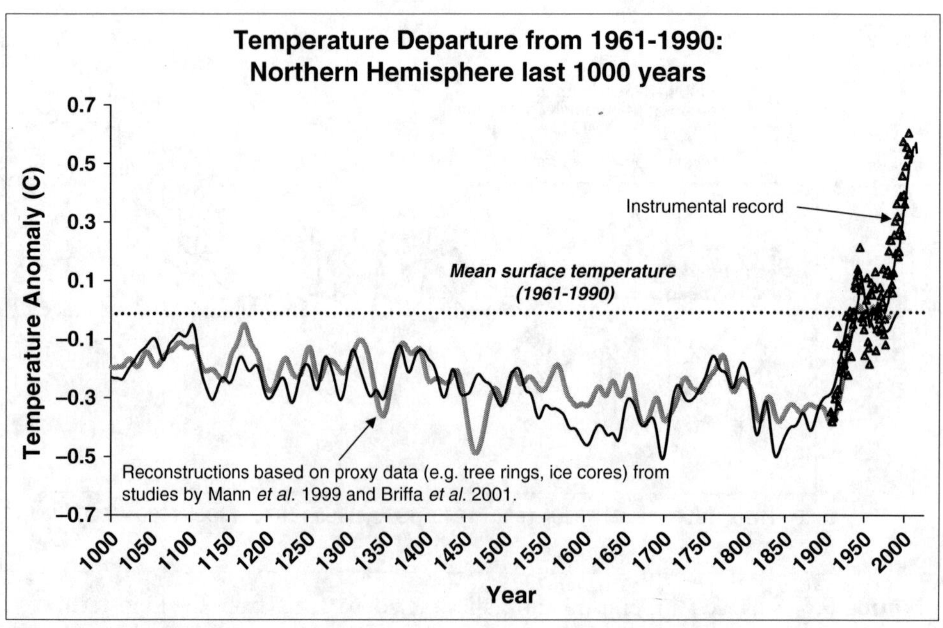

Figure 5.7 Surface temperature anomalies for the last 1000 years, based on direct sampling (i.e., the surface temperature record, shown by the triangles) and proxy evidence (solid lines). (Source: National Oceanic and Atmospheric Administration and National Climatic Data Center—www.ncdc.noaa.gov).

shows ice core data from Antarctica. Here, temperature is calculated using the relative concentrations of various isotopes in the ice. The curve shows (1) periods where global temperatures are ~6 °C colder than the present day (the glacial cycles), which correspond to CO_2 levels of ~200 ppm, (2) periods of warmth (interglacials) where temperatures are even warmer than today, with corresponding CO_2 levels of ~275 ppm, and (3) a dynamically-changing climatic system, with sometimes very rapid changes between warm and cold periods. Although the 20th century warming does not show up when plotted at this scale, we must remember that it is the *rate* of warming during the last century that is unprecedented. The temperature fluctuations shown in Figure 5.8 occur over much longer timescales.

Given the preceding discussion, we are now at a point where I think we can state with reasonable certainty that:

1. atmospheric CO_2 has increased by almost 40 percent since the industrial revolution;
2. current levels of CO_2 are unprecedented over both human history and over longer-term geologic timescales (at least the last 450,000 years);
3. the increase in CO_2 is primarily due to human activity, mostly the combustion of fossil fuels;
4. CO_2 is one of several greenhouse gases that keep our planetary temperatures much warmer than they otherwise would be, the so-called "greenhouse effect"; and
5. global temperatures have risen by about 0.9°C (1.5 °F) during the 20th century. Like the increase in CO_2, this rate is unprecedented over both human history and longer-term geologic timescales.

No one disputes the physics behind the greenhouse effect, not even the most committed global warming skeptic. Increased amounts of CO_2 in the atmosphere will enhance this effect and thus contribute to global warming. But it is here that the more difficult (and controversial) questions begin: Are the increased amounts of CO_2 the primary cause of the observed atmospheric warming? Will CO_2 continue to rise during the 21st century and, if so, at what rate? How will the atmosphere respond? Is this thin envelope of gas that surrounds our planet robust enough to cope with increased levels of CO_2? Will global temperatures begin to level-off, find some equilibrium with the changes in atmospheric composition, or even begin to cool? Or will global temperatures, as many reputed scientists believe, continue to rise or even accelerate during the coming millennium? What will the impacts be? And perhaps most important of all, what, if anything, should be done? In *An Inconvenient Truth*, Al Gore argues that global warming is a moral issue and that it would be deeply unethical to allow it to continue. At stake, according to Gore, is our ability to live on Earth and to have a future as a civilization. But what if the comedian Dennis Miller is more on target? So what if the planet's temperature does continue to rise?

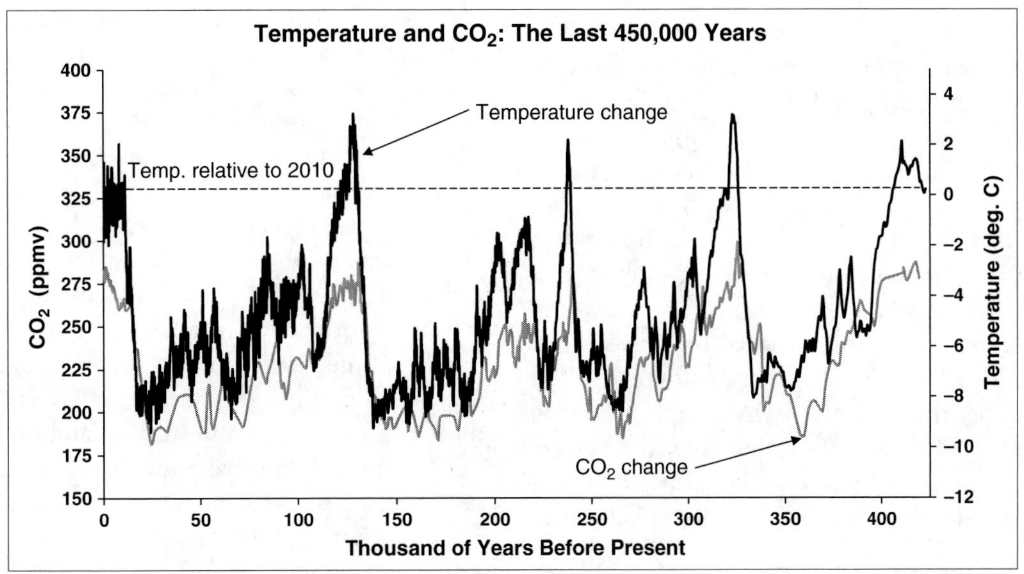

Figure 5.8 Temperature trend for the last 450,000 thousand years (the carbon dioxide trend over the same period is shown as darker lines). Source: National Oceanic and Atmospheric Administration and National Climatic Data Center—www.ncdc.noaa.gov).

> *And then there's global warming. I didn't even know the details on global warming so I looked it up. There are a lot of vying statistics, but I think the crux of it is the temperature has gone up roughly 1.8 degrees over a hundred years. Am I the only one who finds that amazingly stable? I could go back to my hotel room tonight and futz with the thermostat for three to four hours. I could not detect that difference. Then people ask me if I'm worried about the effects of global warming on my kids. Well, obviously I love my kids and I want them to live to be a 100. So that's another 1.8. My kids' kids? Three point six. I'll just tell them we moved to Phoenix.*
>
> Dennis Miller on *The Daily Show* with Jon Stewart, April 20th, 2005

Clearly, Miller, who now commentates on the Fox News channel, does not share Al Gore's view of global warming: that we have a moral imperative to make big changes. And while the views of the Fox News commentators may well be representative of a broader political alignment and ideology concerning the debate, this fact remains: in probabilistic terms, our climate is likely to continue changing during our lifetime. At the very least, we have a duty as scientists to find out why.

PREDICTING FUTURE TRENDS IN CO_2 AND TEMPERATURE

One of the strongest lines of evidence for those who argue for anthropogenically-caused climate change is the plot showing strong correlations between CO_2 and temperature going back several hundred thousand years (Figure 5.8 above). In fact, the correlation between temperature and CO_2 appears very nearly perfect. Many advocates use this as evidence that our emissions of CO_2 will warm the Earth. But if two things, A and B, are correlated, even perfectly, does it imply a particular causal relationship? The answer in simple terms is, no. A strong correlation between two variables does not imply there is a cause-and-effect relationship between the two, even though it is often taken for granted that A is causing B even when no evidence supports this. This is what is known as a logical fallacy because there are several other possibilities:

- B may simply be the cause of A, or
- some unknown third factor is actually the cause of the relationship between A and B (a factor called a lurking variable), or
- the relationship is so complex it can be labeled coincidental—that is, A and B may have no simple relationship to each other besides the fact that they are occurring at the same time.

In other words, *there can be no conclusion made regarding the existence of a cause and effect relationship only from the fact that A is correlated with B.* For example, if researchers found a correlation between individuals' college grades and their income later in life, they might wonder whether doing well in school increased income. It might; but good grades and high income could both be caused by a third (lurking or hidden variable) such as tendency to work hard. I think there is a message here! Unfortunately, we cannot run experiments to determine causation in the context of global warming. We cannot rewind the past 200 years and replay events after making a controlled change to the one important variable—namely CO_2—preferably keeping levels at 280 ppm. What this means is that causation or attribution can only be inferred within some margin of error, and never exactly known. Skeptics of the global warming theory like this and are quick to point out that the CO_2 rise shown in Figure 5.8 actually *follows* the temperature changes (which it does), questioning the direction of the correlation. Surely A must precede B if we are to conclude that A causes B? It certainly seems reasonable. So let's play devil's advocate for a moment. If CO_2 is not the primary driver of global temperature change, then what is? Well, we know that Earth's climate changes, and based on decades of research, we can identify factors that have influenced climate over geologic timescales: tectonic activity, changes in the orbit of Earth about the sun, solar variations, and volcanoes, among others. But with regard to the warming during the 20th century, we can rule out tectonics and orbital variations (they are far too slow to account for warming over mere decades) as well as volcanoes (they affect climate for only a few years). We can also rule out solar variability because our measurements simply have not shown an increase in solar output that would be necessary to explain Earth's temperature increase. Certainly, the climate system is complicated, and so there will be internal variability (such as the El Niño/Southern Oscillation [ENSO], during which certain parts of Earth are much warmer than normal). But there is no evidence (and certainly no data) supporting variability *per sé* as a driver of global warming. The truth is that over timescales of hundreds of thousands of years, climate scientists do not look at CO_2 as a driving or trigger mechanism so much as a feedback mechanism—that is, something that reinforces the effect. What most scientists think happens is that small variations in Earth's orbit cause a small initial warming which leads to CO_2 being released, which then leads to further warming. But in making the argument that CO_2 is causing global warming, we should not really talk about this long-time-scale correlation, whether it exists or not. In the past century, where the record is most reliable, and where the trends are based on measurable data and not inference, humans have come to dominate the carbon cycle. Surely it is only reasonable to suggest that we also now dominate the year-to-year atmospheric changes? In effect, CO_2 has now become a forcing mechanism. In the absence of any other evidence, the only logical conclusion is that the relatively new player in the climate game, human-emitted greenhouse gases, is the most likely cause of increases in the temperature of the surface.

If we accept the above premise, the next questions that must be addressed are: (1) Will CO_2 continue to rise during the 21st century and, if so, at what rate, and (2) how will Earth's climate respond or, more specifically, what will global temperatures and rainfall do? These questions are even more difficult to address because now we move into the world of prediction and, ultimately, climate models.

No one knows for certain what CO_2 levels will be by the end of the 21st century. The rate of rise of CO_2 will depend on a number of uncertain developments, particularly economic, sociological, and technological ones. The Intergovernmental Panel on Climate Change (IPCC), established in 1988 by the World Meteorological Organization and the United Nations Environmental Program, is charged with evaluating the state of climate science as a basis for informed policy action. Led by government and academic scientists and researchers in climate science, the IPCC has published a wide range of future CO_2 scenarios, from 540 ppm to almost 1,000 ppm by the year 2100. Well, which is it? Surely we have to narrow that range and reduce the uncertainty if we are going to be able to predict its effect on temperature, but the truth is we cannot. Uncertainty is just part human inquiry and in a complex system such as the Earth-ocean-atmosphere system, uncertainty is just a fact of life. It would be irresponsible science at best, and scientific misconduct at worst, to pretend otherwise. What we can say, however, is that future CO_2 levels will probably continue rising given the rate of industrial development and our ongoing dependence on fossil fuel usage. The Energy Information Administration (EIA) of the U.S. government estimates that world CO_2 emissions will increase by 1.9 percent annually until 2025, with much of the increase in these emissions expected to occur in the developing world where emerging economies, such as China and India, fuel economic development with fossil energy. Developing countries' emissions are expected to grow above the world average at 2.7 percent annually, and surpass emissions of industrialized countries near 2018. Notwithstanding, what does seem prudent in the emissions scenario debate is to err on the side of caution, and so predictions of future temperatures are now based largely on the assumption of doubled pre-industrial CO_2 levels—that is, 560 to 600 ppm by 2100.

And so to the $1 million question: If CO_2 continues its rise and doubles by the end of this century, what will global temperatures do? Well, given what we have said thus far in relation to uncertainty, you can imagine the dilemma I faced when beginning this section on climate prediction! Ultimately, the answer to this question depends on climate sensitivity which, simply put, is the measure of the climate's response to radiative forcing resulting from increased GHGs and other anthropogenic and natural causes. Climate sensitivity is defined as the change in average surface temperature due to a doubling of the CO_2 concentration ($\Delta T2_x$), and is estimated to lie between 1.0 and 6.0°C (Figure 5.9). These predictions are the result of experiments with general circulation models (GCMs), which are sophisticated computer simulations of how the atmosphere behaves. But these models are far from perfect, and why should we expect them to be given the complexity of the system the scientists are trying to model? The naysayers in the global warming debate most frequently use the "uncertainty of the model projections" to justify their position. A recent article on FoxNews.com by Steven J. Milloy, a commentator for Fox and director of the website Junkscience.com, illustrates this point:

> *So where does all the fuss about manmade CO_2 and global warming come from? Not from actual temperature measurements and greenhouse physics—rather it comes from manmade computer models relying on myriad assumptions and guesswork. Many models incorporate hypothesized "positive feedbacks" in the climate system, which tend to amplify model predictions. But no model has been validated against the historical temperature record. So they don't "radiate" much confidence when it*

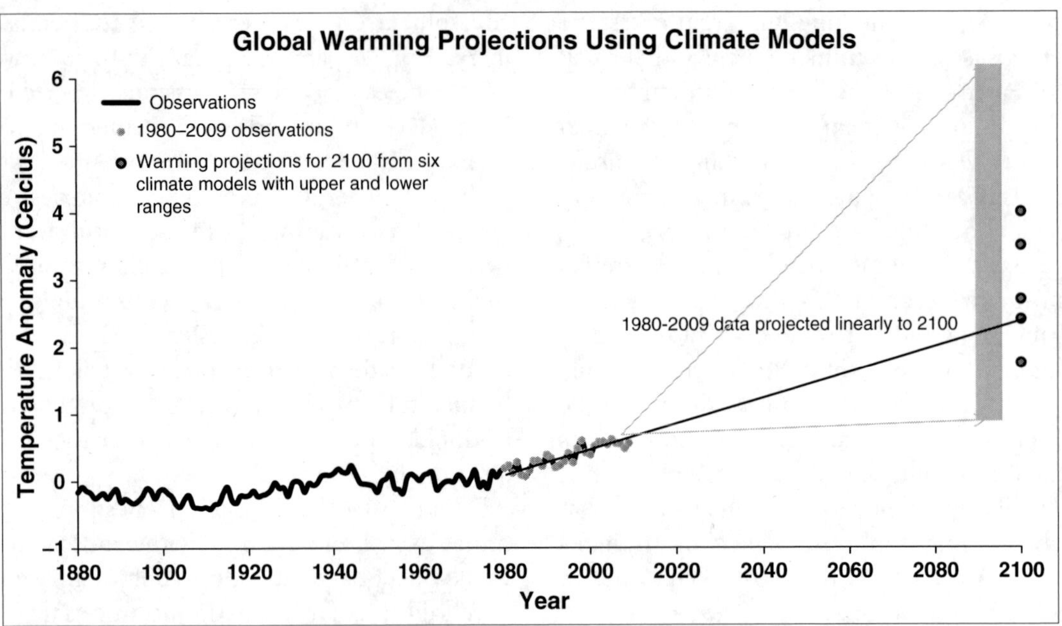

Figure 5.9 Global warming projections using computer models from several climate research centers showing the wide range of possible outcomes through to 2100. The surface record from 1980–2009 are highlighted and used as one projection through to 2100. The circles at 2100 indicate the best estimate and the likely range assessed for six carbon dioxide scenarios. (Source: Intergovernmental Panel on Climate Change—www.ipcc.ch/).

comes to forecasting temperatures. This leaves me to wonder why global warming alarmists are unwilling to explain why they believe in non-validated and always-wrong computer guess-timations of future climate change rather than actual temperature measurements and green-house-effect physics that indicate manmade emissions of greenhouse gases are not a problem.

FoxNews.com, Thursday, April 20, 2006.

Although Milloy has been criticized for making misleading and false claims and for presenting himself as an impartial journalist on health and environmental matters while accepting funding and editorial input from tobacco and oil companies, the fact is many global warming skeptics buy this argument. This is unfortunate, because it completely misrepresents the modeling process and what climate scientists are trying to do, given the complexity of the processes involved. To be sure, no scientific conclusion can ever be proven absolutely. No climate model will ever be perfect. Yet we quite willingly put our faith and money in the hands of financial experts who use highly sophisticated economic and statistical models to make projections about the future state of the financial markets. The complexity and computing power required by these models are entirely on the order of many climate models. Yet any self-respecting portfolio manager would have to agree that modeling financial markets is brutally difficult. All I ask of my financial advisor is to be right significantly more often than she is wrong. And when things do go wrong, I (and probably you too) tend to shrug it off to "volatility" and unforeseen circumstances. Perhaps there really is something to that disclaimer that "Past performance is no guarantee of future results?" Yet we seem to demand far more certainty and predictability from the climate scientists. We simply do not know whether or not climate model forecasts created to date have been correct thus far. In this regard, Mr. Milloy is incorrect: In climate modeling, there has been considerable testing and calibration against observed climate variations. But the approach is basically how well one can fit a climate model to an observed data set such as near-surface temperatures in a publication to see if it indeed matches historical data. There is simply no way to know what the model's *realized* forecast efficacy will be. The cynic may argue that there is incentive to create attention-getting forecasts (e.g., our climate is going to warm dramatically during the next 50 years), a result that is generating a lot of climate research funding without any real accountability as to whether or not the forecasts will later prove to be true. No one knows how a global warming, natural or human-induced, will play out in the real world as opposed to how it plays out in highly sophisticated, yet imperfect, computer models. But researchers are bound by the overall integrity of the scientific process. It doesn't make them infallible, but it does set constraints upon the process.

POSSIBLE EFFECTS OF GLOBAL WARMING

If we are already committed to living in a warmer world, then what are the likely impacts of such warming going to be? The possible effects of global warming generally fall into two categories: the impact on the oceans, specifically rising sea level, and changes in the amount and pattern of precipitation. These impacts will operate at local, regional, continental, and global scales. Let's look at rising sea level first.

The physics behind rising sea levels is well understood. In a warmer world, the oceans themselves will expand, raising the sea level. A warming of the entire world ocean by 1°C would, for example, produce a sea level rise of 1.6 feet. Such a uniform warming of the entire ocean within a short time is, however unlikely. Because the deep ocean warms up much more slowly than the upper layers, water exchange between these two regions is reduced as the warming happens, slowing the whole process of sea level rise down. The figure of a 1.6 feet rise should therefore just be taken as an indication of the order of magnitude of the change possible through thermal expansion. It will most likely be quite a bit lower.

More significant than thermal expansion will be sea level rise due to the addition of fresh water from the melting of land-based glaciers. And this is one area where we are on much firmer footing with respect to degrees of certainty. There is now overwhelming evidence that glaciers around the world are melting and retreating and that the rate of melting is increasing. We all know that a picture is worth a thousand words, and photographs and satellite images showing disappearing ice sheets are now commonplace in the media and scientific literature (see Figure 5.10). The very existence of many of the world's glaciers is now threatened. Recent measurements of glacial ice suggest that total surface area of glaciers worldwide has decreased by 50 percent since the end of the 19th century. Currently, glacier retreat rates have been increasing in the Andes, Alps, Himalaya's, and Rocky Mountains. And as of March 2005, the snow cap that has covered the top of Mount Kilimanjaro for the past 11,000 years since the last ice age has almost disappeared. Observations of glacial recession provide strong qualitative support to the rise in global temperatures since the late 19th century. There is also serious concern about future local water resources in these areas. Glaciers retain water on mountains during wet years, since the snow cover accumulating on glaciers protects the ice from melting. In warmer and drier years, glaciers offset the lower precipitation amounts with a higher meltwater input. Of particular importance are the Himalayan glacial melts that comprise the principal dry-season water source of many of the major rivers of the Southeast Asian mainland. In these areas that are heavily dependent on water runoff from glaciers that melt during the warmer summer months, a continuation of the current retreat will eventually deplete the glacial ice and substantially reduce or eliminate runoff. A reduction in runoff will affect the ability to irrigate crops.

Figure 5.10 In North America, the most visited glacier is the Athabasca Glacier, oce of six glaciers that spill down the Canadian Rockies from the Columbia Icefield in western Canada. Visitors who return to the glacier a few years after their first visit will notice the change wrought by warming temperatures. In the past 125 years, the Athabasca Glacier has lost half of its volume and receded more than 1.5 kilometers (0.93 miles), leaving hills of rock in its place. Its retreat is visible in this photo, where the glacier's front edge looms several meters behind the tombstone-like marker that indicates the edge of the ice in 1992. The Athabasca Glacier is not alone in its retreat: Since 1960, glaciers around the world have lost an estimated 8,000 cubic kilometers (1,900 cubic miles) of ice. That is approximately enough ice to cover a two-kilometer-wide (1.2 mile-wide) swath of land between New York and Los Angeles with an ice sheet that is one kilometer (0.62 miles) tall.

The amount of freshwater added to the oceans from the melting of temperate and alpine glaciers will, however, pale in comparison to the volumes potentially added from melting in the Greenland and West Antarctic Ice Sheets. We know that about 99 percent of all freshwater ice is in the great ice sheets of polar and subpolar Antarctica and Greenland. In Greenland, several very large glaciers that had long been stable have begun to retreat since 2000. Satellite images and aerial photographs from the 1950s and 1970s show glacial stability in Greenland. Now, more sophisticated surveying both from the ground and air shows several glaciers retreating rapidly, some in excess of 100 ft/day. The extent of the Greenland ice melt has been steadily increasing over the past 30 years (Figure 5.11).

The most dramatic example of glacier retreat is on the continent of Antarctica, where large sections of the Larsen Ice Shelf have been lost. The collapse of Larsen Ice Shelf has been caused by warmer melt season temperatures that have led to surface melting and the formation of shallow ponds of water on the ice shelf. The Larsen Ice Shelf lost 965 square miles of its area from 1995 to 2001. In a 35-day period beginning on 31 January 2002, about 1,254 square miles of shelf area disintegrated. The ice sheet is now 40 percent the size of its previous minimum stable extent[2].

Sea level has risen by about 0.65 ft (20 cm) over the past 100 years, and the consensus is that it is generally expected to rise a further 1.6 ft (50 cm) in the next century (0.016 feet per year, or about 5 mm per year, see Figure 5.12). Such a rise would inundate 7,000 square miles of dry land in the United States (an area the size of Massachusetts) and a similar amount of coastal wetlands, erode recreational beaches, exacerbate coastal flooding, and increase the salinity of coastal aquifers and estuaries. Several small island nations will be at great risk; some of them will be inundated. Refugees from highly populated deltas such as Bangladesh will become critical humanitarian issues.

There is some speculation that global warming could lead to cooling, or lesser warming, in the North Atlantic, via a slowing or even shutdown of the thermohaline circulation. This circulation is sometimes called the ocean conveyor belt or the global conveyor belt, and transports warm water to the North Atlantic (Figure 5.13). A melting and influx of fresh water could potentially "turn off" the conveyor. This would affect in particular areas like Ireland, Britain, and Scandinavia that are warmed by the North Atlantic Drift.

A report by the Arctic Climate Impact Assessment—a consortium of eight countries, including Russia and

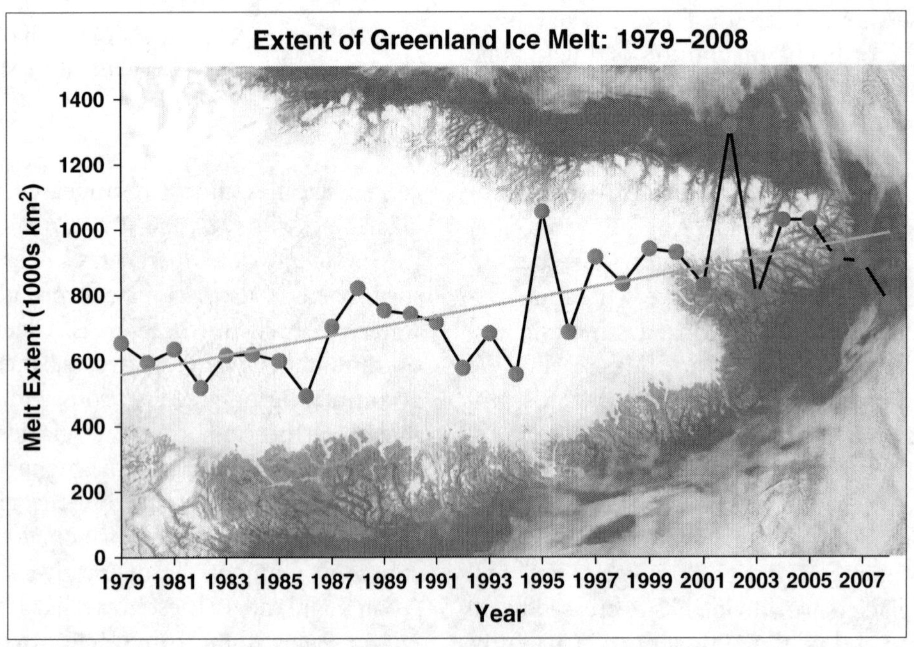

Figure 5.11 Annual estimates of surface melt extent of the Greenland Ice-Sheet from satellite sensors. Source:http//nsidc.org/

[2] National Snow and Ice Data Center (http://nsidc.org/iceshelves/larsenb2002/).

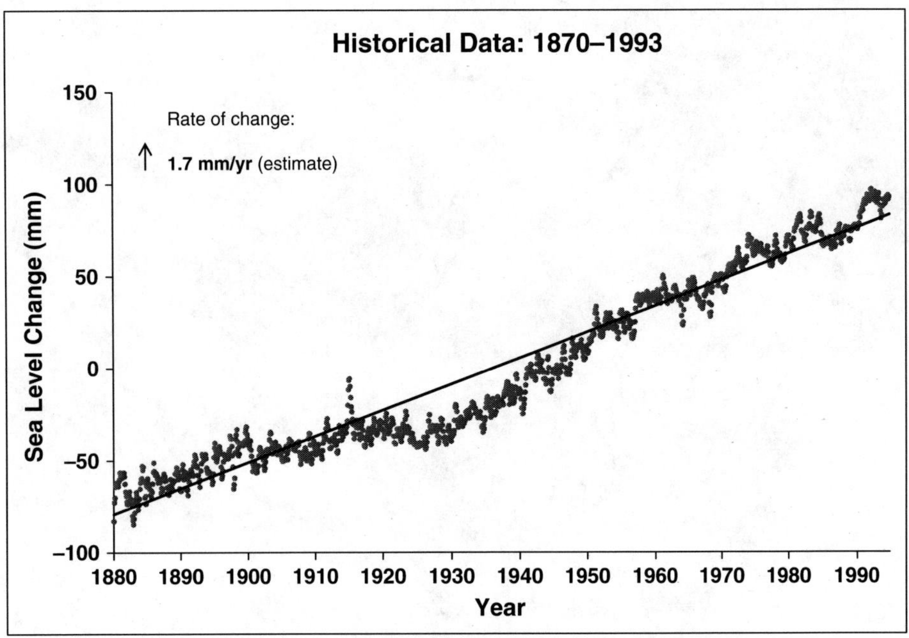

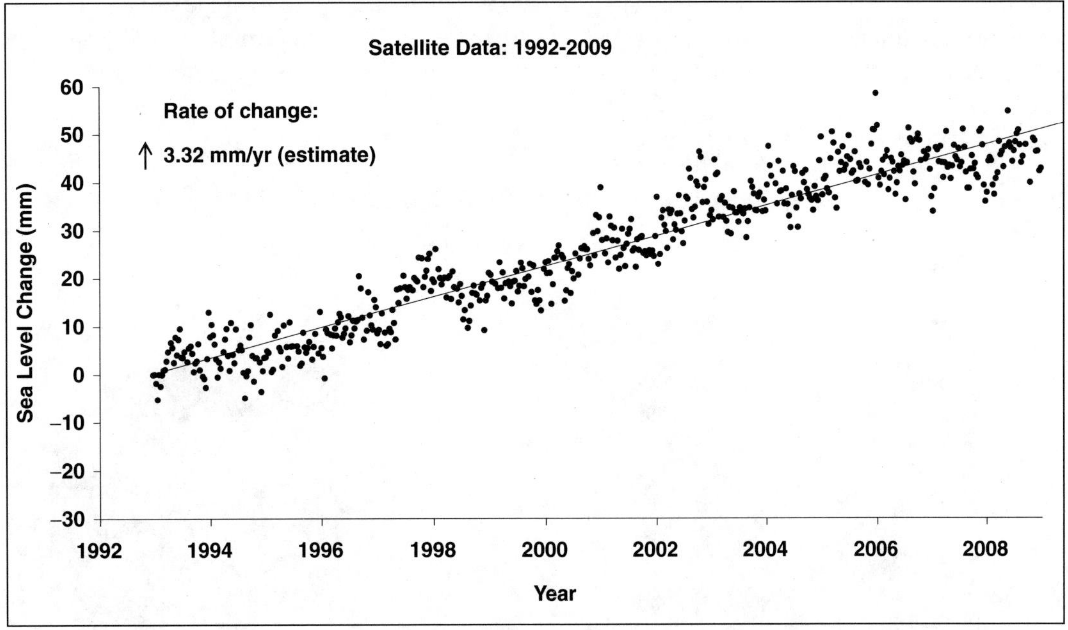

Figure 5.12 Historical sea level data: derived from coastal tide gauge records (1870–1993, top) and average sea level since 1993 derived from global satellite measurements, updated here monthly (bottom). Sea level rise is associated with the thermal expansion of sea water due to climate warming and widespread melting of land ice. Source: http://climate.nasa.gov/

the United States—now confirms that major changes are taking place in the Arctic, affecting both human and nonhuman communities, as predicted by climate models. According to the Canadian Ice Service, the amount of ice in Canada's eastern Arctic decreased by 15 percent between 1969 and 2004 (Figure 5.14). And while the reduction of summer ice in the Arctic may be good news for shipping, particularly if the Northwest Passage opens up in summer, this same phenomenon threatens the Arctic ecosystem, most notably polar bears which depend on ice floes. Subsistence hunters such as the Inuit peoples will find their livelihoods and cultures increasingly threatened as the ecosystem changes due to global warming. Should we care, particularly if an ice-free Arctic cut 5,000 nautical miles from shipping routes between Europe and Asia? An open Arctic Ocean would allow offshore oil drilling and maybe new fisheries access.

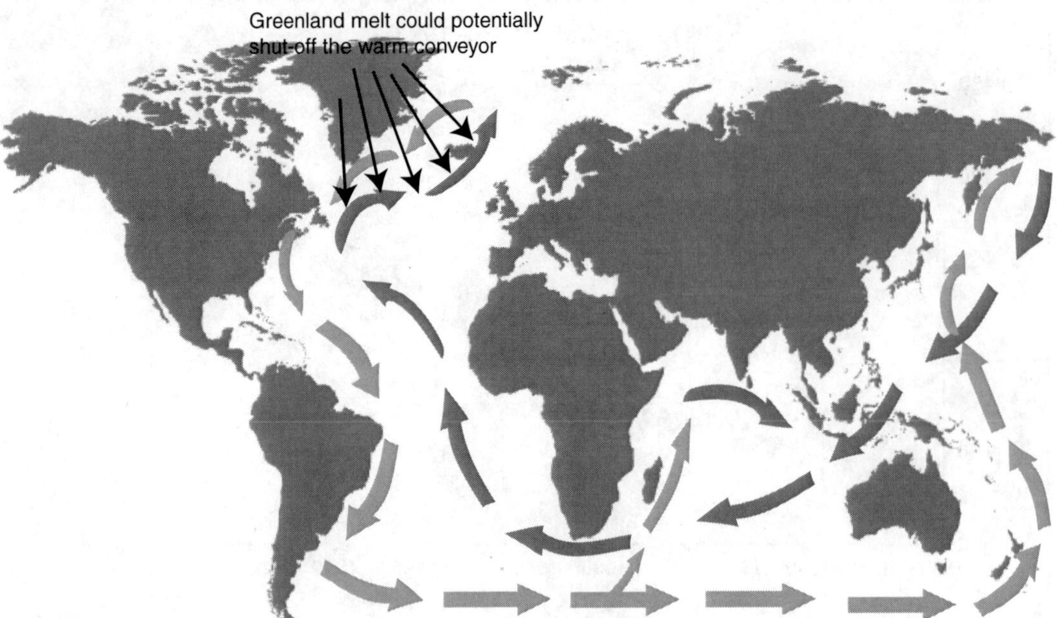

Figure 5.13 Often called a conveyor belt because of its northward transport at the surface, and southward return flow in the abyss in the Atlantic, the ocean circulation system is a slow, three-dimensional pattern of flow involving the surface and deep oceans around the world (Source: http://www.ncdc.noaa.gov).

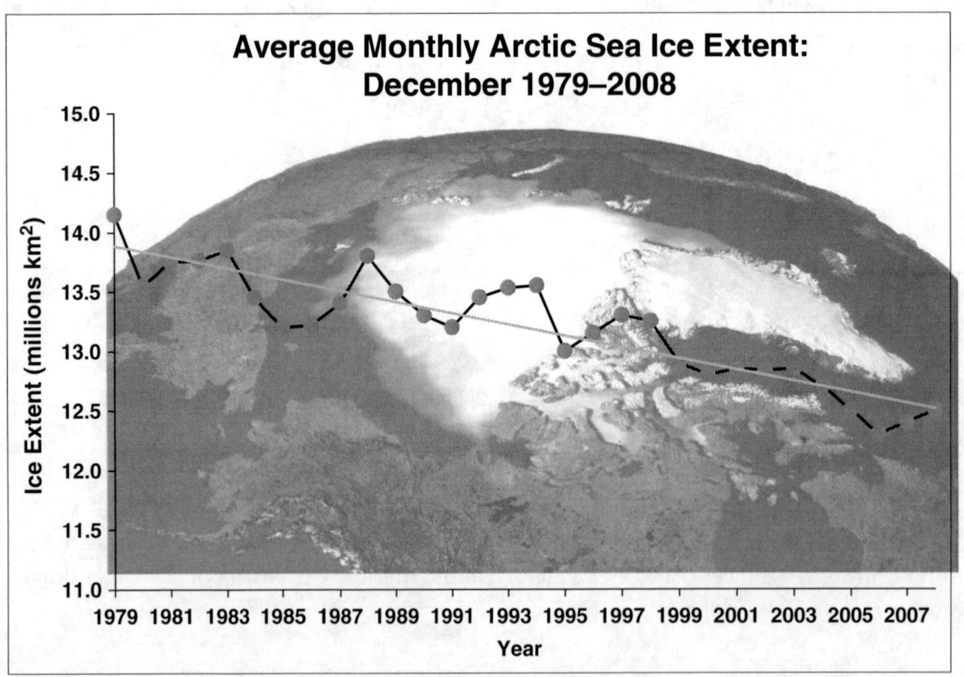

Figure 5.14 Annual monthly Arctic sea ice extent. Sea ice extent over the 30-year monitoring period shows a decline of 3.3 percent perdecade. Source: http//nsidc.org/

Arguably more controversial than global warming's impact on sea level are the possible changes to the planet's precipitation regime. Many have suggested the frequency and intensity of extreme weather events, such as floods, droughts, hurricanes, and tornadoes, will increase. At the end of 2005—the hottest year on record—the Atlantic basin had just wrapped up its most active hurricane season in recorded history. Extreme weather events like hurricanes Rita and Katrina inevitably raised the question: Is global warming to blame?

After Hurricane Katrina impacted the Gulf Coast and became the costliest natural disaster in U.S. history, some Americans began viewing monster hurricanes as the greatest threat posed by a warming world. A host of reputable magazines ran articles on the potential link between global warming and hurricanes. In *Time* magazine, a rather prophetic piece entitled Is Global Warming Making Hurricanes Worse? was published three weeks before Katrina. Yet Max Mayfield, Director of the National Hurricane Center during the 2005 season, noted that science simply does not support a link between global warming and recent hurricane activity. According to Mayfield, Katrina and Rita are part of a natural cycle[3]. The increase in number and intensity of storms since 1995 is hardly unprecedented. Two major hurricanes hit the Gulf Coast only six weeks apart in 1915, mimicking the double whammy of Katrina and Rita. And no sooner do we read that, when scientists from the National Center for Atmospheric Research (NCAR) in Boulder, Colorado, publish a report noting that global warming accounted for around half of the extra hurricane-fueling warmth in the waters of the tropical North Atlantic in 2005, while natural cycles were only a minor factor[4].

These conflicting views on the link between hurricanes and global warming raise the question: Do scientists really know whether the hurricanes we are observing are a direct result of climate change? Can man-made greenhouse gases really be blamed for the intensity of storms like Rita and Katrina? Or are there, as other experts insist, too many additional variables to say one way or the other? We know that 2005s activity was also related to very favorable upper-level winds as well as the extremely warm sea surface temperatures in the Gulf of Mexico. That global warming should, in theory, exacerbate the problem of hurricanes is an easy conclusion to reach: warmer air can easily translate into warmer oceans, and warm oceans are the fuel that drives the hurricane's turbine. The heat energy required to evaporate water (i.e., change its phase from liquid water to water vapor) is hidden in the water molecule but released once the water condenses back in the atmosphere. If you are still unclear on this, put a pan full of water in the sun and another in the shade; which will evaporate first? This hidden or latent heat release will intensify with global warming.

When Katrina hit at the end of August, 2005, the Gulf of Mexico was a veritable hurricane refueling station, with water up to 5°F higher than normal. Rita too drew its killer strength from the Gulf, making its way past southern Florida as a Category 1 storm, then exploding into a Category 5 as it moved westward. But the past 10 stormy years in the North Atlantic were preceded by many very quiet ones, all occurring at the same time that global temperatures were marching upward. A recent analysis of the global hurricane record by scientists at the Geophysical Fluid Dynamics Laboratory, in collaboration with Princeton University, suggests that it is premature to conclude that human activity—and particularly greenhouse warming—has already had a detectable impact on Atlantic hurricane activity. Such human activity may have already caused substantial changes that simply cannot be detected. The study concludes, however, that anthropogenic warming over the next century will *likely* cause Atlantic hurricanes to be more intense (by a few percent on average) and have substantially higher rainfall rates than present-day hurricanes. There is also agreement that such warming more likely than not will lead to greater numbers of very intense hurricanes. The potential impact on just our oil production alone should be cause for concern (Figure 5.15).

MOVING FORWARD

We have heard the term *scientific consensus* at several points in this chapter. What does that really mean? How many scientists does it take to make the term *consensus* a valid one? In December 2004, Naomi Oreskes, Professor of History and Science Studies at the University of California San Diego, published a study in the prestigious journal *Science* in which she analyzed 928 scientific articles published between 1993 and 2003 on global climate change. Her study concluded that 75 percent of the articles either explicitly or implicitly accepted the consensus view that "most of the observed warming over the last 50 years is likely to have been attributable to human activities." In fact, every major scientific institution dealing with climate, ocean, and/or atmosphere agrees that the climate is warming rapidly and the primary cause is human CO_2 emissions. In 2005, the national science academies of the G8 nations, as well as Brazil, China, and India, three of the largest emitters of greenhouse gases in the developing world, signed a statement on the global response to climate change. The statement stresses that the scientific

[3] Article appeared in USAToday, 25 September, 2005.
[4] National Center for Atmospheric Research (http://www.ucar.edu/news/releases/2006/hurricanes.shtml).

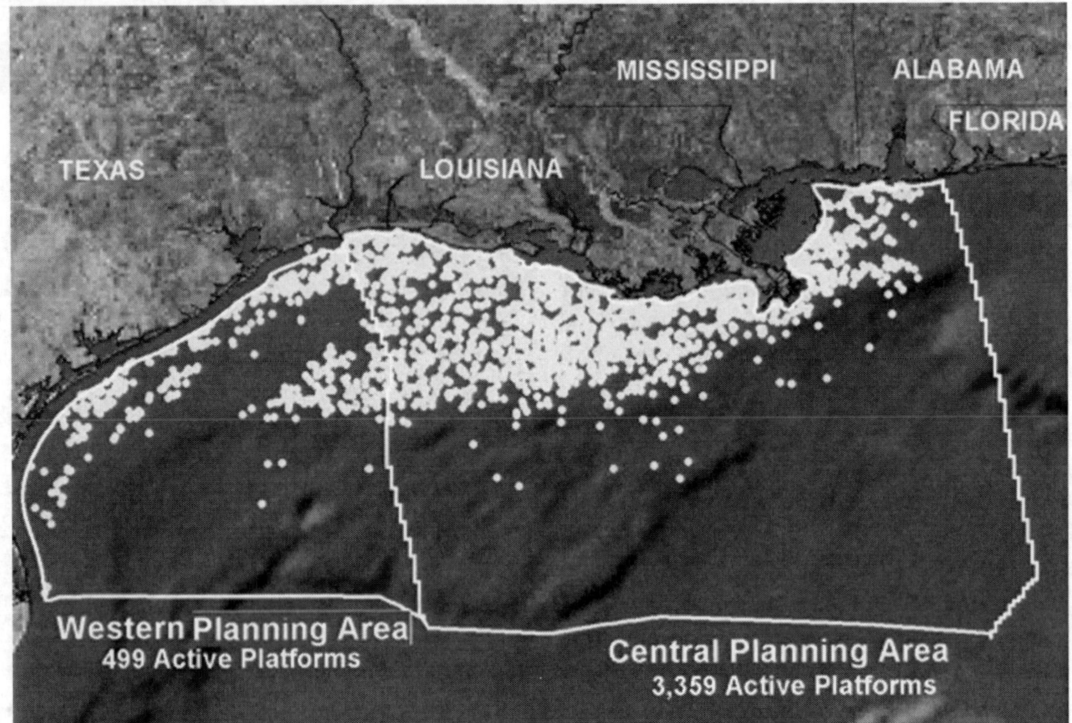

Figure 5.15 Map of northern Gulf of Mexico showing the nearly 4,000 active oil and gas platforms (Source: www.noaa.gov).

understanding of climate change is now sufficiently clear to justify nations taking prompt action[5].

We must acknowledge that there is some scientific uncertainty, including the exact degree of climate change expected in the future, and especially how changes will vary from region to region across the globe. But uncertainty should not be used as justification for complacency. A hotly contested political and public debate has yet to be resolved, regarding whether anything should be done, and what could be cost-effectively done to reduce or reverse future warming, or to deal with the expected consequences. Much of this focuses on the Kyoto Protocol, a global treaty aimed at mitigation of global warming; that is, taking actions aimed at reducing the extent or likelihood of global warming.

The Kyoto Protocol, which was initially adopted in December 1997, came into force on 16 February 2005 and now covers more than 160 countries globally and over 55 percent of global GHG emissions. Countries who have ratified this protocol have committed to reduce their emissions of CO_2 or engage in emissions trading if they maintain or increase emissions of these gases. Between 2008 and 2012, developed countries have to reduce their GHG emissions by an average of 5 percent below their 1990 levels whereas developing economies have no GHG restrictions. Australian Prime Minister John Howard refused to ratify the Agreement during his tenure from 1996 to 2007, arguing that the protocol would cost Australians jobs, since countries with booming economies and massive populations such as China and India have no reduction obligations under the Protocol[6]. China, incidentally, is now the largest emitter of greenhouse gases (Figure 5.16). President George W. Bush also refused to submit the treaty for ratification, not because he did not support the Kyoto principles, but because of the exemption granted to China. Bush also opposed the treaty because of the strain he believed the treaty would put on the economy; he emphasized the uncertainties which he asserted are present in the climate change issue. It is worth remembering that in 1997, the U.S. Senate unanimously passed by a 95–0 vote the Byrd-Hagel Resolution, which stated the sense of the Senate was that the United States should not be a signatory to any protocol that did not include binding targets and timetables for developing as well as industrialized nations or "would result in serious

[5] http://nationalacademies.org/onpi/06072005.pdf

[6] Australia ratified the agreement in December 2007.

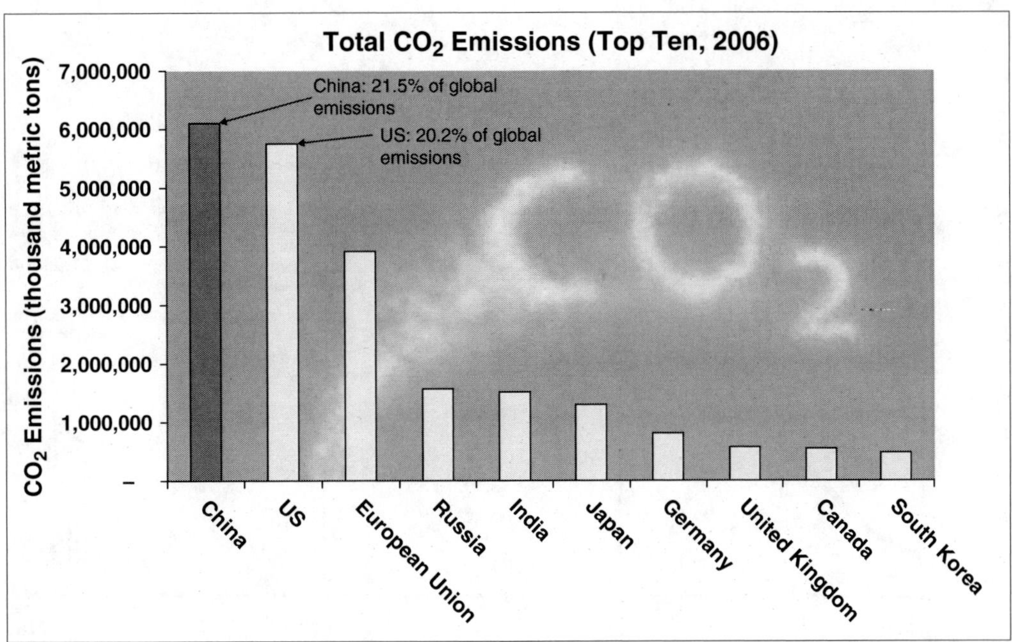

Figure 5.16 Global carbon dioxide emissions, 2006 (Source: www.cdiac.esd.ornl.gov/).

harm to the economy of the United States." The reality is that the U.S. produces about 20 percent of global CO_2 emissions from burning fossil fuels (Figure 5.16), primarily because our economy is the largest in the world and we meet 85 percent of our energy needs through burning fossil fuels. Any global attempt to combat CO_2 emissions without the U.S. at the table is therefore doomed to failure. In Copenhagen, the U.S. appeared much more positive under the new Obama administration but, ultimately, the climate summit failed to deliver a global agreement. The reasons for this are manifold, but one key issue was that the U.S. and the so-called BASIC group of countries (Brazil, South Africa, India and China) tried to hammer out a separate, last-minute deal outside of the UN climate convention where the outcomes were not legally binding. A major reason for this was that President Obama was unable to pledge anything without the support of the U.S. Congress, and this appeared to be a difficult road given the state of the economy and the major health care bills being considered at the time. In the end, he was in a position to offer very little—and other countries responded in kind.

Ultimately, there is no single solution to mitigate the worst effects of global warming. Alternative power (solar, wind, nuclear, or wave) is not going to be sufficient to replace all coal and oil use. Efficiency won't improve fast enough. Sequestration can't bury enough CO_2. These are all true, but only in isolation. The solution that will work comes not as a single bolt from the blue, but from a combination of multiple, varied efforts. Professor Robert Socolow from Princeton University has captured this complexity elegantly in a concept he calls "stabilization wedges" (Figure 5.17). With stabilization wedges, a multitude of projects, from efficiency to de-carbonization to sequestration and renewable energy and more, combine to reduce overall carbon emissions, a task that at times can seem impossible. Individually, the wedges are difficult but achievable. As Scolow is quoted by the *Harvard Gazette*, this approach "decomposes a heroic challenge (eliminating the emissions in the stabilization triangle) into a limited set of merely monumental tasks."

Socolow's model for stabilization attempts to prevent a doubling of the amount of carbon emissions by 2050 by stabilizing at the current rate of 7 billion tons (7 gigatons) of carbon/yr, globally. This is sufficient to prevent the kinds of disastrous results arising from a much higher CO_2 concentration, but would have to be followed by further efforts to reduce emissions once stabilized. Socolow argues that we have more than enough different ways to achieve this goal, with current technologies and practices, and that the real question becomes not "can we do it?" but "what are the best ways to do it?" The stabilization wedge concept, in short, is not a "bright green" approach, but a crystallization of what's possible with relatively mainstream ideas. According to Socolow, if we can adopt seven wedge options, each countering a gigaton of carbon, we can meet this goal. What is really

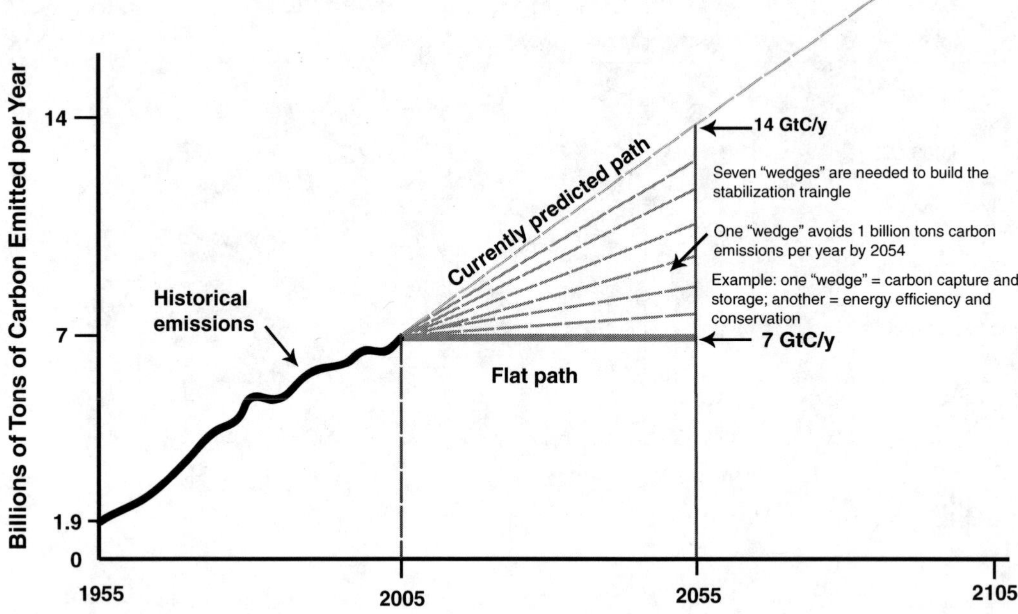

Figure 5.17 Carbon dioxide stabilization wedges. The top curve is a representative emissions path for global carbon emissions as CO_2 from fossil fuel combustion and cement manufacture rises 1.5 percent per year starting from 7.0 GtC/year in 2004. The stabilization triangle shows avoided emissions with actual global emissions fixed at 7 GtC/year. The stabilization triangle is divided into seven wedges, each of which reaches 1 GtC/year in 2054 (Source: Pacala and Socolow, 2004, Science vol. 305)

attractive about this approach is that we don't have to adopt every possible solution, but can instead look for and deploy the ones that give us the best result for the least cost. Many like the "we can do this" spirit of the stabilization wedge model as opposed to the "we're doomed" scenarios often portrayed by scientists and environmentalists.

CONCLUDING THOUGHTS

Climate change is perhaps the most complex scientific issue modern humanity has ever handled. Climate model predictions of the magnitude of temperature increase are uncertain, which means that potential effects of global climate change are also uncertain. This uncertainty intensifies an already controversial political and social debate arguing whether global warming is real. Skeptics argue that the science is simply not mature enough to justify rushing forward with ratifying Kyoto or making major changes that could negatively impact our economy. Still, the ranks of those skeptics are growing thinner as current scientific studies continue to support a global warming scenario.

In the science community, an overall consensus exists that global warming is real and climate change is imminent. This is clearly expressed in the reports of the IPCC: "Human activities . . . are modifying the concentration of atmospheric constituents . . . that absorb or scatter radiant energy. . . . [M]ost of the observed warming over the last 50 years is likely to have been due to the increase in greenhouse gas concentrations."[7] This conclusion represents the results of our best available science and therefore, is our best basis for reasoned action.

What can we do as individuals to help mitigate this issue? The good news is that we can help curb global warming by taking sensible steps. The biggest single step we can take is to require cars and trucks to go farther on a gallon of gas. According to the National Academy of Sciences, currently available technology can make cars and trucks nearly double their gas mileage to an average of 40 mpg within a decade without reducing the size, power, or variety

[7] Third Assessment of the IPCC (2001); http://www.ipcc.ch/.

of cars available to consumers. This will also save Americans billions of dollars and reduce pollution and further GHG emissions. It is vital that we all play a part in identifying cost-effective steps such as these that we can take now, to contribute to the long-term reduction in net global greenhouse gas emissions. Action taken now to reduce the build-up of greenhouse gases in the atmosphere will lessen the magnitude and rate of climate change. As the United Nations Framework Convention on Climate Change (UNFCCC) recognizes, a lack of full scientific certainty about some aspects of climate change and global warming is not a reason for delaying an immediate response that will, at a reasonable cost, prevent dangerous anthropogenic interference with the climate system.

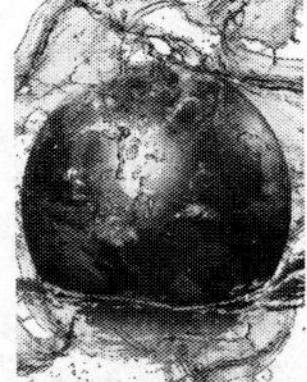

WATER PLANET EXERCISE 5

Name: ______________________________

Water Budgets and Climate

I. Purpose

This exercise requires you to determine a water budget for U.S. cities that will be assigned to you. Read the assigned chapter relating to water budgets and read it carefully.

II. Part I—Water Budgets for American Cities

1. Download the Excel worksheet provided (Table 1).
   The data you will use are located on a second Excel spreadsheet (Table 2). There are data from U.S. cities located along three east-west transects: northern, central and southern United States. Each of you will pick two cities along your assigned transect.

2. Download this Excel spreadsheet (Table 2). All units used are given in millimeters, except of course temperature as that is in degrees Celsius. The data given are for temperature (T), precipitation (P), potential evapotranspiration (PE), and actual evapotranspiration (AE).

3. Enter the values for each city you are assigned in the work sheet (Table 1) in the row next to the T, P, PE, and AE respectively. (You can actually copy the data you need in Table 2 and paste the numbers in Table 1) Using the data you have listed on the worksheet, calculate monthly values for the following water budget data, entering the numbers in the appropriate rows on the worksheet.

   D soil moisture deficit (subtract AE from PE)

   U soil moisture use (if AE > P, subtract P from AE; if P > AE, leave blank)

   R soil moisture recharge (if P > PE, subtract PE from P; if PE > P, leave blank)

   S surplus (subtract PE from P, but only for those months during and following completion of soil moisture recharge)

Calculate the annual total for each of the variables and enter these values in the table. Note that the whole year soil moisture use (U) should equal soil moisture recharge (R). The only time this would not happen is in the case of prolonged drought. Otherwise, soil moisture recharge will usually be completed at some point during the year. After that time, a surplus condition exists and water will run off. If recharge is completed midway through one of the months, assign R only enough of the monthly quantity of P needed to bring the annual total of R equal to the annual total of soil moisture use (U). Assign the balance of that month to surplus (S).

4. Use the scatter line function in the Excel Chart menu to plot the monthly values of P, PE, and AE on one graph. Use the drawing tool in Excel to draw vertical lines on each graph to identify the month in which all of the excess precipitation is recharge and when the excess becomes surplus. Label the three areas between the lines you drew on the graph as: recharge, surplus, and use.

5. On a separate graph, plot the temperature values.

6. Answer the following questions to analyze your water budget diagrams for each city.

Name of City	City 1 =	City 2 =
a. When does the recharge season begin?		
b. How long does recharge take?		
c. When does the surplus season (runoff maximum) begin?		
d. How long does the surplus season last?		
e. When does the deficit season begin? (soil moisture use)		
f. How long does the deficit season last?		
g. Would you expect there to be year-round flow in the rivers? Explain why you reach this conclusion.		
h. When would you expect maximum flow in the rivers? Why do you think this?		

7. What does your data tell you about the relationship between temperature and evapotranspiration?

8. In a particular year, if one of your cities had a long period of below freezing temperatures, how would this modify the relationships shown on your graph?

9. In a particular year, if one of your cities had a long period of summer drought, how would this modify the relationships shown on your graphs

10. In a particular year, if one of your cities had a long period of heavy spring precipitation, how would this modify the relationships shown on your graphs

11. Let's consider how global warming might affect the water budgets of your cities. The Intergovernmental Panel on Climate Change has provided an estimate of temperature change between now and the year 2100. There is a range of estimates given from 0.5°C to 3.5°C because scientists are uncertain how carbon emission rates will change in the future.

    For this analysis, let's take a middle temperature change estimate of 2°C. For simplicity, let's just add 2°C to the temperature data for your cities. On the data table, you will find data for Global Warming Potential Evapotranspiration. Use these data and redo your water budget calculations as you did them above. Use the same precipitation and actual evapotranspiration data that you used before.

Name of City	City 1 =	City 2 =
i. When does the recharge season begin?		
j. How long does recharge take?		
k. When does the surplus season (runoff maximum) begin?		
l. How long does the surplus season last?		
m. Would you expect there to be year-round flow in the rivers? Explain why you reach this conclusion.		
n. When would you expect maximum flow in the rivers? Why do you think this?		
o. How does global warming change the water budget for each city?		

13. Then replot your data as you did above.

14. Using the same questions that you responded to above, explain how the water budgets of your two cities changed as a result of a small increase in temperature.

For this assignment, turn in the questions with answers, and turn in six graphs including:

One Water Budget graph for each city

One Temperature graph for each city

One Global WarmingWater Budget graph for each city

WATER PLANET EXERCISE 6

Name: ______________________________

ENSO and Climate

Use this map centered on the Pacific Ocean to fill in the chart below.

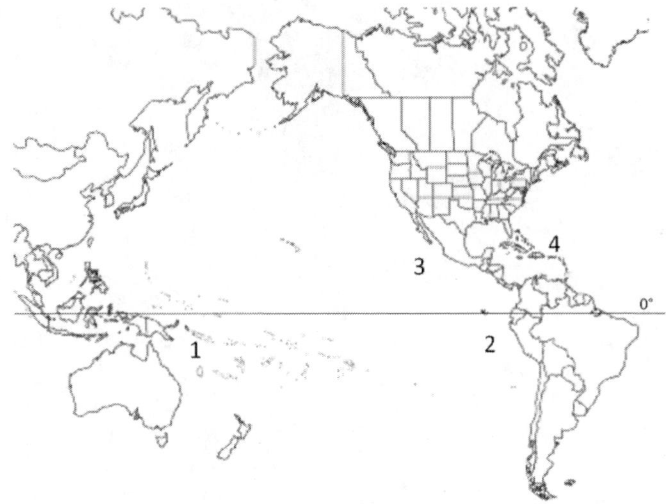

For Sea Surface Temperatures,indicate: cold, cool, warm, hot, or colder or warmer than normal.

For Air Pressure indicate: high, low, or higher or lower than normal.

For Hurricane Risk indicate: increases, decreases, or no particular impact.

Location	ENSO: Neutral	ENSO: El Niño	ENSO: La Niña
Western S. Pacific Ocean (1) **Sea Surface Temp**			
Western S. Pacific Ocean (1) **Air Pressure**			
Eastern South Pacific Ocean (2) **Sea Surface Temp**			
Eastern South Pacific Ocean (2) **Air Pressure**			
Tropical North Pacific Ocean (3) **Hurricane Risk**			
Tropical North Atlantic Ocean (4) **Hurricane Risk**			

Chapter 6

ECOSYSTEM STRUCTURE

A thing is right when it tends to preserve the integrity, stability and beauty of the biotic community. It is wrong when it tends otherwise.

Aldo Leopold

We have what may seem to be a strange request. Think, for a moment, of the languages you studied during high school or college, such as Spanish, French, Russian, or Greek. Before you could hope to read and speak Spanish or Greek, you had to learn the letters and words that are the building blocks of language. Only then could you begin to learn the rules that govern how the letters and words are formed into sentences to communicate ideas. As your understanding grew, you were able to express your own ideas and to read complete passages written in a language that at one time had seemed so alien.

You are probably wondering what this has to do with environmental science. In a real sense, nature, too, has its own language. Ecosystem structure is an alphabet, a collection of letters and words that can be combined in many different ways. In this chapter, we will take a close look at the structural components—the alphabet and words—all ecosystems share.

Knowing letters and words alone does not allow one to speak a language, and so it is with nature. Simply knowing the structure of ecosystems will not allow us to understand how they function, change, and respond to human activities—in short, how to speak the language of nature. To do that, we must learn how the structural components of an ecosystem function as part of a greater whole.

Language, of course, is a cultural artifact, something created by humans for humans. As the makers of language, we establish the rules—grammar—that enable us to communicate with one another. Natural systems, too, have rules that govern how they function and respond to change. Unfortunately, we do not always understand—and sometimes are not even aware of—those rules. Ecology, the study of the structure, function, and behavior of natural systems, is still in its infancy, but already it shows great promise in helping us to understand the rules that govern natural systems. Understanding these rules, in turn, may enable us to decipher the intricate, beautiful language of the biosphere.

WHAT ARE THE LEVELS OF ECOLOGICAL STUDY?

In their quest to understand the structure and function of ecosystems, ecologists study natural systems at many levels: individual, population, community, ecosystem, landscape, biome, and biosphere (Figure 6.1). An individual is a single member of a **species**. A **species** includes all organisms of a particular kind that are capable of producing viable offspring (that is, individuals which can themselves produce offspring). For species that reproduce sexually, the individual members reproduce by mating, or interbreeding.

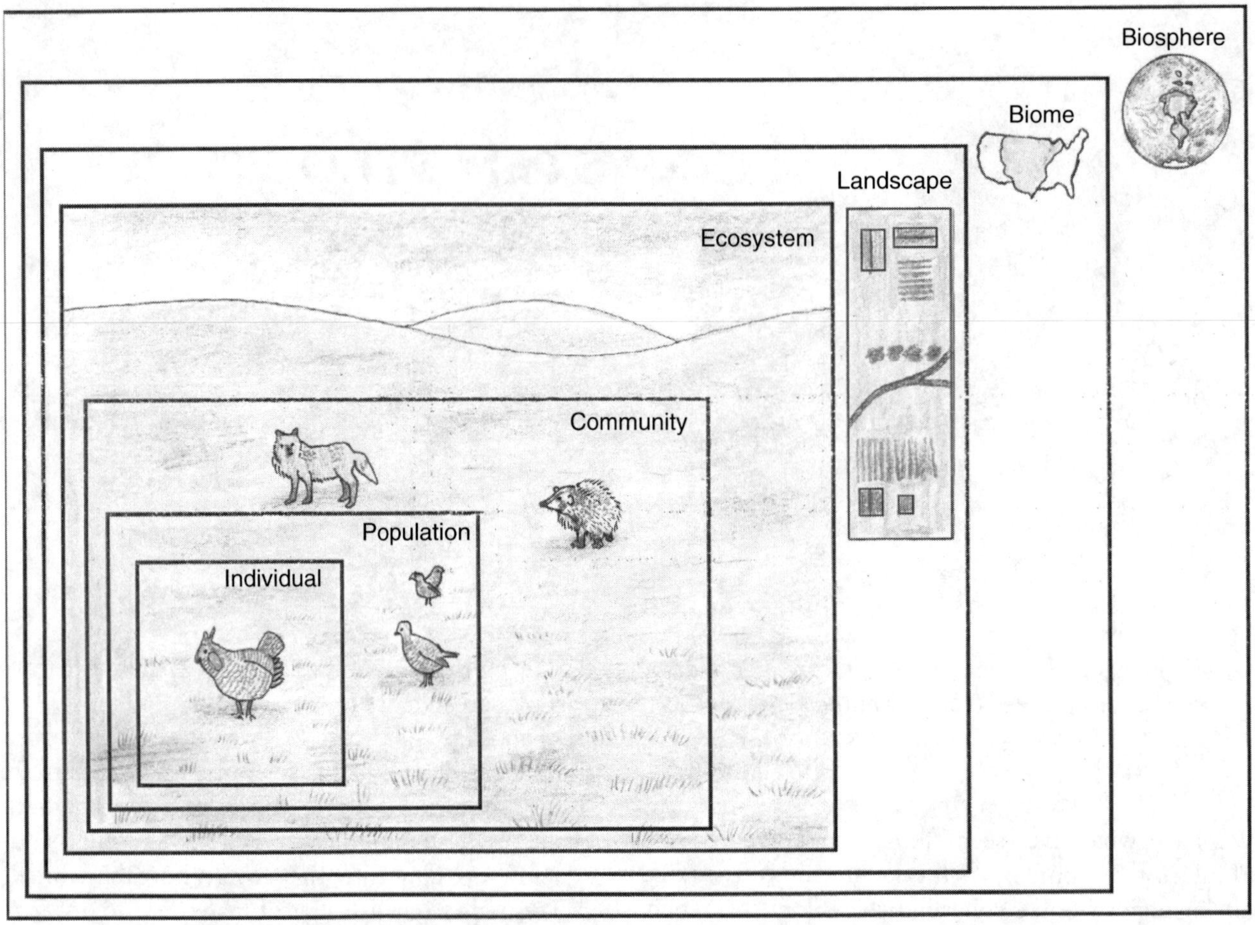

Figure 6.1 Levels of ecological study. The study of ecology spans the continuum from the individual organism (like this greater prairie chicken), to populations, communities, ecosystems, landscapes, biomes (like the temperate grassland shown here), and finally, the biosphere. Information at all these levels contributes to our understanding of the "ecos," our home.

A **population** is a distinct group of individuals of a species that live, interbreed, and interact in the same geographic area, for example, largemouth bass in a particular pond or Canada goldenrod in a single field. Populations have measurable group characteristics such as birth and death rates or seed dispersal and germination rates. Both individual organisms and populations have a place within the physical environment commonly called **habitat**, the place where the organism or population lives. Forests, streams, and soils are just a few examples of habitats where organisms or populations are found.

A **community** includes all of the populations of organisms that live and interact in a given area at a given time. Plants, animals, and microorganisms are bound together by feeding relationships and other interactions, thus forming a complex whole. These interactions are discussed in Chapters 4 and 5.

An **ecosystem** is a self-sustaining, self-regulating community of organisms interacting with the physical environment within a defined geographic area (Figure 6.2). The term 'ecosystem' is derived from two Greek words: *oikos,* meaning home, and *sustéma,* meaning a composite whole. Rivers, lakes, and tidal pools are examples of aquatic ecosystems. Oak-hickory forests, alpine meadows, and high mountain deserts are examples of terrestrial ecosystems.

Ecosystems are not static. Even mature ecosystems like hardwood forests constantly undergo internal changes as a result of changes in their external environments. For example, lack of rainfall can make older trees more susceptible to disease. Diseased trees may die, allowing younger, healthier trees to dominate. Heavy winds can topple trees, opening up the forest floor to increased sunlight and temperature, which promote, for a time, the growth and success of species adapted to these changed conditions.

Sometimes, seemingly minor changes in one component of an ecosystem, such as spraying a field with an insecticide, can have far-reaching effects on other

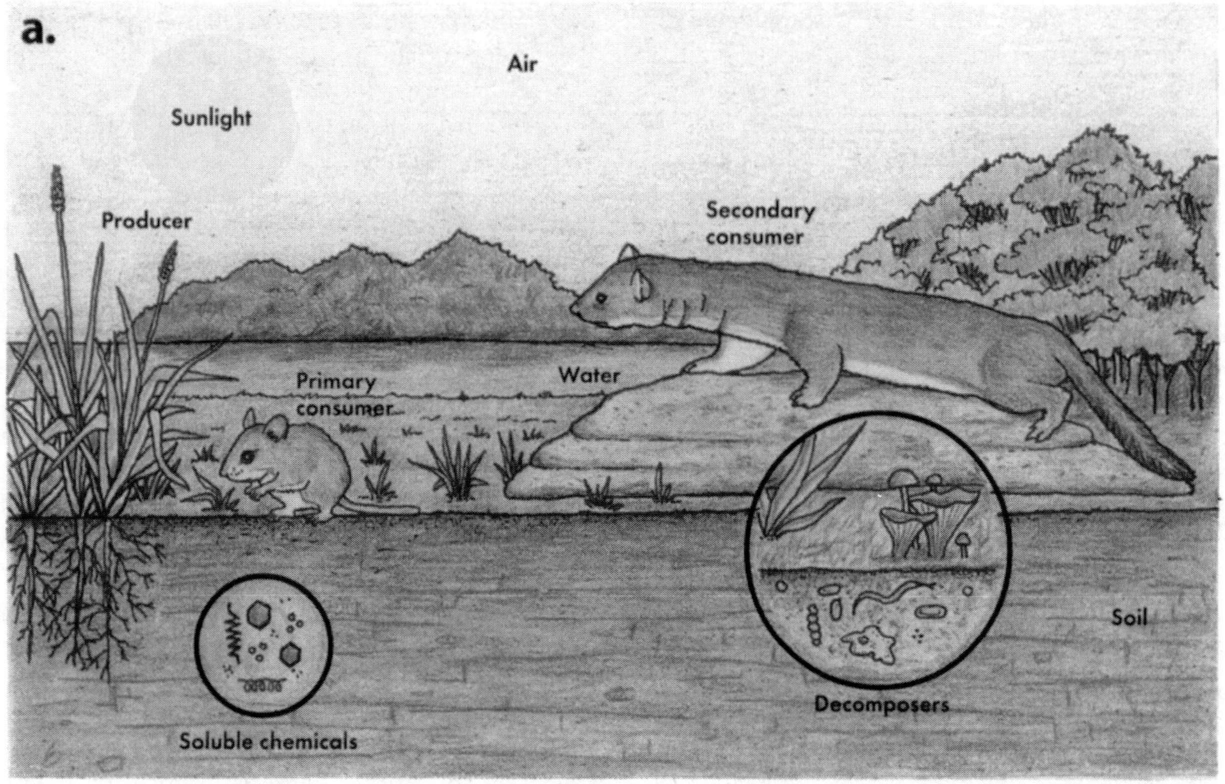

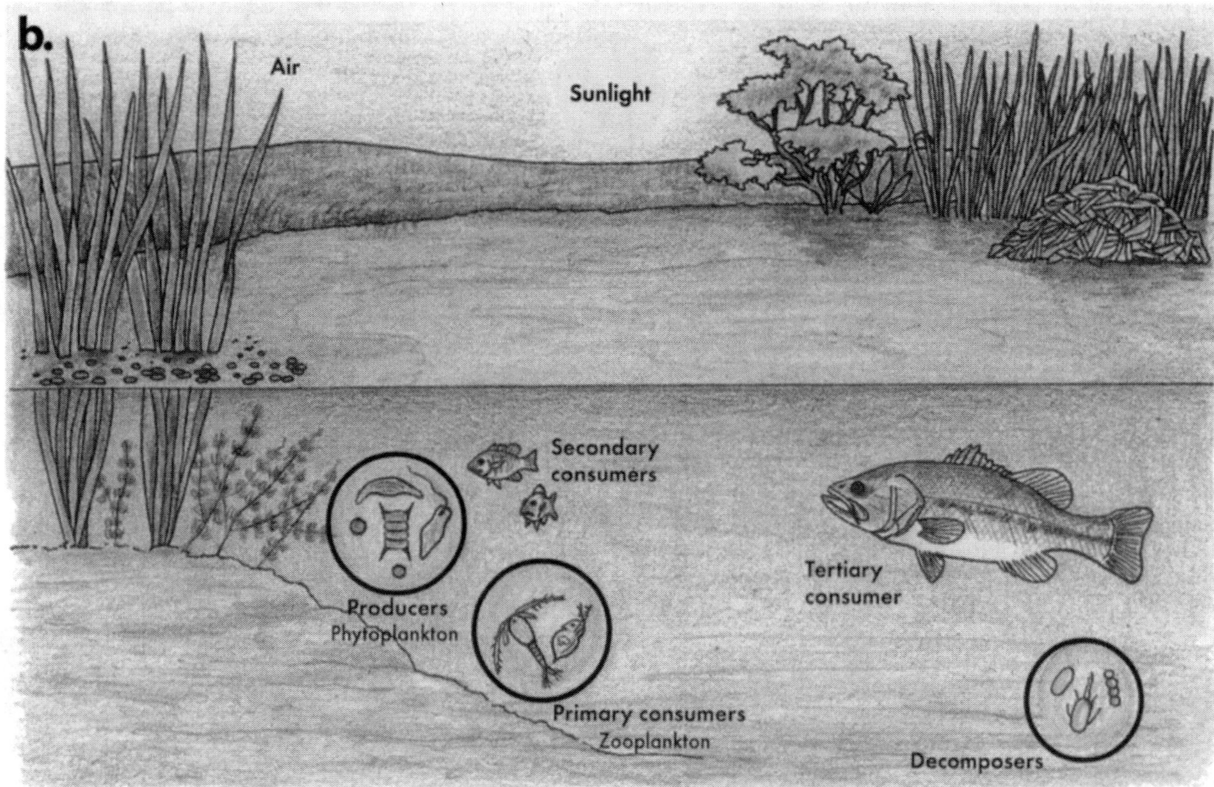

Figure 6.2 Examples of terrestrial and aquatic ecosystems. Ecosystems vary in size and location, but whether it is a field (top) or pond (bottom), every ecosystem is a self-sustaining community of organisms interacting with the physical environment within a defined geographic space.

components of the system. The insecticide might destroy nontarget insects more successfully than it does the insect pest. For example, killing pollinators like honeybees can reduce pollination success in flowers and nectar production for the beehive. In addition, insecticides can kill predators that previously helped to control the target insect population.

Ecosystems usually can compensate for the stresses caused by external changes. But many ecologists believe that individual ecosystems and the biosphere have thresholds beyond which catastrophic, potentially permanent change occurs. For example, at the ecosystem level, thresholds may be exceeded when a lake is acidified, a stream is overloaded with sewage, or a forest is fragmented. Perhaps, if the external stress is eliminated, the system may recover over time. It is uncertain, however, if the system will return to its prestress state. The rapid loss of biological diversity is one example of a potentially disastrous biospheric change.

Many ecosystems taken together are referred to as a **landscape**. Each ecosystem in a landscape has its own distinct elements that, in combination, form the heterogeneous character of the whole. Landscape ecologists are interested in knowing how the ecosystems in a landscape are arranged and how this arrangement affects ecological processes.

A **biome** consists of landscapes grouped across large terrestrial areas of the Earth (Figure 6.3). Biomes are identified and classified according to their dominant vegetation type. Vegetation type is largely the product of climatic conditions, that is, long-term weather patterns, including temperature, precipitation, and the availability of light. The eastern United States, for example, is characterized by temperate deciduous forest, which is dominated by hardwood trees. Beech and maple might dominate in one area, oak and hickory in another and tulip poplar in a third, but the entire area, collectively, is one biome. *Focus On: Biomes* (page 137) takes a closer look at these large terrestrial systems.

Biomes and aquatic ecosystems (such as lakes, the open oceans, coral reefs, and tidal pools) collectively comprise the **biosphere**, the thin layer of air, water, and soil that surrounds the planet and contains the conditions to support life.

WHAT ARE THE COMPONENTS OF AN ECOSYSTEM?

Important research is conducted at all levels of ecological study. In this text, however, we focus on the ecosystem; doing so provides a holistic understanding of natural system structure and function. Ecosystems are composed of nonliving, or abiotic, components and living, or biotic, components. The abiotic and biotic components interact to provide the materials and energy necessary for organisms to survive.

Figure 6.3 World map showing major biomes of the Earth.

Abiotic Components

The abiotic components of ecosystems include energy, matter, and other factors such as temperature and water.

Energy

The ability to do work—to move matter from place to place or to change matter from one form to another—is known as **energy**. We use energy for many purposes: to build shelters and warm or cool them, to process and transport food, and to keep the cells of our bodies active and functioning properly.

Energy reaches the Earth in a continuous but unevenly distributed fashion as solar radiation. Solar radiation is about 45 percent light; the rest is ultraviolet radiation or heat. Less than one percent (0.1–0.3 percent) of the total energy reaching the Earth's atmosphere each day is actually captured through photosynthesis by living organisms; the rest is reflected by the Earth's cloud cover and never reaches the biosphere, or it is radiated by the Earth's surface back into space as heat. Huge amounts of energy, trapped when the planet formed, are stored deep below the Earth's surface. Stored energy makes its way to the surface through volcanoes, deep sea vents, hot springs, and geysers.

Energy cannot be recycled; when it is used, it is changed to another less concentrated form and eventually radiated into space as heat. Consequently, the Earth must be supplied with a constant flow of energy in order to support life. The internal energy of the Earth accounts for only a small percentage of its energy; the vast majority is supplied by the sun. Thus, the Earth is an open system for energy, continuously receiving and using energy from the sun and radiating waste heat into space.

The first law of energy, or **first law of thermodynamics**, states that during a physical or chemical change, energy is neither created nor destroyed. However, it may be changed in form and it may be moved from place to place. Think for a moment about the simple act of eating, which provides us with both nutrients and energy. The ultimate origin of the energy present in all food is the sun. Solar energy is captured by green plants, which then convert it to energy in the chemical bonds of sugars. Thus, plants do not *create* energy; they *capture and convert* solar energy to chemical energy. Here's a second example: The combustion of gasoline in an automobile engine simply releases the energy stored within the chemical bonds of the gasoline. This chemical energy is neither created nor destroyed during the process but is instead transformed through a series of steps into mechanical energy, which then causes the car to move.

The second law of energy, or **second law of thermodynamics**, states that with each change in form, some energy is degraded to a less useful form and given off to the surroundings, usually as low-quality heat. In the process of doing work, high-quality (concentrated) energy is converted to low-quality (dispersed) energy. For example, the energy stored in the sugars we eat is converted to chemical energy; this, in turn, is converted to mechanical energy that moves our muscles and creates heat. Similarly, the high-quality energy available in the chemical bonds of gasoline is converted to mechanical energy (which powers the car) and heat. With each transfer of energy, heat is given off to the surroundings, eventually dissipating to the external environment, through our atmosphere to space, and throughout the universe.

As a consequence of the second law of thermodynamics, energy constantly flows from a high-quality, concentrated, and organized form to a low-quality, randomly-dispersed and disorganized form, a phenomenon called **entropy**. Increasing entropy means increasing disorder. In general, life slows down, but does not stop, the process of entropy. Living organisms temporarily concentrate energy in their tissues and thus, for a time, create a more ordered system. Perhaps the best example of this is the capture and storage of the sun's energy by green plants, algae, and some bacteria. Inevitably, however, these organisms are eaten or die and the energy stored within them is transferred through the ecosystem. As chemical bond energy eventually degrades to heat, the system tends toward entropy (Figure 6.4).

Matter

Anything that has mass and takes up space is **matter**. Although meteors and meteorites sometimes enter the Earth's atmosphere, adding matter to the biosphere, the Earth is essentially a closed system. Most of the matter that will be incorporated into objects in future generations is already present and has been present since the planet came into being.

An **element** is a substance that cannot be changed to a simpler substance by chemical means. Each element has been given a name and a letter symbol. Some familiar elements are oxygen (O), carbon (C), nitrogen (N), sulfur (S), and hydrogen (H). All matter is composed of elements.

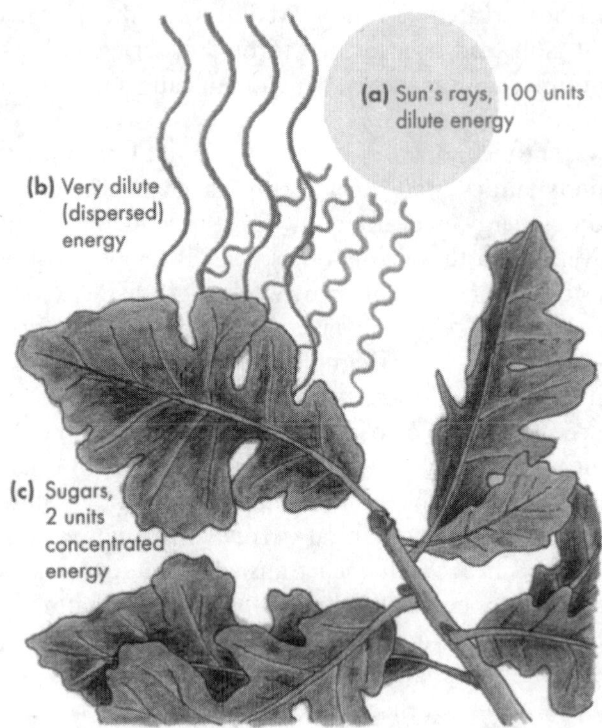

Figure 6.4 The two laws of thermodynamics. The conversion of solar energy (a) to chemical bond energy in food molecules (c) through the process of photosynthesis illustrates the first law of thermodynamics. The second law of thermodynamics maintains that (c) is always less than (a) because heat (b) is lost during the conversion.

There are 92 naturally occurring elements and 15 synthetic ones; each has special characteristics that make it unique from all others. What makes an element unique is its atomic structure. All elements are composed of atoms. Thus, atoms are the basic building blocks of all matter. An **atom** is the smallest unit of an element that retains the unique characteristics of that element; it is the smallest particle of an element that can participate in a chemical reaction.

Only a few naturally occurring elements exist as single atoms; these are known as the 'noble gases'—helium, neon, argon, krypton, xenon, and radon. Single atoms of most other elements cannot exist independently for more than an instant. Oxygen, hydrogen, nitrogen and chlorine, for example, exist in the gaseous state as two atoms joined to form a molecule. A **molecule** is the smallest particle of a substance that has the composition and chemical properties of that substance and is capable of independent existence. A molecule of the substance helium, then, consists of a single atom of helium; a molecule of oxygen consists of two atoms of oxygen; and a molecule of water consists of two atoms of hydrogen and one atom of oxygen. Chemical notation allows us to distinguish between atoms and molecules. For example, O, written by itself, represents one atom of oxygen; 2O represents two atoms; and O_2 represents two atoms of oxygen joined to form a molecule of oxygen.

When two or more elements chemically combine in definite proportions, they form a substance known as a **compound**. For instance, water is a compound in which hydrogen and oxygen combine in a ratio of 2:1; that is, each water molecule consists of one oxygen atom joined to two hydrogen atoms. The chemical notation for water is H_2O. Glucose sugar is a compound formed of 6 carbon atoms, 12 hydrogen atoms, and 6 oxygen atoms; its chemical notation is $C_6H_{12}O_6$. Most matter exists as compounds held together by the forces of attraction in the chemical bonds between their constituent atoms. A compound can be separated into its constituent elements by chemical reactions but not by physical methods.

Organic compounds all contain atoms of carbon. These may be combined with other carbon atoms or with atoms of one or more other elements. Hydrocarbons such as methane (CH_4), chlorinated hydrocarbons such as DDT ($C_{14}H_9Cl_5$), and simple sugars such as glucose ($C_6H_{12}O_6$) are representative of the millions of organic compounds. All other compounds are inorganic.

The **law of the conservation of matter** states that during a physical or chemical change, matter is neither created nor destroyed. However, its form may be changed, and it can be moved from place to place. Ecosystems function within the law of the conservation of matter by using processes that constantly recycle matter.

FOCUS ON BIOMES

Climate, especially temperature and precipitation, is the chief determinant in the formation of biomes; other abiotic factors, including the availability of light and the topography, are also important. While there are many different methods of classifying the world's biomes and some disagreement about the exact number, we discuss nine. Biomes can be distinguished along a continuum of latitude, precipitation, and/or altitude. Beginning at the equator and moving northward, the biomes we discuss are: evergreen tropical rain forest, seasonal (or dry) tropical forest, tropical savanna, desert, chaparral, temperate grassland, temperate deciduous forest, coniferous forest, and tundra.

Evergreen Tropical Rain Forest

The most diverse of all biomes, evergreen tropical rain forests boast a spectacular array of plant and animal life (Figure 6.5). The lush vegetation is supported by abundant annual rainfall—100 to 180 inches (250 to 450 centimeters)—evenly distributed throughout the year. The seasonal variation in temperature is slight, often less than the daily variation (day and night temperatures). Evergreen tropical rain forests occur in three main areas: the Amazon and Orinoco river basins of South America (the world's largest continuous rain forest) and the Central American isthmus; the Indonesian Archipelago; and Madagascar and the Congo, Niger, and Zambezi river basins of central and western Africa.

The natural functioning of tropical forests provides numerous ecosystem services. Rain forests are an important carbon sink, storing large amounts of carbon in trees and other vegetation. Because the clearing of forests accounts for about 25 percent of the carbon released to the atmosphere each year, deforestation has potentially serious implications for global climate change. The dense forest cover also protects the soil, preventing erosion of the thin tropical soils and siltation of local streams and rivers. Rain forests also play a vital role in moderating the global climate, as well as the regional hydrologic cycles where they occur. For instance, the Amazon rainforest generates about half of the rain that falls in the Amazon Basin by the recycling of water through the processes of evaporation and transpiration.

The biological diversity of the tropical rain forests is unequaled. In some Amazonian and Southeast Asian forests, a single hectare (about 2.5 acres) may be home to over 200 different tree species. A study conducted in Peru found over 300 tree species in a one-hectare plot! By comparison, 10 or so are commonly

Shutterstock © gary yim

Figure 6.5 Tropical rain forest, Costa Rica.

(*Continued*)

FOCUS ON TOPICS (*continued*)

found in temperate forests. In general, the trees in tropical forests are almost entirely broadleaved, meaning that the leaves have not been modified into needles or spines. A few conifers, or cone-bearing trees, can be found, such as the klinki pines and hoop pines of New Guinea and Australia. Because of the plentiful rainfall and warm temperatures, the trees retain their leaves year-round and are thus classified as evergreen.

Typically, vegetation in the tropical rain forests is stratified. Broadleaved, evergreen trees 80 to 100 feet tall (25 to 30 meters) form an almost unbroken canopy. Emerging from this great canopy are a few very tall trees (about 200 feet or 60 meters) scattered throughout the forest, perhaps one or two emergent trees per acre. An understory, consisting of smaller tree species, younger trees and shrubs, may also be present, but most of the biodiversity is found in the canopy. Rain forest trees tend to be shallow rooted because the roots do not have to penetrate far to obtain moisture. Many have buttressed stems, swollen bases that help provide support. Common to the tropical rain forest are lianas, climbing plants with a rope-like stem, and epiphytes, plant species that live on the stems and branches of trees and do not touch the soil below. Epiphytes absorb water directly from the humid air or capture the abundant rainfall for later use. Orchids, bromeliads, mosses, and ferns grow on the tree branches, further enriching the plant community. The forest floor is usually dark, owing to the dense tree cover. Even so, it teems with life, chiefly insect scavengers, bacteria, and fungi. Organic material decomposes rapidly under the dark, warm, and very humid conditions. Nutrients are quickly recycled and returned to producers, and detritus does not accumulate to enrich and deepen the soil. Most of the nutrient load in the rain forest is stored in the biomass, and consequently the soils are shallow and nutrient-poor. Thus, if an area is deforested, the soils remain productive for only two to five years.

Like plant species, insect and bird species are found in great abundance and diversity in the tropical rain forest. For example, there are over 20,000 species of insects in a six-square-mile area on Barro Colorado Island, a patch of rain forest in the Panama Canal Zone. In contrast, there are only a few hundred insect species in all of France. One reason given for the multitude of bird species is that many of them are herbivores that feed on the plentiful fruits and seeds of the forest trees. These include the fruit-eating parakeets, toucans, hornbills, cotingas, trogons, and birds-of-paradise. Reptiles, amphibians, and small mammals are also numerous. Most of the animals of the tropical rain forest are arboreal, or tree-dwelling, adapted to life in distinct parts of the canopy or subcanopy. Examples include sloths, monkeys, and small cats. The Costa Rican rain forest harbors 14 ground-foraging mammal species, 59 subcanopy species, and 69 canopy species. Two-thirds of the mammals are arboreal.

Seasonal Tropical Forest

Seasonal tropical forests, sometimes called dry tropical forests, are found in tropical climates that have a pronounced dry season (Figure 6.6). According to the length and severity of the dry season, some or all of the trees lose their leaves. A sweep of color may brighten the landscape just before the leaves fall, or when new leaves begin to bud after the rains return. Asian monsoon forests, dominated by teak and sal trees, have the longest dry season; when the rains fall, they are torrential. Annual rainfall, though seasonal, is still quite high, fostering diverse communities. In fact, among terrestrial systems, seasonal tropical forests are second only to tropical rain forests in terms of species richness.

Tropical Savanna

Savannas are tropical grasslands that contain scattered trees or clumps of trees; they often border tropical rain forests (Figure 6.7). Annual rainfall is 40 to 60 inches (100 to 150 centimeters). Central and East Africa boast the largest tropical savannas, but they are also found in Australia and South America.

Savannas are subject to frequent and extensive fires during the dry season, which are thought to stop the spread of forests. Trees and grasses must be resistant to drought and fire, and consequently the number of species is rather small, especially when

FOCUS ON TOPICS *(continued)*

Shutterstock © gary yim

Figure 6.6 Seasonal tropical forest, Santa Rosa National Park, Costa Rica.

Shutterstock © Pichugin Dmitry

Figure 6.7 The tropical savanna biome, shown here in Serengeti National Park, Tanzania.

(*Continued*)

FOCUS ON TOPICS *(continued)*

compared with the adjacent equatorial forests. A single species of grass or tree may dominate over a large area. The vast African savanna is dotted with thorny acacias and other leguminous trees and shrubs, the large-trunked baobab, and palms.

The distinguishing characteristic of the African savanna may well be its populations of large herbivores, the hoofed mammals. Zebras, giraffes, and antelopes of many kinds (including wildebeests, eland, and impala) graze or browse on the vegetation, hunted by such predators as lions and cheetahs. Insects are plentiful during the wet season, when the area is visited by large numbers of nesting birds.

Desert

The word "desert" may conjure an image of a relentless sun beating down on endless sand dunes, but the world's deserts are actually quite varied (Figure 6.8). Some examples are the hot, very dry Sahara (the world's largest desert), the vast Australian desert, the Atacama in Chile, the Negev in southern Israel, and the cool high deserts of North America, which often see winter snows. All deserts share one characteristic: limited precipitation, less than 10 inches (25 centimeters) per year.

Naturally occurring deserts (unlike areas desertified due to human activity) are healthy ecosystems with communities uniquely adapted to life in a dry and sometimes harsh climate. The vegetation are xerophytes, plants adapted to extremely dry climates. Xerophytic plants have various modifications, such as small leaves, to reduce water loss by transpiration and enable them to live for long periods with little water. Cacti, for example, have leaves that are modified into spines, and they produce a thick, waxy cuticle over their stems, where photosynthesis occurs. However, they are not found in all deserts, as they occur only in the Americas. Similarly adapted species occur in the world's other deserts, but are in different plant families, such as the *Euphorbiaceae*. Saguaro, ocotillo, Joshua tree, creosote bush, sagebrush, agave, cholla, and paloverde are found in the deserts of southwestern North America. Colorful ephemeral annuals bloom soon after the infrequent rains and have a very short life cycle. For many species, a critical amount of rain must fall in order to trigger germination; if the rains fail or too little rain falls, the tough seed coats do not open. They remain dormant, perhaps for several seasons, until sufficient rain finally falls. This favorable adaptation allows them to survive long dry periods.

Figure 6.8 Desert sunset, Guadalupe Mountains National Park, Texas.

FOCUS ON TOPICS *(continued)*

Desert animals include arthropods (especially insects, spiders, and centipedes), reptiles, birds, and small mammals. They too are adapted to desert conditions. The camel, a rare example of a large desert-dwelling mammal, can go for long periods without water because its body tissues can tolerate elevated body temperatures and a high degree of dehydration (conditions fatal to most animals, including humans). The camel does not store water in its hump(s), as is often believed; rather, it conserves water through a special heat exchanger in its nose. Many desert animals, including such predators as owls and rattlesnakes, are nocturnal, avoiding activity during the hot daylight hours. One such species is the desert kangaroo rat of southern California, which remains in its burrow throughout the day. The kangaroo rat is unusual in that it never drinks. Rather, it obtains the water it needs through the moisture contained in its food and the metabolic water it produces through respiration. The animal's efficient kidney produces only small quantities of concentrated urine; most water loss occurs as it breathes. Other adaptive characteristics include oversized ears for cooling and a light-colored coat to reflect the intense sunlight.

Chaparral

The chaparral, or Mediterranean scrub forest, is exclusively coastal, found chiefly along the Pacific coast of North America (California and Mexico) and the coastal hills of Chile, the Mediterranean, southern Africa, and southern Australia (Figure 6.9). Limited winter rainfall of approximately 10 inches (25 centimeters) is followed by drought the rest of the year. However, cool, moist air from the adjacent marine environment moderates the climate of the chaparral, and the vegetation consists of trees or shrubs (or both), that have hard and thick evergreen leaves.

The life forms of the chaparral, like those of the desert, are adapted to drought conditions. In California, for example, mule deer and many birds inhabit the chaparral during the rainy season (November to May) then move north or to higher, cooler altitudes during the dry, hot summer. Resident species include small brush rabbits, wood rats, chipmunks, lizards, wren-tits, and brown towhees. Many chaparral plants are adapted to fire as well as drought. Fire is a natural occurrence brought on by prolonged dry conditions, resinous plants, and a thick layer of dry, slowly decomposing litter on the forest floor. After periodic brush

Shutterstock © Caitlin Mirra

Figure 6.9 Chaparral biome, Santa Monica Mountains, California.

(*Continued*)

FOCUS ON TOPICS (*continued*)

fires sweep through the chaparral, recovery is usually rapid, with shoots sprouting from charred stumps and fire-resistant seeds.

Temperate Grassland

Temperate grasslands occur in areas where average annual rainfall is between 10 and 40 inches (25 to 100 centimeters), depending on the temperature, seasonal distribution of the rainfall, and the water-holding capacity of the soil. Soil moisture is especially important because it limits decomposition and nutrient cycling.

Large grasslands are found in the interior of North America (the prairie, Figure 6.10), southern South America (the Argentine pampas), Eurasia (the steppes), South Africa (the veldt), and Australia. The seasonal nature of the rainfall, and the natural occurrence of periodic fires, discourage the growth of trees. Accordingly, grasses are the dominant vegetation. Which species of grasses are present varies according to local conditions, particularly precipitation. Grasslands may be dominated by annual grasses, perennial bunchgrasses, or perennial sod-forming grasses. Non-grass herbaceous plants may also be seasonally dominant.

This variation in dominant vegetation occurs within all grasslands, and is illustrated by the prairie of central North America. The precipitation increase from west to east results in a continuous

Figure 6.10 Native tallgrass prairie, Agassiz National Wildlife Refuge, Minnesota.

FOCUS ON TOPICS (*continued*)

change from short-grass to mid-grass to tall-grass prairie.

Grasses have adapted numerous mechanisms to cope with limited water. The roots of some species penetrate deeply into soil (as much as six feet) to reach the permanent water table. Other species have diffuse, spreading fibrous roots. Additionally, grasses may become dormant during prolonged dry spells, reviving with the onset of the rains. Some species, such as big bluestem and buffalo grass, have rhizomes, horizontal underground stems with leaves and buds, that serve as a storage organ and means of vegetative propagation. The presence of rhizomes helps to form sod, a dense mat of roots and soil. Much of the biomass of grasses is below ground in the roots; in fact, the roots of healthy perennials may weigh several times as much as the part of the plant above the soil!

Thanks to their productivity, grasslands can support large populations of herbivores, chiefly hooved and burrowing types. In North America, hooved grazers include bison and antelope, while in South America, llamas and alpacas roam the pampas. The large herbivore of the Australian grasslands is the kangaroo. Burrowing mammals include ground squirrels and prairie dogs in North America. Birds and insects are also common grassland residents; the latter are found in especially high numbers in undisturbed areas.

Temperate Deciduous Forest

Much of eastern North America, eastern Asia, and central Europe belong to the temperate deciduous forest biome (Figure 6.11). As its name suggests, the dominant vegetation is deciduous trees, which shed their leaves seasonally. Significant variation occurs within the biome, resulting in certain groups of dominant tree species characteristic of particular regions. Seven such regions are recognized in North America, with widespread dominants such as maples, basswoods, oaks, hickories, and beeches occurring in different abundances throughout the range of the deciduous forest.

With an average annual rainfall of 40 to 60 inches (100 to 150 centimeters), distributed evenly throughout the year, the temperate deciduous forest supports a variety of plant and animal life. The climate is characterized by distinct seasons, with the long growing season giving way to a shorter, but sometimes extreme, period of cold. The plants are characterized by seasonal flowering and fruiting. Depending on the length of the growing season,

Figure 6.11 Temperate deciduous forest biome, as seen in the Great Smoky Mountains National Park.

(*Continued*)

FOCUS ON TOPICS (*continued*)

the forest undergoes a transformation as the leaves change their color from green to brilliant combinations of red, orange, and yellow. The huge amount of biomass falling to the ground as leaves is rapidly decayed, resulting in a rich organic layer and well-developed soils. Animal species have also adapted to the forest's seasons; many migrate (chiefly birds), become dormant, or hibernate. Other animals, such as the rabbit, deer and fox, simply go about their business, managing as best they can until spring returns once again.

Shutterstock © Mark R

Figure 6.12 Coastal temperate rain forest, Glacier Bay National Park, Alaska.

Coniferous Forest

Most of the world's coniferous forests occur in the Northern Hemisphere, but they are also found in smaller areas in South America, Australia, and New Zealand. Coniferous forests are typically dominated by cone-shaped evergreen trees with needlelike leaves. Three of the most common types of coniferous forests include the temperate rain forest, the boreal coniferous forest, and the montane coniferous forest.

The temperate rain forest is a relatively small, but biologically important, vegetation type. Widely scattered throughout the world, temperate rain forests are found on the northwest coast of North America, in southeastern Australia, in New Zealand, and in southern South America (Figure 6.12). Annual precipitation is high, 80 to 150 inches (200 to 380 centimeters). A coastal forest, it benefits from the moderating climatic effects of the ocean. Thus, winters are mild and summers are cool. Thanks to abundant moisture, all temperate rain forests are characterized by a profuse growth of mosses, liverworts, and ferns. A cloak of green covers every tree trunk and rock. Unlike the boreal coniferous forest, this thick understory is well developed wherever light filters through from above. The tree species of the temperate rain forest vary widely throughout the world. In North America, the temperate rain forest on the Olympic Peninsula consists chiefly of conifers such as western hemlock, western arbor vitae, grand fir, and Douglas fir. The southern reaches of the North American rain forest are dominated by the magnificent redwood, the tallest organism on Earth, while Sitka spruce dominates the northern range. The Northern spotted owl, the marbled murrelet, and the red-backed vole are just a few of the many animals that inhabit the North American temperate rain forest. In New Zealand, magnificent stands of southern beeches, kauri pines, and the yew-like podocarps or yellow-woods dominate. The temperate rain forest of Tasmania is home to myrtle, sassafras, and tree ferns.

The vast boreal coniferous forest, also called the taiga, forms a broad belt across both North America and Eurasia. There is no comparable forest in the Southern Hemisphere, which lacks a sufficient land mass at the equivalent latitude. The boreal forests experience long, severe winters and short growing seasons with low temperatures and limited precipitation. They are one of the great lumber-producing regions of the world. Unfortunately, in recent years, unrestricted

FOCUS ON TOPICS *(continued)*

timbering and deforestation have increased rapidly in some areas, including Siberia, site of one of the world's largest stretches of boreal forest.

Evergreen trees—spruce, fir, and pine—are the dominant vegetation of the boreal coniferous forest. Their needle-like or scale-like leaves are covered by a waxy cuticle that retards water loss. This adaptation is essential in the arid environment of the taiga, where groundwater is frozen and thus unavailable to plants for much of the year. The dense evergreens shade the ground, resulting in poorly developed shrub and herb layers. The soil is acidic and covered by a thick layer of partially-decomposed pine needles. Fire is a very important factor in forest development, as most of the tree species have serotinous seed cones that require very high temperatures to release the seeds. Conifer seeds are a primary food source for squirrels and finches such as siskins and crossbills. In disturbed areas, developmental communities of birch, poplar, alder, and willow may be found. These broad-leaved communities are an important food source for many of the taiga's herbivorous inhabitants, such as moose, snowshoe hare, and grouse. Other residents of the coniferous forests include rabbits, porcupines, rodents, elk, deer, grizzly and black bears, wolves, lynx, and wolverines.

Although precipitation is low, the taiga appears quite wet. The topographic relief is largely the product of past glaciation, with extensive bogs, or muskegs. Long ago, such areas were large ponds; they have since developed into the spongy, quaking bogs we see today. They are colonized by plants that are acid-tolerant, including sphagnum moss, cranberry, pine, spruce, and tamarack. Decomposition in a bog is slow, in part because of the cool climate and in part because the oxygen supply quickly becomes depleted in the standing water. Consequently, bogs tend to be far less productive than surrounding forests. Deposits of peat, a brown, acidic material made up of the compressed remains of partially-decomposed plants, accumulate in bogs. Peat can be used to enrich soil or as a potting compost, or it can be dried and used as a fuel.

Montane coniferous forests are found in the mountains of western North America from northern Canada and Alaska down into Mexico, as well as along the higher ridges in the Appalachian mountains of the eastern United States. The coniferous forests of the Rocky Mountains, Sierra Nevadas, and Cascade Mountains are characterized by bands of vegetation corresponding to changing altitude. These bands are lower in the Sierras and Cascades due to the moderating effect of the Pacific Ocean. These mountain ranges are known for high precipitation levels on their west slopes and relatively small amounts on their east sides. This phenomenon is known as the rain shadow effect. As humid air masses move into the mountains and rise, the air cools, the moisture condenses, and the precipitation falls before reaching the eastern slopes.

In addition to altitude, other important environmental factors help to determine vegetation distribution in the montane coniferous forest. Topographic relief (slope exposure and steepness) can determine the extent of such species as subalpine fir, Engelmann spruce, lodgepole pine, Douglas fir, and ponderosa pine. Some of these species have adapted specialized growth forms to deal with the harsh conditions of the timberline, the upper elevational extent of tree growth. Like the boreal coniferous forest, montane coniferous forests have evolved with fire as a naturally reoccurring part of the environment.

Tundra

The tundra is the northernmost biome; it has no equivalent in the Southern Hemisphere, except in a few mountainous areas, where harsh conditions result in an alpine tundra (Figure 6.13). Precipitation is scarce; a scant six inches (15 centimeters) falls annually, much of it as snow. The distinguishing feature of the tundra is the permafrost, a layer of permanently frozen soil lying several inches below the surface.

Low temperatures, a short growing season, and strong winds are the major limiting factors to life. For much of the year, precipitation is also a problem, as the water of the tundra is frozen and unavailable to most life forms. During the long winter, the tundra is a windswept, frozen, and seemingly barren land. But during the summer growing season, which lasts

(*Continued*)

FOCUS ON TOPICS *(continued)*

Figure 6.13 The vast tundra, seen here in Denali National Park, Alaska, is dominated by lichens, grasses, and dwarfed trees.

about two months, surface waters and the top few inches of soil thaw. The permafrost prevents the water from percolating downward and ponds form, dotting the landscape. Although summers are short, summer days are very long, and at these times a vibrant, varied plant community blankets the tundra. Essentially, the "low tundra" of the Alaskan coastal plain is a wet Arctic grassland dominated by grasses, sedges, and dwarfed woody plants such as willows and birches. In many areas, it resembles a thick spongy mat of living and decaying vegetation. A far less profuse growth of lichens, mosses, and grasses is found in the "high tundra," particularly in areas with considerable relief. Most plants of the tundra are long-lived perennials with much of their biomass below ground. Many of the plant species have pigments such as anthocyanin, which help ab sorb sunlight. Tundra animals include caribou, musk oxen, polar bears, wolves, foxes, ptarmigans, bald eagles, snowy owls, snowshoe hares, Arctic ground squirrels, lemmings, and reindeer. In addition, swarms of mosquitoes and flies are legendary. Some species, such as caribou, migrate with the onset of winter, while others, including lemmings and ptarmigans, remain for the season.

Carbon (C), oxygen (O), hydrogen (H), nitrogen (N), phosphorus (P), potassium (K), calcium (Ca), magnesium (Mg), and sulfur (S) are **macronutrients**, chemicals needed by living organisms in large quantities for the construction of proteins, fats, and carbohydrates. These nine macronutrients are the major constituents of the complex organic compounds found in all living organisms. **Micronutrients** are substances needed in trace amounts, such as copper (Cu), zinc (Zn), selenium (Se), lithium (Li), iron (Fe), sodium (Na), cobalt (Co), boron (B), molybdenum (Mo), and chlorine (Cl). These and other micronutrients, along with macronutrients, are regulated by cycles so that they remain available in the physical environment. The chemicals and water that form the complex compounds found in living organisms continually cycle between the abiotic and the biotic components.

Abiotic Factors

In addition to energy and matter, a number of other factors are important to consider when studying the abiotic component of the ecosystem. They include temperature, precipitation, humidity, wind, light, shade, fire, salinity, and available space. These factors do not remain constant, but vary over space and time. They determine the native vegetation found in a particular area, and thus what biome and ecosystems will occur there (Figure 6.14). Together with the available energy and the type, amount and distribution of nutrients, these physical factors help to determine which organisms will comprise the biotic components of that system.

Biotic Components

The biotic components of ecosystems are grouped into two broad categories, producers and consumers, based on nutritional needs and manner of feeding.

Producers.

Producers, or **autotrophs**, are self-nourishing organisms (auto, "self"; troph, "nourishment"). Given water, nutrients and a source of energy, they can produce the compounds necessary for their survival.

Most producers, including green plants, algae and cyanobacteria (blue-green algae), are **phototrophs**. They contain chlorophyll, a green pigment that absorbs light energy from the sun. Through the process of **photosynthesis** (photo, "light"; synthesis, "to put together"), phototrophs use the sun's light energy to convert carbon dioxide and water into complex chemical bonds forming simple carbohydrates such as glucose and fructose. Essentially, light energy is transferred to the carbon bonds that form carbohydrates. In the process, oxygen is given off. Photosynthesis is roughly one to three percent efficient at converting light energy to chemical energy, that is, 100 units of light energy result in one to three units of chemical energy produced.

Phototrophs can then convert simple carbohydrates into more complex carbohydrates (starches and cellulose), lipids (fats and oils), and proteins. They use some of the energy to manufacture cell contents and to carry out life processes. Complex carbohydrates are stored in their tissues, to be used later to meet energy needs. This stored energy (in seeds, roots, or sap) enables plants to call on reserves during germination, after winter, or during prolonged periods of cloudy days.

A small percentage of the Earth's biota depends on the energy stored by **chemotrophs**, autotrophs that use the energy found in inorganic chemical compounds (rather than light energy from the sun) for

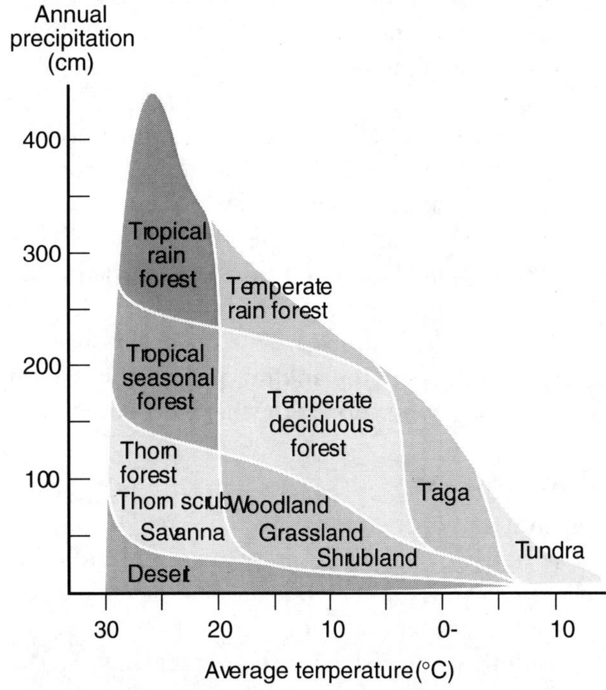

Figure 6.14 Biomes are largely the product of climate, specifically temperature and precipitation. Boundaries between biome types are approximate; other physical factors, including soil type, exposure to frequent fire and maritime versus continental climates, can determine which of the two or more biomes, both adapted to the climate of an area, will actually occur there.

Reprinted by permission of Brad Hinckley

Figure 6.15 Dung beetles, detritivores that feed on the organic wastes of other organisms, gather and transport dung in tandem.

their energy needs. Chemotrophs are represented primarily by species of bacteria that live in and around deep thermal vents in the oceans, at the mud-water interface in high mountain lakes during winter, or in wetlands. Through **chemosynthesis**, they convert the energy in the chemical bonds of hydrogen sulfide to make and store carbohydrates and, in doing so, give off sulfur compounds into the water. Unlike photosynthesis, chemosynthesis takes place without sunlight or chlorophyll.

The importance of producers cannot be emphasized enough, for the energy that they capture and fix supports the Earth's biota. To put it another way, whereas producers capture new energy from the environment, all other organisms simply transfer portions of that energy from their food to themselves. In terrestrial systems, trees, grasses, herbs, and shrubs are the major producers; in aquatic systems, **phytoplankton**, microscopic floating plants and algae, function as the major producers.

Consumers

Consumers, or **heterotrophs** (hetero, "other, different"), eat by engulfing or predigesting the fluids, cells, tissues, or waste products of other organisms. Because consumers cannot make their own food, they rely on other organisms for their energy needs. They can be broadly categorized as macroconsumers or microconsumers.

Macroconsumers feed by ingesting or engulfing particles, parts, or entire bodies of other organisms, either living or dead. They include herbivores, carnivores, omnivores, scavengers, and detritivores. **Herbivores**, or **primary consumers**, (grasshoppers, mice and deer, for example) eat producers directly. Other consumers (such as meadowlarks, black rat snakes, and bobcats) feed indirectly on producers by eating herbivores. Because they eat other animals, they are referred to as **carnivores**, or **secondary consumers**. Consumers that eat both plants and animals (like black bears, Norway rats, and humans) are **omnivores**. Carnivores that eat secondary consumers (such as hawks and large-mouth bass) are **tertiary consumers**.

Many heterotrophs consume dead organic material. Those that consume the entire dead organism are known as **scavengers**. Two familiar examples are vultures and hyenas. Consumers that ingest fragments of dead or decaying tissues or organic wastes are called **detritivores**, or **detritus feeders** (blue crabs, dung beetles, earthworms and shrimp, for example) (Figure 6.15).

Like detritivores, **microconsumers** feed on the tissues of dead organisms; they also consume the waste products of living organisms. They differ in that they digest materials outside of their cells and bodies, through the external activities of enzymes, and then absorb the predigested materials into their cells. Consequently, they are often referred to as **decomposers**. Decomposers live on or within their food source. The result of the activity of decomposers is what we call rot or decay. Eventually, decomposers reduce complex molecules to simple molecules and return them to the physical environment for reuse by producers. Microconsumers include some bacteria, some protozoans, and fungi (for example, yeasts and molds).

Decomposers play the major role in reducing complex organic matter to inorganic matter and returning nutrients and necessary chemicals to the physical environment in a form that can be used by producers. The importance of decomposers is often overlooked. We are only now beginning to get a clearer picture of how they perform their vital functions. Consider what it would be like if leaves were not decomposed after they fell from trees. How quickly nutrients in the soil would be depleted if decomposers did not continually recycle them after the deaths of producers and consumers! Decomposers form the vital link in the cycle that returns nutrients and chemicals to the soil, enabling material to proceed from death to life in ecosystems.

WHAT DETERMINES THE STRUCTURE OF ECOSYSTEMS?

No organism, population, or community is distributed evenly about the Earth. Instead, each occupies a particular environment or habitat. Some organisms are distributed throughout large areas, while others live in very specific habitats (Figure 6.16). Some organisms are found only in the leaf litter of deciduous forests, under rocks in fast moving streams, or in the minute cracks of rocks in the Antarctic. Some organisms are found on the forest floor, but not in the forest canopy; some survive at great ocean depths, but not in shallow waters. Some organisms are successful in the wetter, cooler conditions on the western slopes of the coastal ranges of western North America, while others are successful in the drier, warmer conditions of the eastern slopes.

The species, populations, and communities found in an ecosystem or biome are the result of **limiting factors**, abiotic and biotic regulators that determine the distribution and success of living organisms.

Abiotic Limiting Factors

Temperature, light, precipitation, and available phosphorus, oxygen, and carbon are examples of abiotic limiting factors. As we saw in Figure 6.14, a difference in average rainfall separates the major plant communities into forests, grasslands, or deserts. Typically, regions with more than 40 inches (100 centimeters) of precipitation per year are forests, 10 to 40 inches (25 to 100 centimeters) are grasslands, and less than 10 inches (25 centimeters) are deserts. Temperature is another important limiting factor. If an area usually gets 40 inches of rainfall per year and is hot, it will sustain a tropical savanna; if the area is temperate, it will sustain a deciduous forest (beeches, maples, oaks). Soil types within a forest are also a limiting factor. In a temperate climate with adequate rainfall, oaks and hickories are more successful on low-nutrient soils, while beeches and maples are more successful on high-nutrient soils. Abiotic factors form a complex set of interactions that limit or control the activities of organisms, populations, and communities. Ecologists do not understand fully all the ways in which these factors interact.

In an aquatic ecosystem, oxygen, sunlight, and nutrients (phosphorus and nitrogen) are the most significant abiotic limiting factors. Generally, the availability of phosphorus (as the compound phosphate) in lakes and streams limits the growth of aquatic plants and algae. Increasing the amount of phosphates increases the growth of plants and algae. Nutrient enrichment of a lake, stream, or estuary can set in motion a mix of physical, chemical, and biological

Figure 6.16 Habitat and distribution of species. (a) Some species are widely distributed. The giant ragweed is found throughout North America from Mexico to Canada. (b) Other species, like the giant, blood-red tube worm, are found in very specific habitats, such as near thermal vents on the ocean floor.

changes that collectively are known as **eutrophication**, the natural aging of a lake. The high input of nutrients may be the result of natural erosion or it may be related to human activities, as in the case of runoff from agricultural fields that have been treated with fertilizers. When human activities lead to nutrient enrichment of a body of water, ecologists say that the aquatic system has undergone cultural eutrophication.

The single largest marine system affected by cultural eutrophication is an area known as the "Dead Zone" in the Gulf of Mexico. Eutrophication in the Dead Zone has resulted in hypoxic conditions, which are characterized by low oxygen levels. According to a 2000 report by the National Science and Technology Council (NSTC) Committee on Environment and Natural Resources, the primary cause of the hypoxia is excess nitrogen that flows into the Gulf from the Mississippi-Atchafalaya River Basin. This river basin is the largest in the country, covering 41 percent of the continental United States and containing 47 percent of the nation's rural population and 52 percent of its farms. Waste, including nitrogen-based fertilizer, from this area drains directly into the Gulf of Mexico, resulting in spring and summer "blooms," or dense mats, of algae. The first Dead Zone was recorded in the early 1970s. Originally, the hypoxic events occurred every two to three years; however, they now occur annually. By the early 1990s, the zone covered approximately 3,670 square miles (9,500 square kilometers); by 2001, the area had doubled to 8,000 square miles (20,800 square kilometers), an area larger than the State of New Jersey. The zone occurs in one of the most important commercial and recreational fisheries in the country and could threaten the economy of Gulf States such as Texas and Louisiana. According to the NSTC report, efforts are underway to reduce nitrogen flows into the Gulf.

Cultural eutrophication is also a problem in many freshwater systems, including Lake Erie, part of the 2,000-mile-long Great Lakes system. Historically, the ecosystem teemed with diverse wildlife, including such fishes as blue pike, lake whitefish, lake sturgeon, and cisco. The young of these and other species fed on the mayfly, a once-plentiful insect that, in its larval stage, lives on the lake bottom. However, by the 1950s, dense algal blooms, particularly of *Cladophora*, became commonplace in the lake's western and central basins during periods of calm, warm weather in mid to late summer. The blooms were caused by a high influx of phosphates, which entered the lake in agricultural runoff, detergent-laden wastewater, and insufficiently treated sewage. When the algae died and sank to the bottom, the decomposition of such large amounts of organic matter depleted the water's oxygen supply, and the mayfly population crashed. As it did, the populations of fish species whose young depended on the larva also plummeted. By the 1960s, the blue pike, lake whitefish, lake sturgeon, and cisco were extirpated from Lake Erie. To learn more about the effect of cultural eutrophication on Lake Erie's biotic community, the progress that has been made in reducing nutrient loads to the lake, and the challenges that remain in the effort to restore and protect the ecosystem, read *Environmental Science in Action: Lake Erie* by going to www.EnvironmentalEducationOhio.org and clicking on "Biosphere Project."

Living organisms, populations, and communities have a range of tolerances for each of the abiotic limiting factors, a concept known as the **law of tolerances**. Tolerances range along a continuum from the maximum amount or degree that can sustain life to the optimum or best amount for sustaining life to the minimum amount that can sustain life (Figure 6.17). Any change that approaches or exceeds the limits of tolerance, either the maximum or the minimum, becomes a limiting factor. For example, laboratory trials have demonstrated that speckled trout prefer water temperatures of 57° to 66° F (14° to 19° C), although they can tolerate temperatures as high as 77° F (25° C) for short periods of time. This finding is corroborated by field studies, which show that speckled trout are not found in streams where the temperature exceeds 75° F (24° C) for an extended period of time.

Some organisms have wide ranges of tolerances and others have narrow ones. Aquatic insects such as mayflies, fish such as hogsuckers, and flatworms such as planaria all have narrow tolerances for oxygen that limit their success in aquatic habitats. When the concentration of dissolved oxygen in streams or lakes is reduced, these species disappear quickly and are replaced by species more tolerant of lower oxygen levels, such as mosquito larvae, rat-tailed maggot, and carp. A mayfly (or hogsucker or planaria) is an **indicator species**, a species that indicates, by either its presence or absence, certain environmental conditions (in this case, the amount of dissolved oxygen). If mayflies are abundant in a stream, the amount of dissolved oxygen must be relatively high; if they are absent, it is probably low. Scientists look for the presence of such organisms when determining the ecological health of both aquatic and terrestrial ecosystems.

Limiting factors have important implications for humans. For example, the success of a crop is

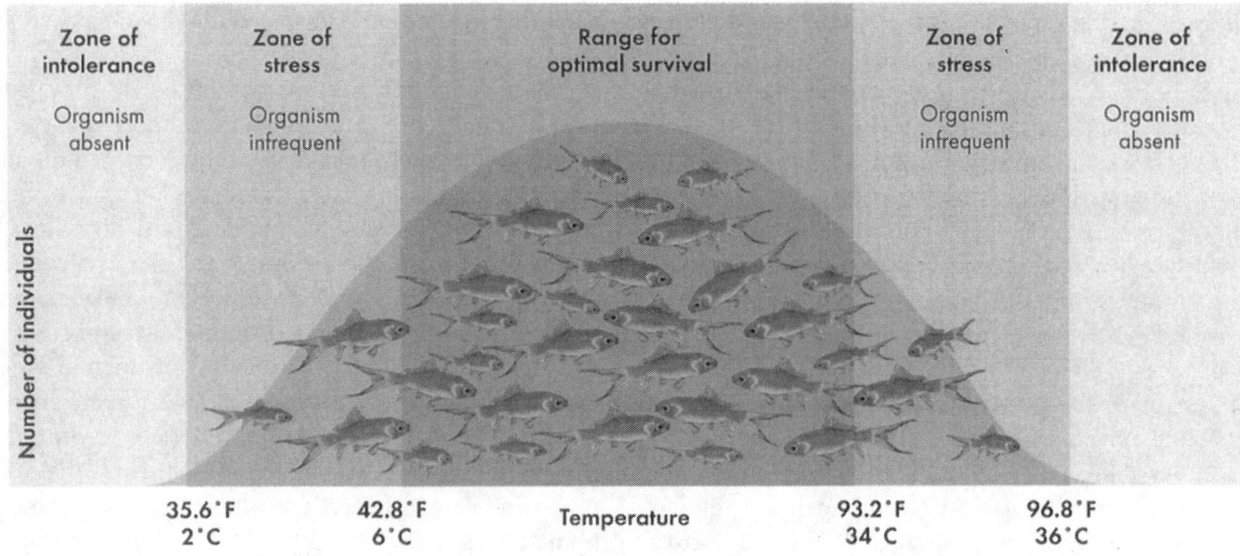

Figure 6.17 Law of tolerances. Goldfish can live at temperatures ranging from 35.6°F (2°C) to 96.8°F (36°C) but cannot tolerate temperatures above or below this range.

sometimes limited by micronutrients, such as iron for soybeans or molybdenum for clover, even if macronutrients (phosphorus, nitrogen, and potassium) are applied in large quantities for that particular crop. We manipulate limiting factors when we try to maintain optimum conditions for growth to ensure or increase our harvest from gardens, farms, and ponds.

Biotic Limiting Factors

Ecosystem structure is also affected by the interactions between species, such as competition for food or shelter. One such interaction occurs when **prey**, living organisms that serve as food for other organisms, are inhibited or eliminated by **predators**, organisms that obtain their food by eating other living organisms. For example, if the population of bass, a predator, in a pond increases, the population of prey species such as bluegills may decrease. The resultant drop in the bluegill population may then lead to an increase in the small animals (zooplankton) that the bluegills eat. The increase in zooplankton, in turn, may cause a decrease in the population of producers, or phytoplankton, in the pond.

Ecologists are beginning to understand the effects that organisms can have on community structure. Beavers are an excellent example of a biotic regulator. Through the construction of dams, beavers significantly alter the ecosystem structure of their habitats. Beaver dams alter stream channels and slow down the flow of water, creating and maintaining wetlands, thereby encouraging the growth of plants and animals that are successful in flooded areas and discouraging the growth of those successful in drier areas. By altering their habitats, beavers significantly influence the diversity of the community. For this reason, they are known as a **keystone species**, a species that has a significant role in community organization due to its impact on other species.

The rabbits of southern England are a second example of a keystone species. A drastic reduction in the rabbit population through disease allowed a thick growth of meadow grass. The heavy grass caused the local extinction of open-ground ants and, in turn, the extinction of the large blue butterfly, whose caterpillar fed on the ants. The loss of a keystone species, the rabbit, caused the successful growth of a plant species, the meadow grass, and the local extinction of two animal species, the ant and the butterfly.

SUMMARY

Ecologists study the natural world at many levels: individual, population, species, community, ecosystem, landscape, biome, and biosphere. An individual is a single member of a species. A species includes all organisms that are capable of breeding to produce viable, fertile offspring. Individuals of a particular species that live in the same geographic area comprise populations; populations have measurable group characteristics such as birth rates, death rates, seed dispersal rates, and germination rates. The place where the individual organism or population lives is its habitat. All of the populations of organisms that live and interact with one another in a given area at a given time are collectively known as a community. A community and its interactions with the physical environment comprise an ecosystem. A landscape is a heterogeneous "patchwork" of many ecosystems taken together. A grouping of many landscapes is a biome, which is identified and classified by its dominant vegetation type. The union of all terrestrial and aquatic ecosystems—and the largest system of life-physical interactions on Earth—is called the biosphere.

Ecosystems are composed of biotic components (communities) and abiotic components (physical surroundings). Energy, matter, and physical factors like temperature and rainfall constitute abiotic components. According to the first law of energy, or first law of thermodynamics, energy can neither be created nor destroyed but may be changed in form and may be moved from place to place. The second law of energy, also known as the second law of thermodynamics, states that with each change in form, some energy is degraded to a less useful form and given off to the surroundings, usually as heat. Consequently, in the process of doing work, high-quality energy is converted to low-quality energy. Energy constantly flows from a high-quality, concentrated, and organized form to a low-quality, randomly-dispersed and disorganized form, a phenomenon called entropy.

Matter is anything that has mass and takes up space. Elements, substances that cannot be changed to simpler substances by chemical means, comprise all matter. An atom is the smallest unit of an element that retains the unique characteristics of that element. Molecules are formed when two or more atoms combine. Compounds are molecules composed of two or more different elements. Compounds containing atoms of carbon are known as organic compounds. According to the law of the conservation of matter, matter is neither created nor destroyed, but its form may be changed, and it can be moved from place to place.

Biotic components are composed of producers (autotrophs), consumers, and decomposers (heterotrophs). Autotrophs that convert the energy of the sun into chemical energy are called phototrophs. Autotrophs that use the energy found in inorganic chemical compounds in order to produce starches and sugars are known as chemotrophs. Consumers are categorized as macroconsumers or microconsumers. Macroconsumers include herbivores (primary consumers), which eat plant matter; carnivores (secondary consumers), which feed on animals; and omnivores, consumers that eat both plants and animals. Carnivores that feed on secondary consumers are called tertiary consumers. Some consumers feed on dead organisms: Scavengers consume the entire organism; detritivores ingest fragments of dead or decaying tissues or organic wastes. Microconsumers, or decomposers, digest organic material outside of their bodies through the activities of enzymes; they then absorb the predigested material into their cells. Because they break down wastes and dead plant and animal matter, microconsumers return nutrients to the environment to be used once again.

The species, populations, and communities in an ecosystem or biome are the result of limiting factors, abiotic and biotic regulators that determine the distribution and success of living organisms. Abiotic factors include precipitation, temperature, and nutrient levels. According to the law of tolerances, living organisms, populations, and communities have a range of tolerances for each of the abiotic factors that operate in a specific ecosystem. An indicator species is a species that indicates, by its presence or absence, certain environmental conditions with respect to limiting factors (such as the amount of dissolved oxygen in a stream). Examples of biotic limiting factors include predator-prey interactions and keystone species. A keystone species is one that has a significant role in community organization due to its impact on other species.

WATER PLANET EXERCISE 7

Name: ______________________________

WATER BALANCE, CLIMATE, AND VEGETATION

Purpose

In this exercise you will learn:

a. The water balance diagram for different climates of the world

b. How to construct a simple (but useful) moisture index

c. The relationship between vegetation patterns and climate.

Plotting Water Balance Data

Download the water balance data file (from Blackboard). Plot the values for PRECIPITATION and POTENTIAL EVAPOTRANSPIRATION listed in the data table for each location. Use the Scatter Plot function with month on the x axis and precipitation and potential evapotranspiration on the y axis.

1. Describe the water situation in each of the six locations. What is the implication of this for water runoff? For plant growth? (4 pts ea.)

   A. Akassa

   B. Cairo

   C. Rome

   D. Caracas

   E. Bergen

   F. Macon

MOISTURE INDEX

The verbal discussion of the water situation for each place that you completed above is fine, but wouldn't it be good if there was a way to quantitatively compare them! Actually, there is . . . it's called a moisture index. One simple moisture index compares the relationship between precipitation (P) and potential evapotranspiration (PE) in a mathematical way like you did verbally. In a very basic way, if P > PE, then we can say it is a humid region, but if P < PE it would be an arid region. When we talk generally about climate on a continental scale, it is a very crude index of moisture availability. A more useful index can be computed.

2. First, take the sum of precipitation and potential evapotranspiration for each of the six places and enter the numbers in the table below.

City:	Akassa	Cairo	Rome	Caracas	Bergen	Macon
P						
PE						

3. Compute the moisture index (MI) for each place using the following equation:

$$MI = 100 \times \frac{(P - PE)}{PE}$$

City:	Akassa	Cairo	Rome	Caracas	Bergen	Macon
MI						
Climate Type						

4. Use the following scale of moisture index values to determine each place's climate type and fill that in the table above.

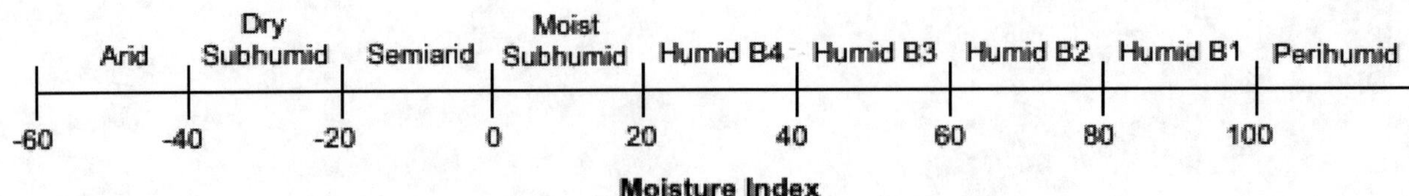

The Moisture Index is useful because it can tell us about the availability of water. Temperature is also important because it will determine whether living organisms can be active year round. The Moisture Index does this in a way because PE is used to calculate the index and PE is a measure of energy.

The Moisture Index does not help us very much in terms of temperature. The figure below will help determine the climatic zone of a place if you know total annual precipitation and average annual temperature. Consult the graph and identify the climate for each of the six study sites. There may be places that are on the boundary between zones.

5. Use your judgment to select the zone that best corresponds to each location.

City:	Akassa	Cairo	Rome	Caracas	Bergen	Macon
Zone						

CLIMATE AND VEGETATION

We now need to relate climate to vegetation cover. Plants have one basic role: to convert solar energy to other forms of energy that can be used by other living organisms. Of course, to live, they have other requirements. The primary need is for water, but they also need various nutrients to perform their tasks. The efficiency with which plants convert solar energy to other forms of energy is called **net primary productivity**. It is the result of the amount of solar energy they absorb (called gross primary productivity) minus the amount of energy required to do the work of converting solar energy to usable energy. One way of measuring net primary productivity is to see how much living material accumulates in the plants. This is called **biomass**. This is the dry weight of all living plant matter in a specified area. Dry weight implies that water is removed from the plants.

Scientists have determined that biomass is a function of light intensity (to represent the amount of energy received) and precipitation (the amount of water available to plants). The two graphs below suggest the relationship between biomass and these two independent variables.

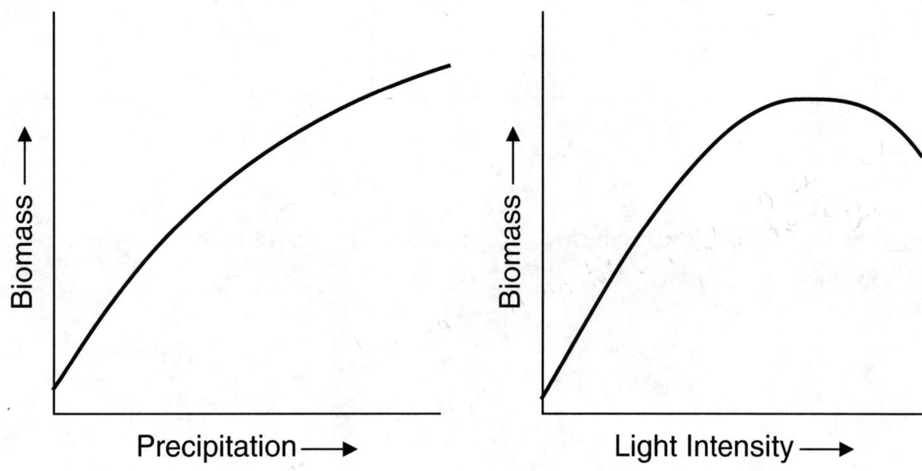

6. What overall levels of biomass production would expect in each of the six places we have been examining here? Use general descriptive terms: high, a lot, low, medium, some, etc.

City:	Akassa	Cairo	Rome	Caracas	Bergen	Macon
Biomass Production						

7. For each place, when would biomass production be at its maximum? (When is the best combination of light intensity and precipitation?) Refer to the water balance diagrams to determine seasonal characteristics of precipitation and temperature. Identify a month or several months when biomass is at a maximum and at a minimum.

City:	Akassa	Cairo	Rome	Caracas	Bergen	Macon
Maximum months						
Minimum months						

If you have not yet figured it out, biomass reflects the type of vegetation you find in a place. The biomass of a forest is much greater than the biomass of a grassland. So, if we could relate vegetation type to the independent variables, we would have a great way to identify vegetation type according to energy and precipitation. The Vegetation and Climate graph below does that.

8. For each of the six study locations, use the Vegetation and Climate graph above to identify the vegetation type, based on its moisture index and total annual potential evapotranspiration.

City:	Akassa	Cairo	Rome	Caracas	Bergen	Macon
Vegetation Type						

9. Finally, discuss the overall relationship between vegetation zone and climate zone based on the observations you have made for the six study sites.

INSTRUCTIONS FOR USING EXCEL IN THIS EXERCISE

1. Open Excel file from Blackboard.
2. Highlight rows 4 to 15 columns A thru D.
3. Go to chart icon at top of Excel.
4. Select Column option and first Sub-type (left).
5. Click Next.
6. Click on Series at top on window.
7. Highlight Series 1 in box on lower left.
8. Click Remove.
9. Then highlight Series 2.
10 In Name box type "Precipitation."
11. Highlight Series 3.
12. In Name box type "potential evapotranspiration."
13. Click Next.
14. In Chart title box, type "Akassa, Nigeria."
15 Click Finish.
16. Print your chart.

After you print your chart of Akassa,

1. Go to top of Excel window and click on Chart.
2. Select Source data.
3. Click on Series.
4. Go to Values box… at the right side, there is a little arrow.
5. Click on the arrow.
6. In the box that appears, you highlight the words, then place your cursor on the precipitation column on the Excel spreadsheet, under a different city… drag down the column from January to December
7. Click on the little arrow again; the graph will change with new data.
8. Repeat procedure by highlighting first on "potential evapotranspiration" in the box on the lower left.
9. Click OK.
10. Go back to Chart menu and click on Chart options.
11. In the new box change the title to the new city.
12. Print the new chart.

Repeat the above procedure with each of the six cities.

Chapter 7

COASTAL REGIONS AND LAND LOSS

Coastal regions, where the land meets the ocean or a large lake, are attractive places to live or vacation. Because large bodies of water moderate temperatures, coastal areas are cooler in summer and warmer in winter than farther inland. Humans have always been attracted to the coastal regions, to take advantage of the milder climate, abundant seafood, easy transportation, recreational opportunities, and commercial benefits. It is no wonder that the coastlines have become heavily urbanized and industrialized. Approximately 60 percent of the world's population lives within 100 kilometers of ocean coasts. In the United States alone, coastal population increased by 38 million between 1960 and 1990, and today 55 percent of the population live in coastal counties along the Atlantic and Pacific Oceans, the Gulf of Mexico, and the Great Lakes. This percentage is estimated to rise to over 70 percent by 2025.

Increasing coastal development is of major concern to geologists because they know that coastlines are among Earth's most geologically active environments. Water in oceans and lakes is constantly in motion due to winds, tides, currents, and, occasionally, tsunami. Therefore, coasts are dynamic and constantly changing from interactions between the energy in the water and the land. These coastal changes occur on two very different time scales. Short-term change (years to decades) is largely due to coastal erosion from waves, storms, and coastal flooding, while long-term changes (hundreds to thousands of years) are due to slower sea-level rise that causes a landward shift in the coastline. These natural processes posed no problem until people began to live along coasts.

Hurricanes and coastal storms are major hazards affecting most coasts in the United States, due to the high energy waves they bring to these areas. As these coasts become increasingly developed, they are highly vulnerable to these natural hazards, and storm damage continues to rise dramatically. Many coasts are affected by multiple hazards such as landslides caused by cliffs continually being undermined by large waves. Today, coastal erosion affects businesses, homes, public facilities, beaches, cliffs, and bluffs (cliffs along lakes) built close to the water's edge. It is estimated that within the next 60 years, coastal erosion may claim one out of four structures within 150 meters of the coastline of the United States.

Even though the coasts are dynamic environments, predicting future coastal change is often difficult, because of the many variables inherent in world climate, weather, nature of the coastline, and human activity. However, scientific studies show evidence that sea level will continue rising, and that storms will become more common and powerful in the coming years. If our present patterns and rates of development along coasts continue, then we are on a collision course with more disasters and catastrophes. It is therefore important to understand the nature of coastal processes and their inherent natural hazards as future development is planned along the coastal zone.

shutterstock © tropicdreams

Figure 7.1 The shoreline serves as a boundary between the hydrosphere, geosphere, and atmosphere, where all three meet and interact.

COASTAL PROCESSES

Coastal Basics

The coastline is a unique boundary where the geosphere, atmosphere, and hydrosphere meet and the systems interact (**Figure 7.1**). At this boundary, dynamic processes of erosion and deposition are constantly at work shaping and reshaping the landscape. Coastal processes active along the coasts are the result of interactions within the climate system and the solar system. Coastal surf and storms result from interactions between the atmosphere and the hydrosphere, with the Sun as the ultimate source of energy driving them. Wave activity that derives from blowing winds is the most important process acting along lake and marine coastlines. Gravity is also an important source of energy in producing rising and falling tides and currents that mostly affect oceanic coastlines. Tides are produced by gravitational interactions between Earth, the Sun, and Moon. Thus waves and tides are important processes in bringing energy to the coasts for erosion of the land and the transport and deposition of sediment on beaches.

Waves

Wave Generation

A **wave** is simply energy in motion that is the result of some disturbance. The energy that causes waves in water to form is called a disturbing force. For example, a rock thrown into a still lake will create waves that radiate in all directions from the disturbance. Mass movement into the ocean, such as coastal landslides and calving glaciers (creating icebergs) produce waves commonly known as splash waves. Sea floor movements change the shape of the ocean floor and release tremendous amounts of energy to the entire water column and create very large waves. Examples include underwater avalanches, volcanic eruptions, and fault movement, all of which can generate a tsunami. Human activities can also generate waves, such as when ships travel across a body of water and leave behind a wake, which is a wave. Wind blowing across a body of water disturbs surface waters and generates most waves that we commonly see on the surface of the oceans or large lakes. Wind-generated waves represent a direct transfer of kinetic energy from the atmosphere to the water surface. In all these cases, some type of energy release creates waves; however, wind-generated waves provide most of the energy that reaches land and shapes and modifies the coastlines.

Wave Characteristics

When wind blows unobstructed across the water, it deforms the surface into a series of wave oscillations. The highest part of the wave is the **crest**, and the lowest part between crests is the **trough** (**Figure 7.2**). The vertical distance between the crest and the adjacent trough is the **wave height**. The horizontal distance between any two similar points of the wave, such as two crests or two troughs, is the **wavelength**. The **wave period** is the time it takes for one full wavelength to pass a given point. The **wave speed** is the rate at which the wave travels and is equal to the wavelength divided by the period. **Wave steepness** is the ratio of wave height to wavelength. If the wave steepness exceeds 1/7, the wave becomes too steep to support itself and it **breaks**, or spills forward, releasing energy and forming whitecaps, often observed in choppy waters or the surf area along a beach. A wave can break anytime the 1:7 ratio is exceeded, either in the open ocean or along the shoreline.

Wave Motion

Waves are a mechanism by which energy is transferred along the surface of the water. Waves can travel many kilometers from their place of origin. Waves generated in Antarctica have been tracked as they traveled over 10,000 kilometers through the Pacific Ocean before finally expending their energy a week later on the shores of Alaska. But it is important to note that the water itself does not travel this great distance. The water is merely the medium for the waveform (the energy) to travel through, similar to earthquake seismic waves as they travel through solid rock.

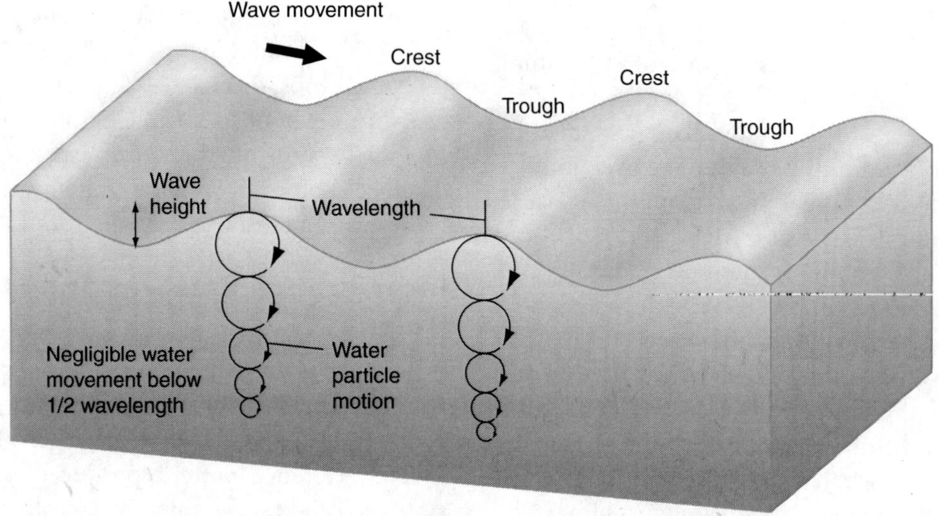

Figure 7.2 Wave form with characteristics. Crests and troughs alternate across the wave form. Note that water motion dies off at a depth of about one-half the wavelength.

In the open water, water particles pass the energy along by moving in a circle (**Figure 7.3**). This is known as **circular orbital motion**. This motion can be observed easily by observing a floating object as it bobs up and down and sways back and forth as the wave passes, but the object itself does not travel along with the wave. From the side, the object can be viewed moving in a circular orbit with a diameter at the surface equal to the wave's height. Beneath the surface, the orbital motion of the water particles diminishes downward with depth. At a depth equal to approximately one-half the wavelength, there is no movement associated with surface waves. This bottom depth of orbital motion is known as the **wave base**. Submarines can avoid large ocean waves by submerging below the wave base. Even seasick scuba divers can find relief by submerging into the calm water below the wave base. If the water depth is greater than the wave base, the waves are called deep-water waves and do not contact the ocean floor. The motion of water in waves is therefore distinctly different from the motion of water in currents, in which water travels in a given direction and does not return to its original position.

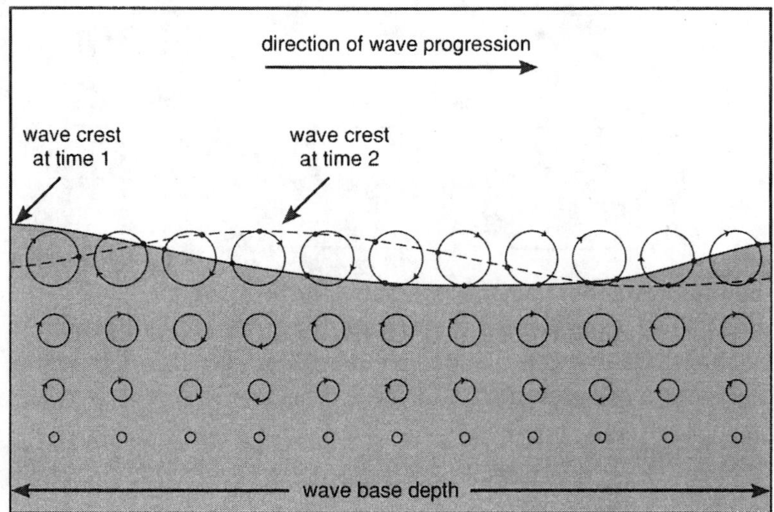

Figure 7.3 Circular motion of a wave form in open water. Individual particles of water rotate in a circle, producing an overall lateral movement of a wave.

Wave Energy

As wind blows over the surface of a body of water, some of its energy is transferred to the water. The mechanism of energy transfer is related to frictional drag resulting from one fluid (the air) moving over another fluid (the water). Waves that crash along the coast in the absence of local winds are generated by offshore winds and storm events, sometimes thousands of kilometers away. The energy of a wave depends on its height and length. The higher the wave's height, the greater the size of the orbit in which the water moves. The height, length, and period of a wave depend on the combination of three factors: (1) wind speed (the stronger the wind speed, the larger the waves), (2) wind duration (the longer time the wind blows, the more time the wind can transfer energy to the water, and the larger the waves), and (3) **fetch**, the distance over which the wind blows (a longer fetch allows more energy to be transferred and form larger waves). If we compare waves on a lake and on the ocean, when wind speed and duration are the same, the waves will be higher on the ocean because the fetch is far greater than on a lake. When the maximum fetch and duration have been reached for a given wind speed, waves will be fully developed and will grow no further. This is because they are losing as much energy breaking as whitecaps as they are receiving from the wind.

In areas where storm waves are generated, waves will have different lengths, heights, and periods. When the wind stops, or changes direction, waves will separate into waves of uniform length called **swells**. Swells moving away from the storm center can travel great distances before the energy of the wave is released by breaking and crashing onto the coast.

Interference Patterns and Hazardous Rogue Waves

When swells of deep water waves from different storms run together, the waves interfere with one another to produce different interference patterns (**Figure 7.4**). The interference pattern produced when two wave systems collide is the sum of the disturbance that each would have created individually. Constructive interference occurs when two waves having the same wavelength come together in phase (meaning crest to crest and trough to trough). The wave height will be the sum of the two, and if it becomes too steep, the wave may break forming whitecaps. Destructive interference occurs when waves having the same wavelength come together out of phase (meaning the crest of one will coincide with the trough of the other). If the wave heights are equal, the energies will cancel each other and the water surface will be flat. If the waves are traveling in opposite directions, the waves will return

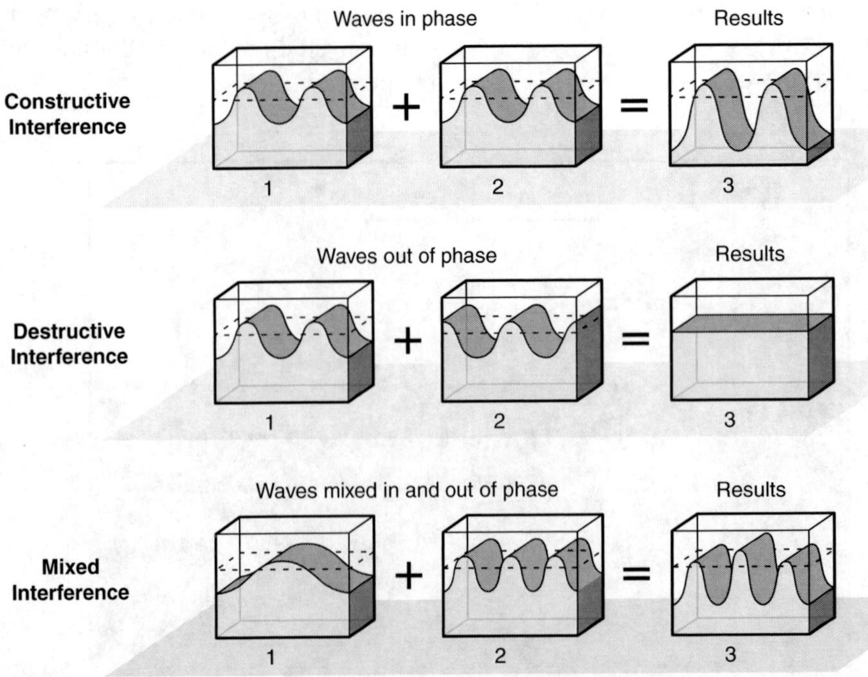

Figure 7.4 Interference patterns in water. Constructive interference creates larger waves, destructive interference reduces the waves to a flat surface, and mixed interference generates a mixture of small and large waves.

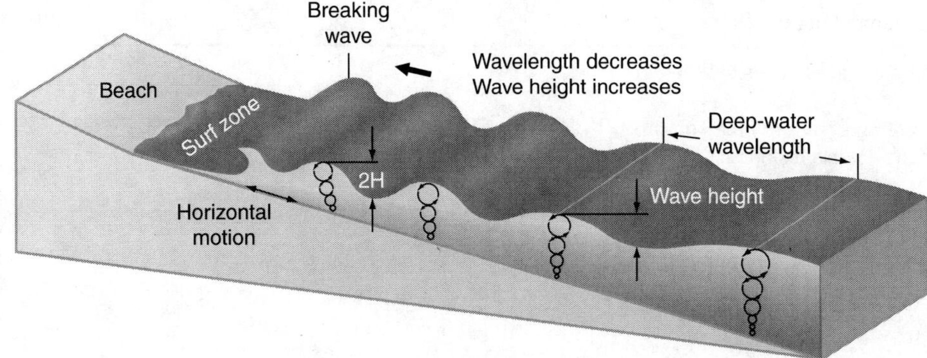

Figure 7.5 Wave hitting the shore with the bottom of the wave intersecting the sea floor. Waves form breakers and move toward the beach as the surface of the water moves faster than the water underneath.

to their normal heights once they travel through the interference area.

It is common for mid-ocean storm waves to reach 7 meters in height, and in extreme conditions such waves can reach heights of 15 meters. However, solitary waves called **rogue waves** can reach enormous heights and can occur when normal ocean waves are not unusually high. The word *rogue* means unusual, and in this case the waves are unusually large—monsters up to 30 meters in height (approximately the height of a 10-story building)—that can appear without warning. Rogue waves appear to be caused by an extraordinary case of constructive interference that can be very destructive and have been popularized in movies such as *The Poseiden Adventure* and *The Perfect Storm*.

In 1942 during World War II, the RMS *Queen Mary* was carrying 15,000 American troops near Scotland during a gale and was broadsided by a 28 meter high rogue wave and nearly capsized. The ship listed briefly about 52 degrees before the ship slowly righted herself.

Waves Reach the Shore: Shallow-Water Waves and Breakers

When deep-water waves approach shore, the water depth decreases and the wave base starts to intersect the seafloor. At this point the wave comes in contact with the bottom and the character of the wave starts to change (**Figure 7.5**). In this zone of shoaling (shallowing) waves, they grow taller and less symmetrical. Because of friction at the bottom, the wave speed decreases, but its period remains the same, and thus, the wavelength will decrease. The circular loops of water motion also change to elliptical shapes, as loops are deformed by the bottom. As the wave moves farther shoreward, the wavelength shortens considerably and the wave height increases. The increase in wave height, combined with the decrease in wavelength, causes an increase in wave steepness. With continued forward motion at the top of the wave and friction at the bottom, the front portion of the wave cannot support the water as the rear part moves over, and the wave breaks as surf. Here in the **surf zone**, actual forward movement of water itself occurs within the wave as all the water releases its energy as a wall of moving, turbulent surf known as a **breaker**.

There are three main types of breakers (**Figure 7.6**). **Spilling breakers** form on shorelines with gentle offshore slopes and are characterized by turbulent crests spilling down the front slope of the wave. **Plunging breakers** form on shorelines with steeper offshore slopes and have a curling crest that moves over an air pocket. Plunging breakers are prized waves for surfing. **Surging breakers** form when the offshore slopes abruptly and the wave energy is compressed into a shorter distance and the wave surges forward right at the shoreline.

After the breaker collapses, a turbulent sheet of water, the **swash**, rushes up the slope of the beach (called the swash zone). The swash is a powerful surge that causes landward movement of sediment (sand and gravel) on the beach. When the energy of the swash is dissipated, the water flows by gravity back down the beach toward the surf zone as **backwash**. Therefore, as a wave approaches the shore, it breaks, and the stored energy in the wave is expended in the surf and swash zones, causing erosion, transport, and deposition of sediment along the coast (**Figure 7.7**).

Wave Refraction

As waves approach an irregular shoreline, or at an angle to the shore, the wave base will initially encounter shallower water areas first and begin to slow down

Fundamentals: Breakers

There are three types of breakers:

- **Spilling breakers** break gradually over considerable distance.

- **Plunging breakers** tend to curl over and break with a single crash. The front face is concave, the rear face is convex.

- **Surging breakers** peak up, but surge onto the back without spilling or plunging. Even though they don't "break," surging waves are still classified as breakers.

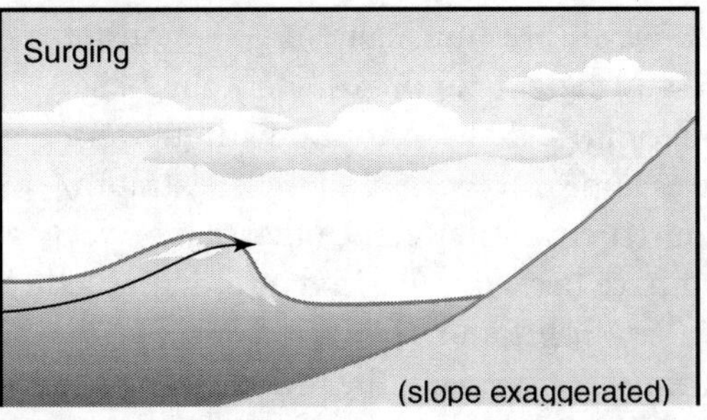

U.S. Army

Figure 7.6 Spilling, plunging, and surging breakers. Sea floor topography plays a key role in the type of breaker that forms.

© Dmitry Naumov, 2010. Underlicense from Shutterstock, Inc.

Figure 7.7 Swash forms as a breaking wave moves up the flat surface along the shore. Receding water produces the backwash.

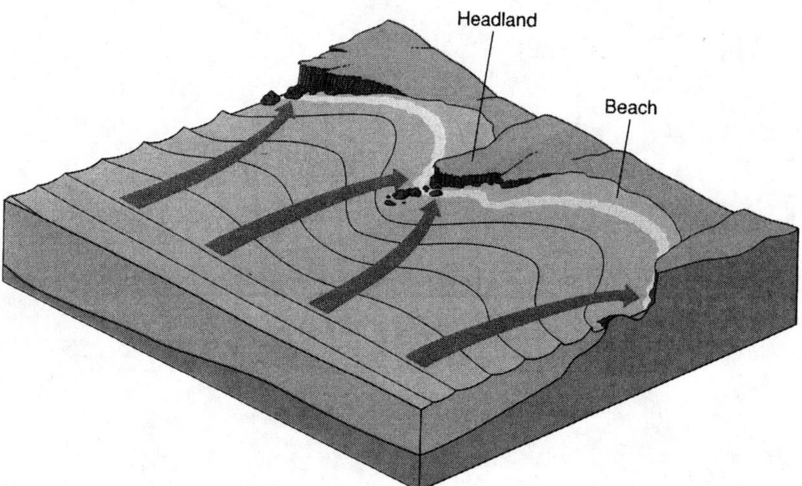

Figure 7.8 Refraction of wave energy around a headland. Incoming wave energy is bent or refracted toward the headland due to changes in the sea floor topography that cause the wave to change speed. This produced a zone of high energy that erodes the protruding headland.

before the rest of the wave does resulting in **wave refraction**, or bending of the wave. Refraction of waves approaching coastlines concentrates wave energy on protruding **headland** areas and dissipates energy in the bays (**Figure 7.8**). The concentrated energy on headlands erodes them into cliffs and causes deposition of sediment in the bays; thus, headlands erode faster than bays due to stronger wave energy. The result of wave refraction is to erode headlands and smooth out the coastline. The eroded sediments are deposited offshore, on beaches, or in bays.

Tides

Tides produce short-term fluctuations in sea level on a daily bases. **Tides** are the rising and falling of Earth's ocean surface caused by the gravitational attraction of moon and the Sun on the Earth. Because the moon is closer to the Earth than the Sun, it has a greater effect and causes the Earth's water to bulge toward it, while at the same time a bulge occurs on the opposite side of the Earth due to inertial forces. These different bulges remain stationary while Earth rotates and the tidal bulges result in a rhythmic rise and fall of ocean surface, which is not noticeable in the open ocean but is magnified along the coasts. The changing tide produced at a given location is the result of the changing positions of the moon and Sun relative to the Earth, coupled with the effects of Earth rotation and the local shape of the sea floor.

The regular fluctuations in the ocean surface result in most coastline areas having two daily high tides and two low tides as sea level rises and falls onto the shore. A complete tidal cycle includes a **flood tide** that progresses upward on the shore until high tide is reached, followed by an **ebb tide** falling off the shore until low tide is reached and exposing the land once again. Tidal ranges between high and low tides along most coasts range about 2 meters. However, in narrow inlets tidal currents can be strong and cause variations in sea level up to 16 meters. High and low tides do not occur at the same time each day but instead are delayed about 53 minutes every 24 hours. This is because the Earth makes a complete axis rotation in 24 hours, but at the same time, the moon is orbiting the Earth in the same direction, which means the Earth must spin an additional 53 minutes for the same point on Earth to be directly beneath the moon again (and thus in the bulge at its highest). This explains why the moon rises in the sky about 53 minutes later each day, and in the same manner, why the tides are also about 53 minutes later each day.

Because the Sun also exerts a gravitational attraction on the Earth, there are also monthly tidal cycles that are controlled by the relative position of the Sun and moon to the Earth. Although the sun's gravitational pull on the oceans is smaller than the moon's, it does have an effect on tidal ranges (the difference in elevation between high and low tides). The largest variation between high and low tides, called **spring tides**, occurs when the sun and the moon are aligned on the same side of the Earth (new moon) or on opposite sides of the Earth (full moon) (**Figure 7.9**). Here the gravitational attractions of the moon and sun amplify each other and produce higher and lower

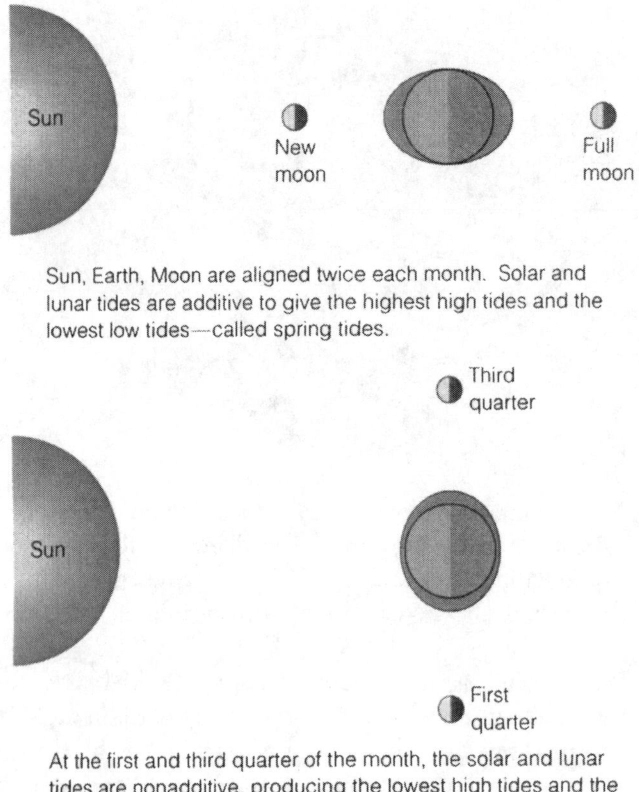

Figure 7.9 The tidal ranges are affected by the position of the moon with respect to Earth. New and full moons produce spring tides, while first and third quarter moons produce neap tides.

tides. The lowest variation between high and low tides, called **neap tides**, occur when the moon is at right angles relative to the Earth and Sun (quarter moons).

The timing when hazards, such as storms or tsunami events, strike the shoreline, especially at spring tides phases, is very important. The intensity of a disaster is magnified when rising water from a storm surge or tsunami arrives at the same time as the highest high tides. The combination of these events often sends the destructive power of the water farther inland, producing much more catastrophic results.

COASTAL EROSION

The erosion of the coastlines is due to the constant battering of waves which causes the land to retreat. Most coastal erosion occurs during intense storms when waves and storm surges are more energetic. The rate of wave erosion varies greatly along coasts of different compositions but is typically rapid along sandy coasts and slower along rocky coasts. Water weathers and erodes coastlines by processes of hydraulic action, abrasion, and corrosion.

The force of water alone, called hydraulic action, is an effective erosional process. Breaking waves exert a tremendous force on the shores by direct impact of the water and are very effective on cliffs composed of sediment or fractured rocks. A large wave 10-meter high storm wave striking a 10-meter high cliff produces four times the thrust energy of the space shuttle's three main orbiter engines. A wave striking a cliff drives water into cracks or other openings in the rock and compresses air inside. As this happens, the water and air combine to create hydraulic forces on the surrounding rock that is large enough to dislodge rock fragments or large boulders. Repeated countless times, hydraulic action wedges out rock fragments from cliff faces which fall to the bottom of the cliff or sea bed. The debris can be picked up and used for another erosive wave action–abrasion. Loose sand is easily moved by wave action and by currents that run parallel to the shoreline.

Landforms of Erosional Coasts

Along coasts where erosion dominates, rocky coastlines are common. Since erosion occurs at sea level, abrasion and hydraulic action undercut exposed bedrock forming a wave-cut cliff. As the cliff continues to erode, it leaves behind a flat or gently sloping **wave-cut platform** (**Figure 7.10**). Farther offshore a wave-built platform can be formed by transported sediments that are deposited as the water moves seaward. Locally, refraction of waves onto a narrow headland can cut a cave into the rock which may eventually erode all the way through the headland forming a **sea arch**. When the sea arch collapses, a small prtion of the headland may be isolated from the retreating sea cliff and remain as a **sea stack** (**Figure 7.11**). As waves continue to batter the rocks, eventually the sea stacks crumble. The overall effect is to produce a rugged shoreline that is constantly being hit by incoming waves (**Figure 7.12**).

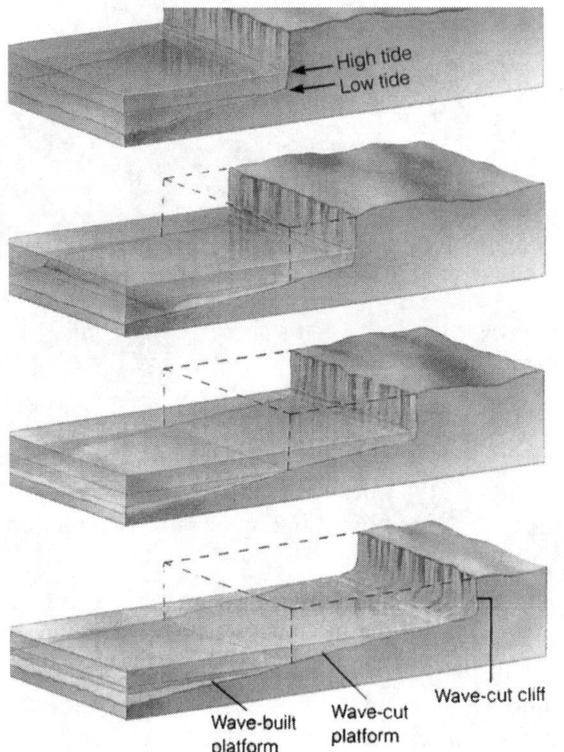

Figure 7.10 Wave-cut platforms and wave-cut cliffs are formed by active erosion produced by incoming tides.

COASTAL SEDIMENT TRANSPORT

Sediment that is created by the abrasive and hydraulic action of waves, or sediment brought to the coast by streams, is picked up by the waves and transported. One of the most important processes of sediment transport within the shoreline area is longshore drift. Sediment is also transported by rip currents and tidal currents.

Longshore Drift and Currents

Longshore drift is the net movement of sediment parallel to the shore. The process starts when waves approach the shore obliquely, even after refraction. Waves striking the shore at an angle, as opposed to straight on, will cause the wave swash to move up the beach at an angle. The swash moves the sediment particles (typically sand) up the beach at this angle, while the backwash brings them directly down the beach slope, under the influence of gravity. This has the net effect of gradual movement of the sediment along the shore by the swash and backwash. The swash of the incoming wave moves sand up the beach in a direction

Figure 7.11 Arches represent the remains of a once-protruding headland that reached out into the ocean. The sea stack in the distance seen through the arch is the remnants of a collapsed arch.

Figure 7.12 Waves strike a rugged shoreline in the Channel Islands National Park, California.

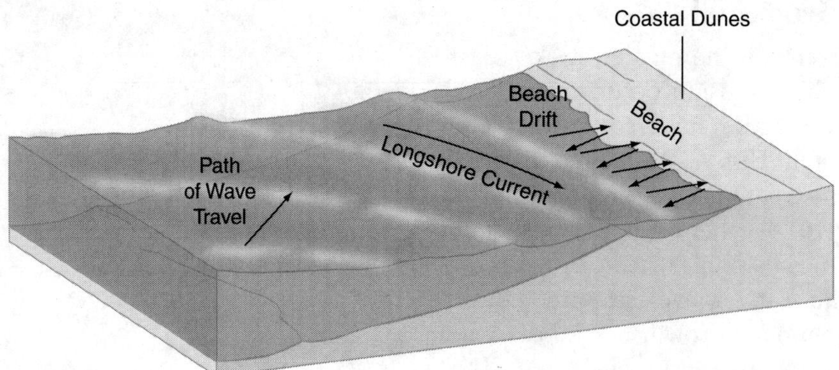

Figure 7.13 Beach drift is created by incoming waves hitting the beach at an angle moving sand that returns to sea in a direction perpendicular to the beach. Longshore current is the overall movement of water parallel to the beach but in the same general direction as the incoming wave direction.

perpendicular to the incoming wave crests and the backwash moves the sand down the beach perpendicular to the shoreline. Thus, with successive waves, the sand will move along a zigzag path along the beach parallel to shore. This process is known as **beach drift** (**Figure 7.13**).

A similar process, known as a **longshore current**, develops in the surf zone and a little farther out to sea (**Figure 7.14**). The movement of swash and backwash in and out from the shore at an angle creates turbulent water in the surf that transports sediments along the shallow bottom in the same direction as the beach drift. Substantially more sediment is transported along many beaches as a result of longshore currents than beach drift. Thus longshore currents and beach drift work together as longshore drift to transport huge amounts of sediment along a coast (Figure 7.14). At Sandy Hook, New Jersey, approximately 2000 tons of sediment per day moves past any point on the beach. No wonder beaches are often referred to by coastal geologists as rivers of sand.

Hazardous Rip Currents

There are times when waves can pile volumes of water on the beach that are much greater than normal. The only way this water can return to the ocean is to ebb back in a channel through the surf zone. This creates a **rip current** that typically flows perpendicular to the shore and the strong surface flow can have sufficient force to be a hazard to swimmers (**Figure 7.15**). It is often incorrectly called a "rip tide" or "riptide," because the occurrence is not related to tides, and also as an "undertow," athough they do not drag people

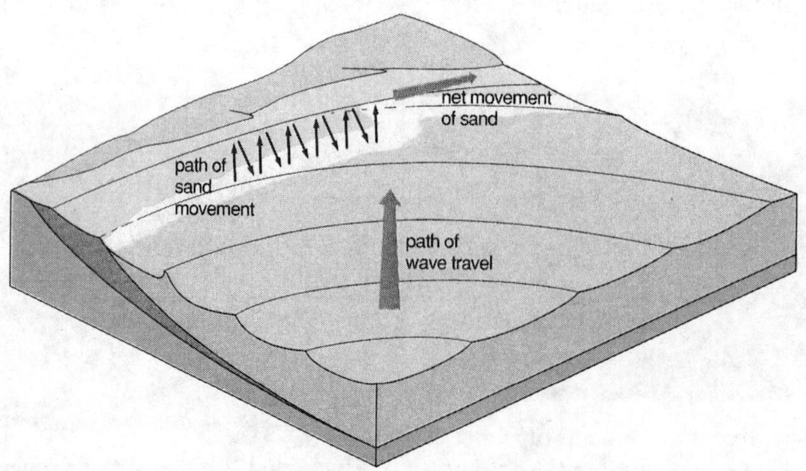

Figure 7.14 Longshore drift creates a net movement of sand along the beach and shallow water zone.

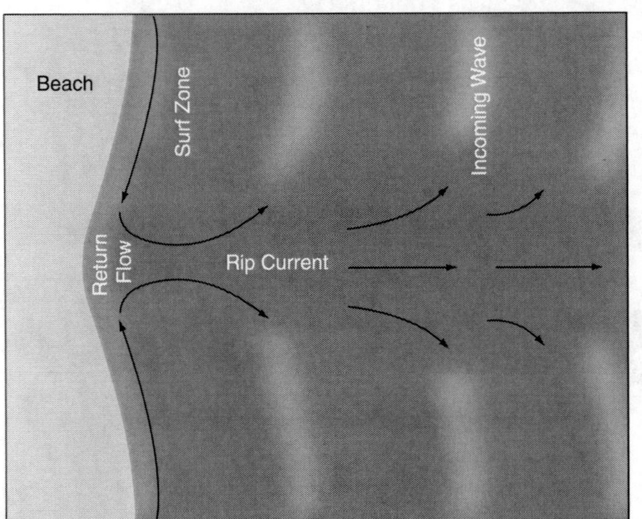

Figure 7.15 Rip currents form when too much water is pushed up onto the beach. Its return to the sea causes a rapid movement of water seaward.

under water. Rates of return flow can range from 0.5 meters per second to as much as 2.5 meters per second. The position of rip currents can shift along the beach during the day as differing amounts of water are pushed up onto the shore.

Often two characteristics are present that allow us to identify a rip current. As the water is receding toward the ocean, its force counteracts the incoming force of the waves, thereby canceling out the waves. Thus a relatively smooth surface will be flanked by incoming waves. Also the receding water can carry along large amounts of sand and silt, which will discolor the water. It is advisable to look for the existence of a rip current before heading into the water. Such currents can be extremely dangerous, dragging swimmers away from the beach and leading to death by drowning when they attempt to fight the current and become exhausted. The United States Lifesaving Association reports that rip currents cause approximately 100 deaths annually in the United States, mainly on unguarded beaches. Over 80 percent of rescues by beach lifeguards are due to rip currents, totaling more than 37,000 lifeguard rescues in 2008.

If a swimmer is caught in a rip current, one should not try to swim directly back to shore but rather swim parallel to the shoreline in order to get out of the current. Rip currents can be between 15 and 45 meters wide. If you see a person caught in a rip current, yell at them to swim parallel to the shore and you should move along the shoreline in a direction that leads them out of the current.

Coastal Sediment Deposition and Landforms

Sediment transported along the shore is deposited in areas of lower wave energy and produces a variety of landforms. Common landforms include *beaches, spits, tombolos,* and *barrier islands.* Erosion of headlands and sea cliffs is the source of some sediment, but probably no more than 5 to 10 percent of the total. The primary source of sediment is that transported to the coast by rivers that drain the continents and then redistributed along the shore by longshore drift.

Beaches

A **beach** is an accumulation of unconsolidated sediment along part of the coastline that is exposed to wave action. Beaches are formed from the wave-washed sediment along a coast, and represent interconnected zones of onshore and offshore sediment accumulation. Most beaches can be described in terms of three geomorphic zones (**Figure 7.16**). The **offshore zone** is the

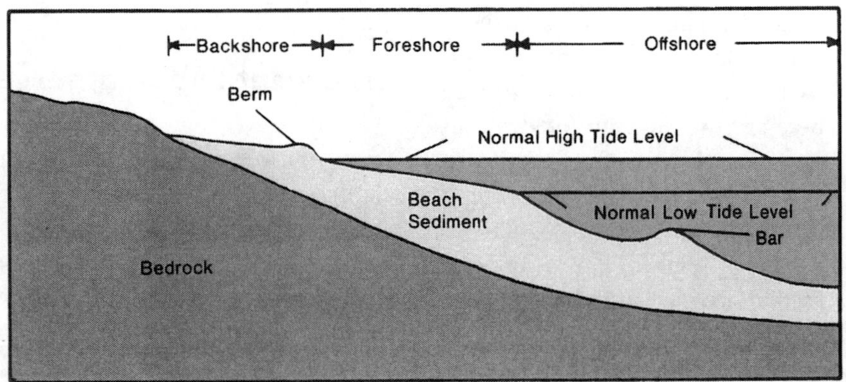

Figure 7.16 The topographic features of a beach area show the different "shore" zones that extend from the land out to sea.

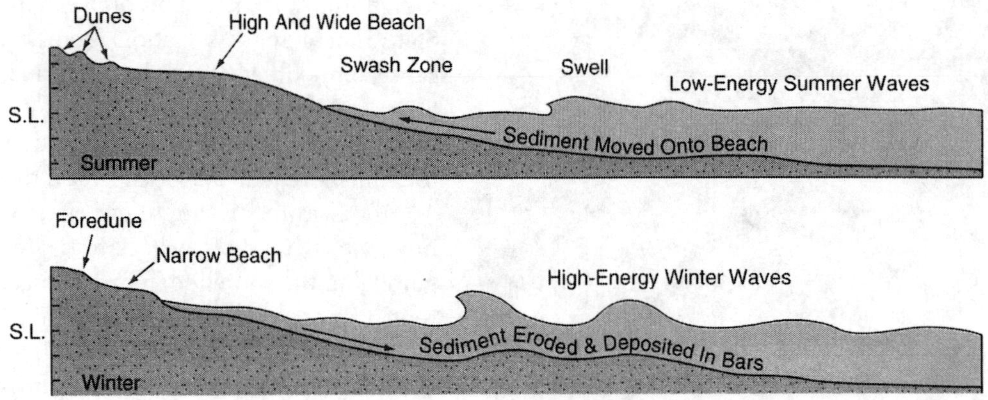

Figure 7.17 Beach profiles during the summer and winter differ in that the lower energy of the summer allows the beach to become enriched with sand. Winter storms erode most of the summer buildup and reduce the size of the beach.

portion of beach that extends seaward from the low tide level. Strong backwash currents usually transport some sediment off exposed portions of the beach and deposit it offshore as submerged offshore bars. The foreshore zone represents the area between low and high tide levels. The **backshore zone**, which is commonly separated from the foreshore by a distinct ridge, called a **berm**, is the part of the beach extending landward from the high tide level to the area reached only during storms. Sediments in this zone are frequently redistributed by wind to form sand dunes. Behind the backshore may be a zone of cliffs, marshes, or additional sand dunes.

Even though beaches are areas of deposition, they are in a constant state of change, and dynamically responding to variations in the energy of waves and currents. The effect that waves have depends on their strength. Strong, also called destructive waves, occur on high energy beaches and are typical of winter storms (**Figure 7.17**). They reduce the quantity of sediment present on the beach by carrying it out to offshore bars under the sea. Constructive, weak waves are typical of low energy beaches, and occur usually during summer months. These are the opposite of destructive waves because they increase the size of the beach by removing sand from the offshore bars and piling it up onto the berm. This strong and weak wave activity alternates seasonally at most beaches. The weak wave activity produces a high and wide sandy beach at the expense of the offshore bars. The strong wave activity produces a narrow beach during the winter months and builds prominent offshore bars.

Barrier Islands

A **barrier island** is a long narrow offshore island of sediment running parallel to the coast and separated from it by a lagoon (**Figure 7.18**). Spits can form at the ends of barrier islands and as sand is transported into inlets by longshore and tidal currents.

Barrier islands are mostly between 15 and 30 kilometers long and from 1 to 5 kilometers wide. The tallest features are wind-blown sand dunes that reach heights of 5 to 10 meters (**Figure 7.19**). Barrier islands are common features along the Atlantic and Gulf coasts of the United States which forms the longest chain of barrier islands in the world. However, barrier islands are dynamic coastal features as they grow parallel to the coast by longshore drift and are often eroded by storm surges that often cut them into smaller islands. Despite their transient nature, many barrier islands are heavily populated with homes and resorts. Even several major cities occupy barrier islands, including Miami Beach, Atlantic City, and Galveston.

Emergent and Submergent Coastlines

While sea level fluctuates daily because of tides, long-term changes in sea level have also occurred. Such changes in sea level result from uplift or subsidence along a coastline. Many coastal geologists classify coasts based on changes that have occurred in the past with respect to sea level. This commonly used classification divides coasts into two categories: *emergent* and *submergent.* An **emergent coastline** is a coastline that has experienced a fall in sea level, because of global sea

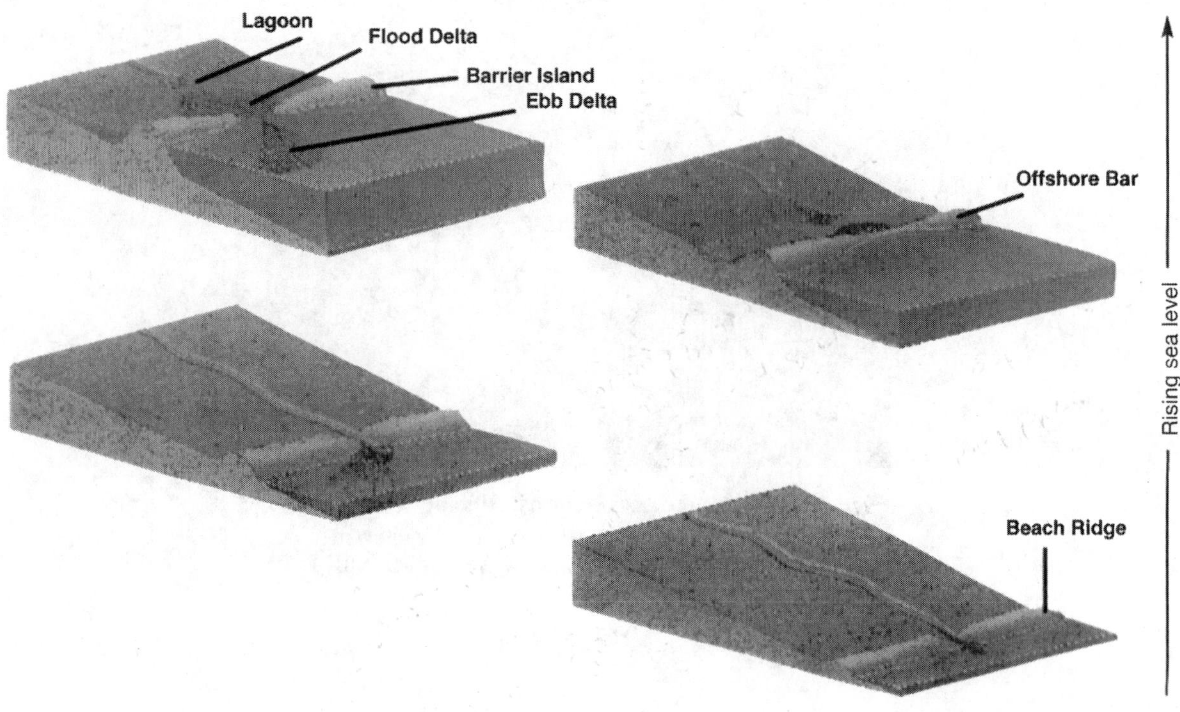

Figure 7.18 Barrier islands formed from sand deposited along low energy beachs. These islands provide protection of the shoreline during storms and period of high energy. During period of very high water these islands are overrun with water.

level change, local land uplift, or isostatic rebound. Emergent coastlines are identifiable by the coastal landforms which are now above the high tide mark, such as raised beaches or raised wave cut benches (marine terraces) (**Figure 7.20**). Alternatively, a **submergent coastline** is one that has experienced a rise in sea level, due to a global sea level change or local land subsidence. Submergent coastlines are identifiable by their submerged, or "drowned" landforms, such as drowned valleys and fjords.

The type of coast produced is controlled mainly by tectonic forces and meteorological conditions (climate and weather). Tectonic processes can cause a coastline to rise or sink while lithospheric isostatic adjustment can depress or elevate sections of a continent. The tectonics at active plate margins can produce uplift or subsidence of a coast. In the northwestern United States, the coastline is slowly rising due to subduction of the Juan de Fuca plate beneath the North American plate. During the 1964 Alaska earthquake, parts of the coast rose and other parts subsided beneath sea level from a single event. Different isostatic adjustments to the land do not have to occur along plate margins.

During glacial periods, large continental ice sheets can displace the lithosphere into the plastic asthenosphere. About 18,000 years ago, a huge continental glacier covered most of Scandinavia, causing the land to sink isostatically. As the lithosphere sank, the displaced asthenosphere flowed southward, causing the Netherlands to rise. After the ice melted, the process was reversed and the asthenosphere flowed back north from below the Netherlands to Scandinavia today, Scandinavia is rebounding and the Netherlands is sinking. During the same glacial episode in North America, Canada was depressed by ice, and asthenosphere rock flowed southward. The asthenosphere is flowing back north and much of Canada is rebounding while much of the United States is now sinking.

Global changes in sea level can also occur. Such global sea level changes are called **eustatic** changes and can occur by three mechanisms: the growth or

Figure 7.19 Sand dunes serve as a line of defense against storm water that can overrun the beach zone. Salt-resistant sea grasses are often planted to stabilize the dunes.

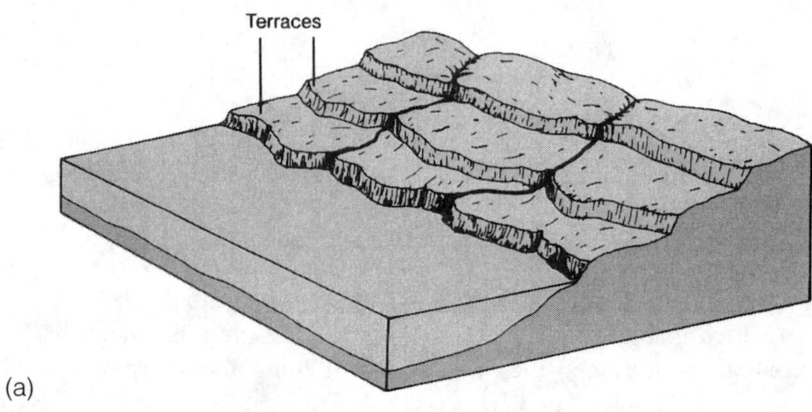

(a)

(b)

Figure 7.20 (a) An emergent coastline often has wave-cut terraces that represent odler period of higher sea level. (b) This wave-cut terrace is part of an emergent shoreline at Baker's Point, California.

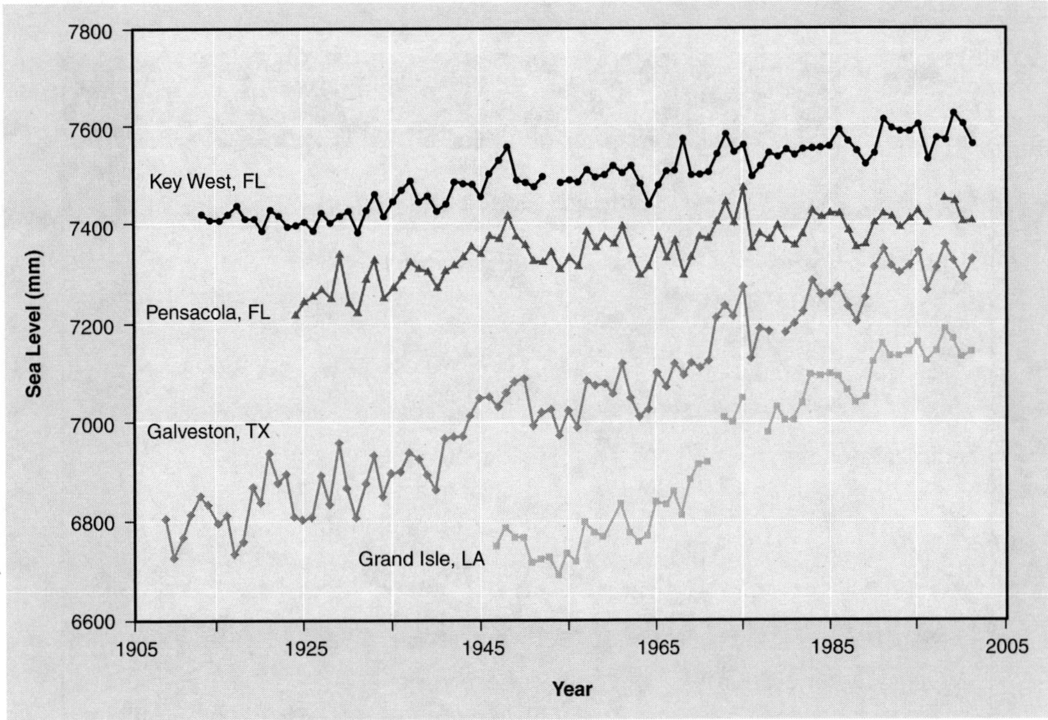

Figure 7.21 Long-term trends in average annual sea level at selected tide gauges in the Gulf of Mexico. Data are from the National Ocean Service.

melting of glaciers, changes in water temperature, and changes in the volume of the mid-ocean ridges. During glacial periods large amounts of water evaporated from the oceans becomes stored on the continents as glacial ice and causes sea level to become lower, resulting in global land emergence. Similarly, when glaciers melt, water flows back into the oceans and sea level rises globally, causing land submergence.

Changes in the volume of mid-ocean ridges can also affect sea level. Growth of a mid-ocean ridge displaces seawater upward. If lithospheric plates spread slowly from the ridge they create a narrow mountain ridge system that displaces relatively small amounts of seawater, resulting in lower sea level. In contrast, rapidly spreading plates produce a high-volume ridge system that displaces more water upwards, resulting in higher sea level. At times during Earth's history, sea floor spreading has been relatively rapid, and as a result, global sea level has been higher.

COASTAL HAZARDS: LIVING WITH COASTAL CHANGE

From our discussion of our coastal areas it is apparent that diverse and complex processes are at work continually changing the coastal landscapes. Vast areas of coastal land have been lost since the mid 1800s as a result of natural processes and human activities (**Table 7.1**). The most important causes that have the greatest influence on coastal land loss are relative sea level rise, erosion from frequent storms, and reductions in sediment supply; whereas the most important human activities are sediment excavation, river modification, and coastal construction. Any one of these causes may be responsible for most of the land loss at a coast, or the land loss may be the result of several of these factors acting at the same time.

From a hazard point of view, coastal erosion is the most widespread and continuous process affecting the world's coastlines and contributing to land loss destruction. Global warming and sea level rise are slow-onset hazards that greatly contribute to the erosional process. However, catastrophic, rapid-onset events play a very significant role both for coastal erosion and human suffering. These include erosion and destruction from storms, landslides, and tsunami.

Coastal Land Loss by Global Sea-Level Rise and Subsidence

A significant amount of coastal erosion presently plaguing today's coastlines is the result of gradual but sustained global sea level rise (**Figure 7.21**). Most of this

Table 7.1 Common Physical and Anthropogenic Causes of Coastal Land Loss

Agent	Examples
Natural Processes	
Erosion	waves and currents storms landslides
Sediment Reduction	climate change stream avulsion source depletion
Submergence	land subsidence sea-level rise
Wetland Deterioration	herbivory freezes fires saltwater intrusion
Human Activities	
Agent	**Examples**
Transportation	boat wakes, altered water circulation
Coastal Construction	sediment deprivation (bluff retention) coastal structures (jetties, groins, seawalls)
River Modification	control and diversion (dams, levees)
Fluid Extraction	water, oil, gas, sulfur
Climate Alteration	global warming and ocean expansion increased frequency and intensity of storms
Excavation	dredging (canal, pipelines, drainage) mineral extraction (sand, shell, heavy mins.)
Wetland Destruction	pollutant discharge traffic failed reclamation burning

Source: United States Geological Survey.

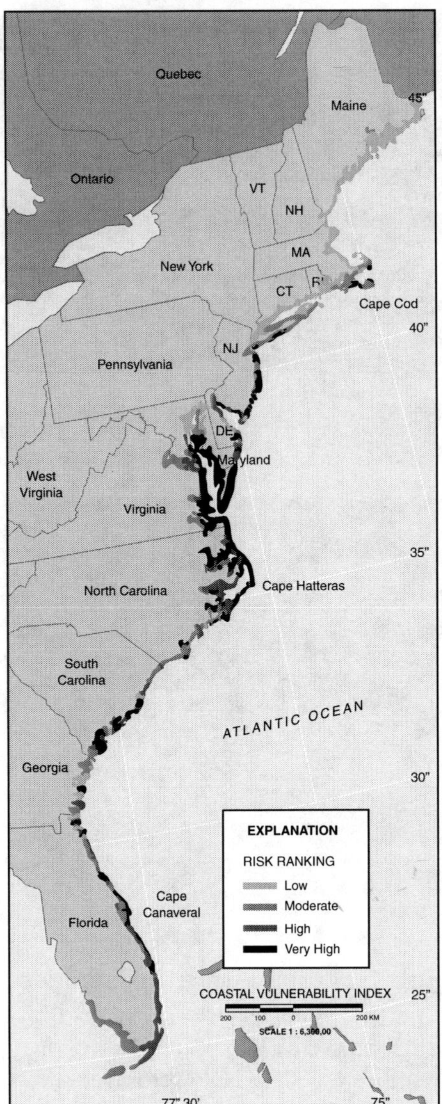

Figure 7.22 Map of the Coastal Vulnerability Index (CVI) for the U.S. East Coast showing the relative vulnerability of the coast to changes due to future rises in sea level. Areas along the coast are assigned a ranking from low to very high risk, based on the analysis of physical variables that contribute to coastal change.

rise is from the melting of polar continental ice sheets, coupled with expansion of the water itself as global temperatures increase. The sea level rise is currently estimated at about 0.3 meter per century. Although this amount does not sound very threatening, additional factors increase the risk. First, the slope of many coastal areas is very gentle so that a small rise in sea level results in a far larger inland advance of the coast than steeper sloping areas. The vulnerability of coastal regions along the eastern seaboard of the United States shows a wide range of potential risks (**Figure 7.22**). Estimates of the amount of coastline retreat in the United States from a sea level rise of 0.3 meters would be 15 to 30 meters in the northeast, 65 to 130 meters in California, and up to 300 meters in Florida. Second, the documented rise of atmospheric carbon-dioxide levels (discussed in Chapter 5) suggests that global warming from the increased greenhouse-effect will melt the glaciers more rapidly, as well as warming the oceans more, thereby accelerating the rise of sea level. Some estimates put the anticipated rise in sea level at 1 meter by the year 2100. In addition to increased beach erosion, it would also flood 30 to 70 percent of coastal wetlands in the United States that protect shores from storm flooding events.

The most widely assessed effects of future sea level rise are coastal inundation (submergence), erosion, and barrier migration. The USGS estimates the primary impacts of a sea level rise on the United States to be: (1) the cost of protecting ocean communities by pumping sand onto beaches and gradually raising barrier islands in place; (2) the cost of protecting developed areas along sheltered waters through the use of levees (dikes) and bulkheads; and (3) the loss of coastal wetlands and undeveloped lowlands. The total cost for a one meter rise is estimated to be $270–475 billion, ignoring future development.

Coastal submergence refers to permanent flooding of the coast caused by either a rise in global sea level or subsidence of the land, or both. At many coastal sites, submergence is the most important factor responsible for land loss and as sea level rises, or the land subsides, it will inundate present unprotected low-lying coastal areas and cities such as: Boston, New York, Charleston, Miami, and Los Angeles. Submergence also accelerates coastal beach erosion and landslides because it facilitates greater inland penetration of storm waves. In addition to accelerated land loss, coastal submergence causes intrusion of salt-water into coastal aquifers.

Coastal Land Loss by Erosion: Impacts from Storms and Landslides

Superimposed on the slower sea level rise are shorter duration water fluctuations caused by storm events. The most damaging coastal storms for the United States are tropical cyclones (hurricanes) and extratropical cyclones (winter storms) that form around low-pressure cells (see Chapter 3 and 4 for discussions of these storms).

Hurricanes form in the tropics during summer to early fall and migrate northward and westward into temperate regions of the Atlantic and Gulf coasts. The extratropical storms occur mostly in winter (like nor'easters) and can cause erosion of the coastline at much higher rates than normal. Although each type of storm is unique, there are several factors common to all storm types which include strong winds, generation of large waves, and elevated water levels known as a storm surge.

Storm Impacts

Strong storms bring more energy to the coastline causing higher rates of erosion (**Figure 7.23**). Higher erosion rates are due to several factors:

- Wave velocities are higher during storms and thus larger particles can be carried in suspension causing sand on beaches to be picked up and moved offshore. This leaves behind coarser grained particles such as pebbles and cobbles, thus reducing the width of sandy beaches;
- Storm waves reach higher levels onto the coast and destroy and remove structures and sediment from areas not normally reached by normal waves;
- Wave heights increase during a storm and crash higher onto cliff faces and rocky coasts. Larger rock debris or debris from destroyed structures is flung against the rock causing rapid rates of erosion by abrasion;
- Hydraulic action increases as larger waves crash into rocks. Air and water occupying fractures in the rock becomes compressed and thus the pressure in the fractures is increased which causes further fracturing of the rock.

Figure 7.23 Upper figure shows erosion and property damage near Floridana Beach, Florida, caused by Hurricane Frances on September 4, 2004. The lower image shows the same area following the arrival of Hurricane Jeanne on September 25, 2004. Jeanne produced much greater beach erosion.

Storm surge is responsible for about 90 percent of all human fatalities and damage during storms (**Figure 7.24**). A **storm surge** is an onshore flood of water created by a low pressure storm system. The surge is caused primarily by the strong winds of the storm blowing over the sea surface and causing the surface water to pile up above sea level. Low pressure at the center of the storm also elevates the surface water upward and enhances the height of the mound of water. As the storm nears land, the shallower sea floor prevents the piled-up water from collapsing and it floods inland as a deadly storm surge. Storm surges are at their highest and most damaging when they coincide with high tide (especially at the high tides during the spring tide cycles), combining the effects of the surge and the tide.

Dune and Beach Recession

High storm-generated waves erode large quantities of sediment from dune and beach areas. From March 5 through 8, 1962 a major coastal storm, known as the "Ash Wednesday" storm, moved northward and became stalled against the middle Atlantic coast through five high tides. The documented erosion that occurred at Virginia Beach, Virginia, showed that 30 percent of the beach and dune sand was removed. The crest of the dunes at Virginia Beach was reduced from an elevation of 4.9 to 3.4 meters thus enabling future storm surges to rise over the dunes and flood inland areas.

Figure 7.24 Property damage caused by a storm surge associated with the Patriot's Day nor'easter that struck New England in 2007.

Dune and Beach Breeching and Overwash

Large amounts of sediment can be eroded from a beach and dunes during a major storm with some migrating along the shore by accelerated longshore currents and some moved offshore. In addition, storm waves may wash sediment through low areas between the dunes of islands and onto the back side it. This **overwash** is important because it maintains the barrier island's width as its front is eroded but can be devastating to homes and other structures). Overwash fans are lobe-shaped deposits eroded from the ocean side of a shore and deposited in the bays and lagoons behind barrier islands.

Barrier Island Breeching

Severe storms can cut through a barrier island to produce a tidal inlet and tidal delta. A storm-produced tidal inlet often is short-lived as it closes naturally in a few weeks by longshore drift deposits that cross the inlet and fills it. The filling of a tidal inlet produces a flat area that invites future housing development. However, this area will be the first to flood in a future storm and time and time again, barrier islands have been breached at the same location where they were cut through many years before.

El Niño Events

Along the Pacific coast, winter storms and unusual oceanographic conditions such as El Niño cause the most erosion and land loss. Approximately every four to five years, El Niño conditions cause warm surface water of the Pacific Ocean to flow eastward piling up water along the west coast of North and South America. The elevated water levels and the unusually strong storms during El Niño events cause extensive flooding and erosion beaches and cliffs. In 1983, an unusually strong El Niño caused torrential rainfall, rapid beach erosion, and massive landslides along the Pacific coast of the United States. Land loss was concentrated along the southern California coast where numerous expensive homes built on cliffs were damaged or destroyed.

Two more major El Niño storms hit California in October 1997 and six months later in April 1998. Coastal areas were heavily eroded by these two events (**Figure 7.25**).

Landslides and Cliff Retreat

Coastal landslides occur where unstable slopes fail and land is both displaced down slope (**Figure 7.26**). Some of the fundamental causes of slope failures that lead to land loss are: (1) slope over-steepening (2) slope overloading, (3) shocks and vibrations, (4) water saturation, and (5) removal of natural vegetation. Sea level rise can elevate waves so they can erode and undercut cliffs at higher elevations, initiating mass movements. Cliffs may stay relatively stable and then retreat several meters in a single storm event which makes building

Figure 7.25 Coastal region near Ventura, California. Upper image shows the coast following the El Niño storm of October 1997; lower image shows a definite change in the coastal morphology following the April 1998 El Niño storm.

Figure 7.26 The small community of La Conchita, California, lies along the coast of the Pacific Ocean. Bluffs that overlie the town have collapsed twice since 1995 due to heavy rainfall that saturated the ground.

structures near the edge of cliffs an especially risky during times of sea level rise.

Coastal Land Loss by Human Activities

There is increasing evidence that recent land losses in many coastal regions are largely anthropogenic and attributable to human alteration of the coastal environment. Land losses indirectly related to human activities are difficult to quantify because they promote alterations and imbalances in the primary factors causing land loss such as sediment budget, coastal processes, and relative sea level changes. Human activities causing land loss are: transportation networks that tend to increase erosion, coastal construction projects that typically increase deficits in the sediment budget, subsurface fluid extraction and climate alterations that accelerate submergence and excavation projects that cause direct losses of land.

There are countless examples of human interference with coastal processes. The beach at Miami Beach must be restored periodically by sand pumped from offshore. In Louisiana the land is subsiding as sea level rises causing loss of natural coastal wetlands. Many California beaches are eroding due to the damming of rivers for irrigation and flood control. The river-supplied sediment that normally replenishes the beaches is being trapped in reservoirs behind dams. Since this sediment is not being supplied to the ocean, longshore currents cannot resupply the beaches with sediment. Instead, longshore currents carry the existing sediment in the downdrift direction, resulting in significant erosion of the beaches. Eliminating wetlands for development and agriculture removes the natural flood protection and storm-swollen estuaries now flood barrier islands from the bay side as storms move inland. Where dunes are removed, the most effective barrier to storm waters has been lost overwashing is more common. Groins built to trap sediment and widen updrift beaches have caused serious erosion problems downdrift. Over the last 10,000 years, most of the state of Louisiana has formed from the deposition of sediments by the flooding of the Mississippi River. Humans, however, have prevented the river from flooding by building levee systems that extend to the mouth of the river. As previously deposited sediments become compacted they tend to subside. Since no new sediment is being supplied by Mississippi river flooding, the subsidence results in a relative rise in sea level. This, coupled with a current rise in eustatic sea level, is causing coastal Louisiana to erode at an incredible rate.

Tsunami

A tsunami is a shallow water sea wave generated by earthquakes, volcanic eruptions, meteorite impacts in the ocean, or landslides. Tsunami can cause coastal flooding and catastrophic destruction thousands of kilometers from where they where generated. Such waves can have wave heights up to 30 meters, and have great potential to wipe out large coastal cities.

Lessons from the Geologic Record

Since the oceans formed over four billion years ago, they have influenced the coastlines of the newly forming continents. Sea level has risen and fallen repeatedly in the geologic past, and its coastlines have subsequently submerges and emerged throughout Earth's history. The rock record shows countless examples of seas transgressing and regressing over the continents. Marine fossils found thousands of kilometers inland from the present coast attests to this fluctuation in past sea levels.

At times during Earth's long history, tectonic movements arranged the continents into very different configurations from those of today. When there were large amounts of land near the poles, the rock record shows unusually low sea levels during past ice ages due to large ice sheets forming on the continents. During times when the land masses clustered around the equator, ice ages had much less effect on sea level. However, over most of geologic time, long-term sea

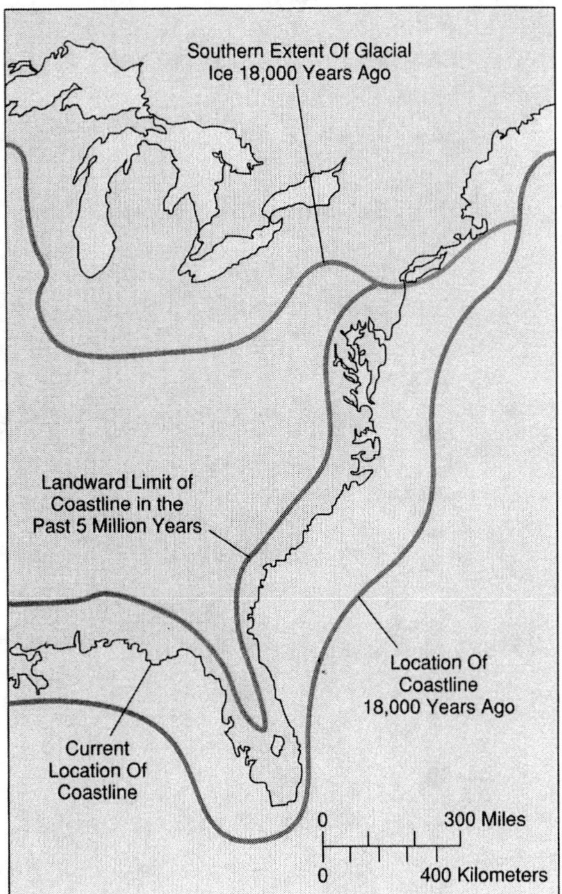

Figure 7.27 Coastlines have fluctuated about 400 km over the past five million years. Notice that sea level was much lower in the past 18,000 years.

level has been higher than today. Only at the Permian-Triassic boundary about 250 million years ago was long-term sea level lower than today.

The world's present coastlines are not the result of present-day processes but were affected by the rise of sea level caused by the melting of the Pleistocene glaciers beginning between 15,000 and 20,000 years ago (**Figure 7.27**). The rising sea flooded large parts of the low coastal areas, which are now part of the continental shelf, and moved the coastlines inland. Sea-level has risen about 130 meters since the peak of the last ice age about 18,000 years ago. It was during this time of very low sea level that there was a dry land connection between Asia and Alaska over which humans migrated to North America over the Bering Land Bridge. However, for the past 6,000 years (a few centuries before the first known written records), the world's sea level has been gradually approaching the level we see today.

Lessons from the Historic Record and the Human Toll

The increase in coastal populations together with rising sea level and intense storms combine to make coastal erosion and flooding very costly and life-threatening. Since the early 1900's, property damages in the United States have been on the rise. However, the death tolls have generally decreased (at least until Hurricane Katrina) because of advanced warnings and evacuations to the weather-related storm events. Unfortunately, people continue to build more structures along migrating shorelines and are unaware of the dynamic balance between erosion and deposition (refer to **Box 7.1**). Nearly all human intervention with coastal processes interrupts natural processes and thus can have an adverse effect on coastlines.

Coastal environments are a delicate setting in which conflicts arise when humans and natural processes attempt to coexist. With about 58 percent of people in the United States living within 150 km of a shoreline, it is inevitable that problems will develop. These problems are all too common when cyclonic storms hit a coastline. The rising waters and wind cause large amounts of damage to property, and unfortunately take people's lives. Examples are well known to those who live in these areas, and others who live elsewhere become aware of the issues when large storms hit. The case of Hurricane Katrina striking the Gulf Coast region of the United States in late August 2005 brought these problems to everyone's attention.

MITIGATION: ADAPTING TO COASTAL EROSION

Barrier islands and beaches, since they are made of unconsolidated sediment, and sea cliffs, since they are susceptible to landslides due to undercutting, are difficult to protect from the erosive action of the waves. Human construction methods can attempt to prevent erosion, but cannot always protect against abnormal conditions. In addition, other problems are sometimes caused by these engineering structures.

Protection of the Shoreline

Shoreline protection can be divided into two categories: hard stabilization in which solid structures are built to reduce wave action, and soft stabilization which mainly refers to adding sediment back to a beach as it erodes.

BOX 7.1 One Case Study Made By the United States Geological Survey

Ocean City, Maryland: An Urbanized Barrier Island

Relative recent changes in the shoreline have occurred in populated regions of the United States. USGS Circular 1075 provides a good summary of the events that have involved the shoreline near Ocean City, Maryland. For more than a century Ocean City, Maryland, has been a popular beach resort for vacationers from the Northeast and Mid-Atlantic States (Box Figure 7A). During the Roaring 1920s, several large hotels and a boardwalk were built to accommodate visitors and development continued slowly until the early 1950s. Then a period of rapid construction began that lasted almost 30 years. Concerns about the coastal environment were raised in the late 1970s and led to Federal and State laws to limit dredging and filling of wetlands. The resort is built on the southern end of Fenwick Island, one of the chain of barrier islands stretching along the east coast (Box Figure 7B). The Great Hurricane of 1933 (before names were assigned to hurricanes) opened the Ocean City Inlet by storm-surge overwash from the bay side. To maintain the inlet as a navigation channel, two large stone jetties were constructed by the U.S. Army Corps of Engineers. These jetties helped stabilized the inlet, but they have drastically altered the sand-transport processes near the inlet. The net longshore drift at Ocean City is southerly; it has produced a wide beach at north of the jetty, but Assateague Island, south of the inlet, has been starved of sediment. The result is a westerly offset of more than 500 meters in the once-straight barrier island.

The most damaging storm to hit Ocean City within historic times was the Five-High or Ash Wednesday northeaster of early March 1962 which caused severe erosion and flooding along much of the middle Atlantic Coast. For two days, over five high tide cycles, all of Fenwick Island, except the highest dune areas was repeatedly washed over by storm waves superimposed on a storm surge measuring 2-meters high. Property damage in Ocean City was estimated at $7.5 million. Given the dense development of the island over the last 20 years, damage from a similar storm would today be hundreds of millions of dollars.

Figure 7A The beaches at Ocean City, Maryland, are a popular vacation spot for many people who live in the heavily populated Atlantic Seaboard of eastern United States. Large amounts of construction are at risk along the beaches of the United States form cyclonic storms.

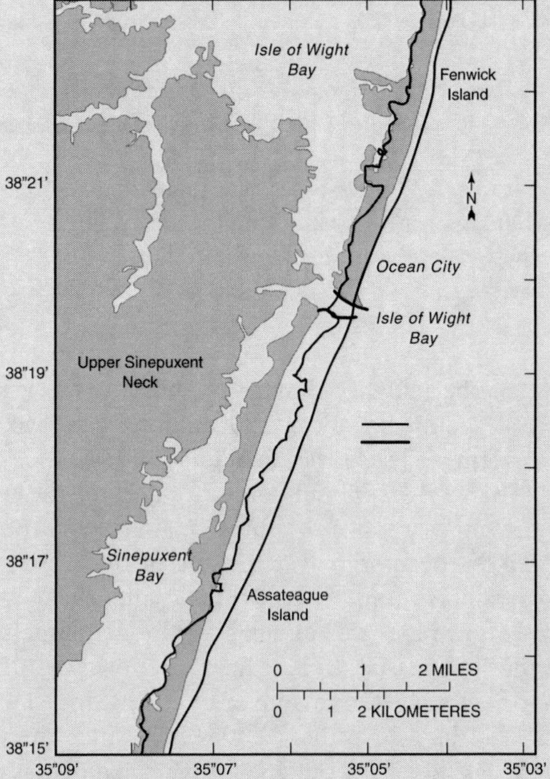

Figure 7B The natural sediment transport along the Fenwick Island-Assateague Island region has been altered by the construction of two large jetties at Ocean City Inlet. The landward shift of the southern barrier island was caused by a change in the longshore currents in the area.

Hard Stabilization

Two types of hard stabilization are often used. The first type interrupts the flow of sediment along the beach. These structures include **groins** (**Figures 7.28** and **29**) and **jetties** (**Figure 7.30**), built at right angles to the beach to trap sand and widen the beach. The second type interrupts the force of the waves. **Seawalls** are built parallel to the coastline to protect structures on the beach (**Figures 7.31**) by allowing waves to crash against it and preventing them from running up the beach. **Breakwaters** serve a similar purpose, but are built offshore parallel to the beach (**Figure 7.32**), again preventing the force of the waves from reaching the beach and any structures.

While hard stabilization usually works for its intended purpose, it does cause sediment to be redistributed along the coast. A breakwater, for example, causes wave refraction, and alters the flow of the longshore current. Sediment is trapped behind the breakwater, and the waves become focused on another part of the beach where they can cause significant erosion (Figure 7.32). Similarly, because groins and jetties trap sediment, areas in the downdrift direction are not resupplied with sediment by the longshore current, and beaches are eroded and become narrower in the downdrift direction.

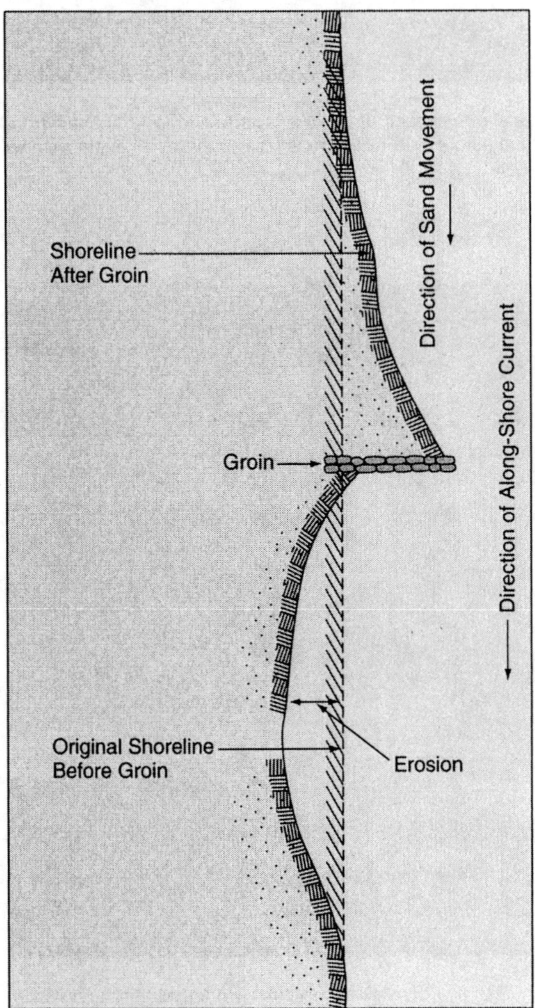

Figure 7.28 The effects of constructing a groin on a beach are that portions of the beach undergo erosion while others down drift experience erosion.

Soft Stabilization

Soft stabilization is primarily accomplished by adding sediment to the coastline which is called **beach nourishment**. This is usually done by dredging sediment from offshore and pumping it onto the coastline. Adding sediment is necessary when erosion removes too much sediment, however, because the erosive forces are still operating, additional sediment will need to be periodically replenished at continuing expense (**Figure 7.33**). Less invasive approaches include construction of access walkways and steps to reduce erosion of fragile dunes, as well as planting and protection of well-rooted vegetation.

Abandonment

Protecting ourselves from coastal hazards, such as beach erosion and coastal flooding, requires long-term strategic planning. Should we continue to attempt to defend the coasts from rising seas and ever larger storms? Or do we recognize awesome power of natural processes and strategically abandon the coast? Both methods are very costly and decisions will most likely require passage of governmental

Courtesy of David M. Best

Figure 7.29 This groin along the English Channel is constructed along a beach that consists of pebbles and cobbles rather than sand.

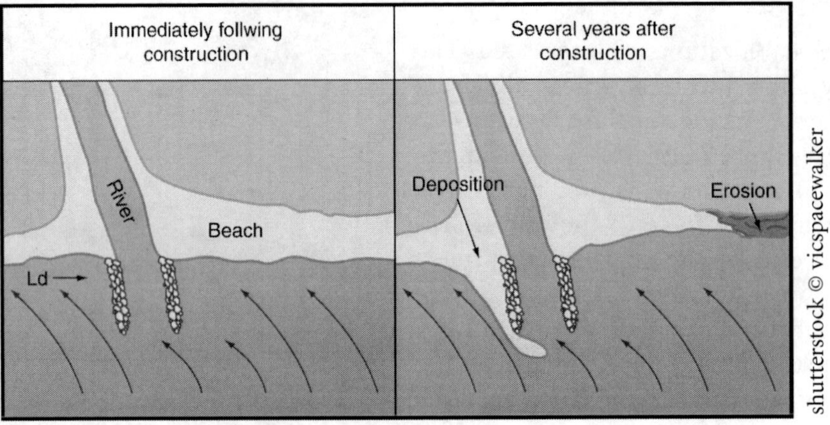

Figure 7.30 Jetties are extensions of pre-existing channels or river channels. Notice how depositional patterns change and sand begins to migrate around the jetty, eventually becoming a hazard to the entrance to the river.

Figure 7.31 This rock sea wall is built to absorb the energy of storm waves coming off the ocean. Unfortunately this feature removes the possibility of having a recreational beach.

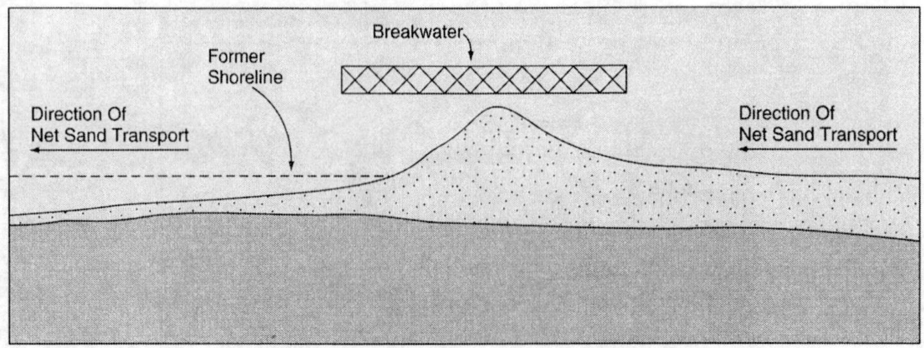

Figure 7.32 The construction of a breakwater off shore and parallel to the shoreline creates a buildup of sand that extends from the shoreline out to the breakwater.

Figure 7.33 The replenishment of beach sands is key to maintaining the health of the shoreline. Each year millions of cubic yards of sand are added to coastal regions to maintain the balance between the ocean and the land.

regulations. Presently, public policies are encouraging the development of hazardous areas by providing federal flood-insurance and disaster relief programs which encourages homeowners and businesses to rebuild after a disaster.

Many coastal geologists believe that instead of rebuilding our eroding beaches, we should return more of them to public use after they are devastated by a storm. Examples of such public coastal resources are the National Seashores, such as Cape Cod in Massachusetts, Padre Island in Texas, Hatteras in North Carolina, and Point Reyes in California. National Seashores are kept in as natural a condition as possible for all to enjoy. Storms will continue to damage their roads, parking lots, bathhouses, and concessions, but these can inexpensively be rebuilt, compared to the cost of restoring high-rise hotels, condominiums, and beach homes.

SUMMARY

Coastlines are among Earth's most geologically active environments and are continually changing because of the dynamic interaction between the water and the land. Coastal changes occur on two very different time scales. Short-term change is largely due to seasonal severe storm events, while long-term changes are due to slow sea-level rise. Waves, longshore currents, and tidal currents interact with the geologic structures and plate tectonic processes of the coast to shape coastlines into a multitude of landforms.

Waves are formed by wind forces acting on the water surface and transfers energy in circular motion through the water. Motion in a wave ceases at a depth equal to one-half its wavelength. As a wave enters shallow water, its wave base intersects the bottom and the wave begins to break. Most of the energy carried within a wave is then released within the surf zone by breakers. Sediment is moved along the shoreline by longshore drift and into and out of tidal inlets by tidal currents. Beaches are accumulations of sediment along the shoreline.

Coastal storms and hurricanes are inherent natural hazards along most U.S. shorelines. As population and development continues to increase, storm damage has risen dramatically. Many coasts are affected by multiple hazards such as storm erosion, landslides, tsunami, and coastal flooding. Many scientists see evidence that sea level is rising, that storms and hurricanes will continue to occur as frequently as they do today, and that their magnitude may increase as global temperature rise.

Human interference with coastal processes and landform development is causing serious problems. Seawall construction protects structures against wave attack, but causes beach erosion. Groins cause the updrift beach to grow, but the downdrift beaches erode. Breakwaters and jetties prevent erosion of beaches in some areas, but their effect is to cause sand to move to other positions along the beach and waterfront. Hard and soft stabilization of beaches is only a short-term solution in the overall process.

REFERENCES AND SUGGESTED READINGS

Bush, D. M., O. H. Pilkey, Jr., and W. J. Neal. 1996. *Living by the Rules of the Sea.* Durham, NC: Duke University Press.

Coch, N. K., 1995, *Geohazards, Natural and Human.* Prentice Hall: Upper Saddle River, NJ.

Douglas, B. C., and W. R. Peltier, 2002. The Puzzle of Global Sea-Level Rise. *Physics Today* 55 (3): 35–41.

Komar, P. D. 1997. *The Pacific Northwest Coast:* Duke University Press: Durham, NC.

Morton, R. A. 2003. An overview of coastal land loss: with emphasis on the southeastern United States. U.S. Geological Survey, Open File Report 03-337.

Thompson, G.R. and Turk, J., 2007, *Earth Science and the Environment.* Thomson & Brooks/Cole: Belmont, CA.

Trujillo, A. P. and H. V. Thurmann. 2008. *Essentials of Oceanography.* Pearson Prentice Hall: Upper Saddle River, NJ.

Williams, S. J., K. Dodd, and K. K. Cohn, 1990. Coasts in Crisis. U.S. Geological Survey Circular 1075.

WEB SITES FOR FURTHER REFERENCE

http://solidearth.jpl.nasa.gov/PAGES/sea01.html
http://coastal.er.usgs.gov/hurricanes/cch.html
http://coastalchange.ucsd.edu/index.html
http://pubs.usgs.gov/of/2003/of03-337/
http://marine.usgs.gov/kb/views/cch/index.php

QUESTIONS FOR THOUGHT

1. How are waves that affect coastlines generated?
2. Explain longshore currents and how they cause sediment transport on beaches.
3. Describe what happens to waves as they shoal in shallow water.
4. What are the main causes of coastal erosion?
5. What are the main coastal hazards?
6. What are barrier islands, and how do they form?
7. Describe ways in which the relative elevation of land and sea may change.
8. What is the present trend in global sea level and what effect does it have on the coasts?
9. Describe the motion of a water particle as a wave passes.
10. Why are beaches often called rivers of sand?
11. What is wave refraction, and how does it affect coast erosion and deposition?
12. What influence do tides have on coastal processes and hazards?

Now it is time to examine some other sites from around the world. To do this, go up to the top of the page and click on Pick a different site. This time go to Alphabetic list of all tidal height sites. Once there, select P and find Provincetown, MA.

Location	What is the daily tide range? (include units of feet or meters)	What is the monthly tidal range?	What is the magnitude classification of the tide?	What is the cyclic classification of the tide?
Provincetown, MA				

Next find the following locationsand answer the same four questions you did for Provincetown:

Location	What is the daily tide range? (include units of feet or meters)	What is the monthly tidal range?	What is the magnitude classification of the tide?	What is the cyclic classification of the tide?
Gisborne, New Zealand				
Charlotte Amalie, St. Thomas, Virgin Islands				
San Francisco, California				
Busselton, Australia				
Hantsport, Nova Scotia				

In this report, in addition to your answers on the tables, print out the monthly tidal plots for each of the places you have looked at (six graphs in addition to the two for Nags Head).

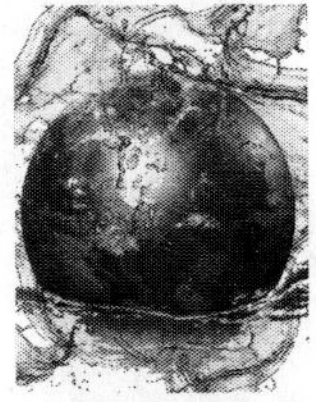

WATER PLANET EXERCISE 9

Name: ___________________________

Waves

1. Using information from lecture or your textbook, fill in this chart comparing wave processes:

	Regular Beach Waves	Rogue Waves	Tsunami Waves
How are they created?			
Where are they found? (at sea, along coasts, where in the world?)			
What size can they reach and where are they noticeable? (at sea, at beach, inland?)			
What kinds of materials and landforms can they create, move or affect?			
Are there any warning signs or indications for each wave type?			

2. What, if any, is the relationship between tides, waves, and surface currents?

____

____

____

3. Which process—tides, waves, currents—are you most affected by in your daily life and why?

____

____

WATER PLANET VIDEO RESPONSE 3

Name: ______________________________

"Tsunami: The Wave That Shook the World"

This video recounts the tale of scientists monitoring the tsunami generated by the 9.0 magnitude earthquake off the coast of Indonesia in December 2004 and examines the reasons for the widespread devastation. A lack of physical warning systems and also hazard education about tsunamis greatly worsened the death toll, but led to improvements that were adapted before Japan's 2011 tsunami.

1. Why are places around the Pacific Ocean susceptible to tsunamis? Is there a warning system there?

2. How do tsunamis form in the ocean? Are they noticeable in the open ocean? Are they related to "tides" when called tidal waves?

3. What can tsunamis do, in terms of damage?

4. How can people survive them? Are there any natural warnings you can detect and respond to?

5. Why was the2004 Indian Ocean tsunami so devastating (other than a lack of warning)? What human behavior increasedthe risk of dying on beaches? What part was due to culture, building styles, etc.?

6. Why was there no warning system in the Indian Ocean in 2004? Would a warning system have helped everyone at risk around the Indian Ocean? How does a warning system operate?

Chapter 8

GLACIERS

Glaciers form in areas of Earth where more snow falls in the winter than what melts away in the summer, so year after year new snow keeps piling on top of old snow, which turns the bottom layers of it into ice. The weight of continued accumulation eventually causes the ice to move outward from its area of accumulation producing a moving glacier.

Glaciers form in two areas: high latitudes and high altitudes. The two types of glaciers—***continental glaciers*** and ***mountain glaciers***—reflect the division between formation areas. Both types of glaciers produce distinctive landforms.

Glacial periods have occurred on Earth for hundreds of millions of years. The last period of glaciation, which began about 1 to 2 million years ago, is known as the Pleistocene Ice Age. There were four major glacial advances during the Pleistocene, and there might have been as many as 30 or 40 smaller advances. The four major ice advances (from oldest to youngest) were the Nebraskan Glacier, the Kansan Glacier, the Illinoian Glacier, and the Wisconsin Glacier, which only left the state of Indiana about 10,000 to 14,000 years ago. Periods of warmth known as ***interglacial stages*** occupied the time spaces between the major advances. Today, we might still be living in the Pleistocene Ice Age; perhaps the warm climate we are now experiencing is an interglacial stage between the last glacier, the Wisconsin, and the next glacier yet to arrive.

CONTINENTAL GLACIERS

Continental glaciers, as the name implies, cover large land areas. Both the modern Greenland and Antarctic ice sheets are continental glaciers. The continental glaciers today are found in the high latitudes, but about 20,000 years ago there was an ice sheet covering the northern half of Indiana, including the site that Indianapolis now occupies. The Wisconsin Glacier was the last Ice Age glacier to invade Indiana and the northern United States. It originated in the Hudson Bay area in Canada. A second ice sheet covered much of northern Europe at the same time; it was centered on the Gulf of Bothnia between the countries of Sweden and Finland. The area of the United States (excluding Alaska and Hawaii) that was glaciated by at least one of the four continental glaciers of the Pleistocene Ice Age is shown in Figure 8.1.

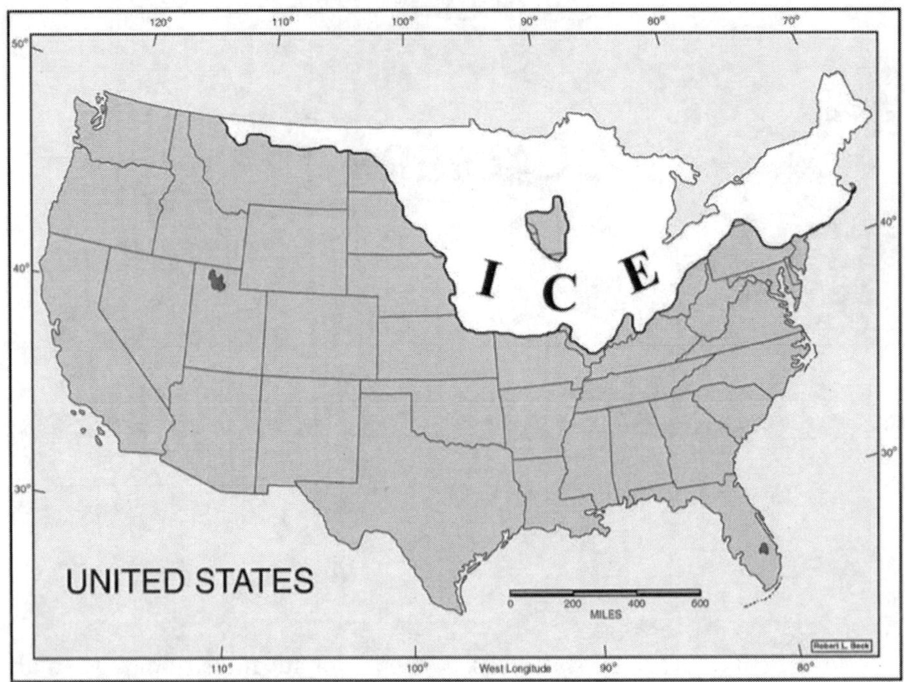

Figure 8.1 Area of the U.S. Covered by the Pleistocene Continental Glaciers.

As continental glaciers advance outward from their area of origin, they scrape off the soil and loose material they come in contact with. Some of these substances will become incorporated into the ice, but others, including large rocks, will be pushed by the ice in front of it much like a bulldozer moves objects of various sizes. If you ever have a chance to walk on a glacier, you will probably be able to see some of the loose debris carried by it (Fig. 8.2).

It is necessary to distinguish between glacial ***movement*** and glacial ***advance***. Glaciers **move** when the weight of the ice at the center causes the ice underneath to expand outward, but if the glacier is melting at the same rate of speed the ice is moving, then the glacier won't be advancing (pushing into new territory). If a glacier, however, is moving faster than it is melting, then it will be advancing into a previously unglaciated space. This brings up an important point

Figure 8.2. Debris Carried by a Mountain Glacier, Alaska.

concerning glaciers—they are either in equilibrium or disequilibrium with their climate.

A glacier in equilibrium with its climate will neither be advancing nor retreating, but it will still be moving! It will act like a big conveyor belt picking up rocks and loose material beneath the ice and transporting those substances to the edge of the glacier where they will be thrown out to produce a landform known as a ***moraine***; which is a long, linear hill along the edge of the ice (Figs. 8.3a and 8.3b). If the moraine is at the

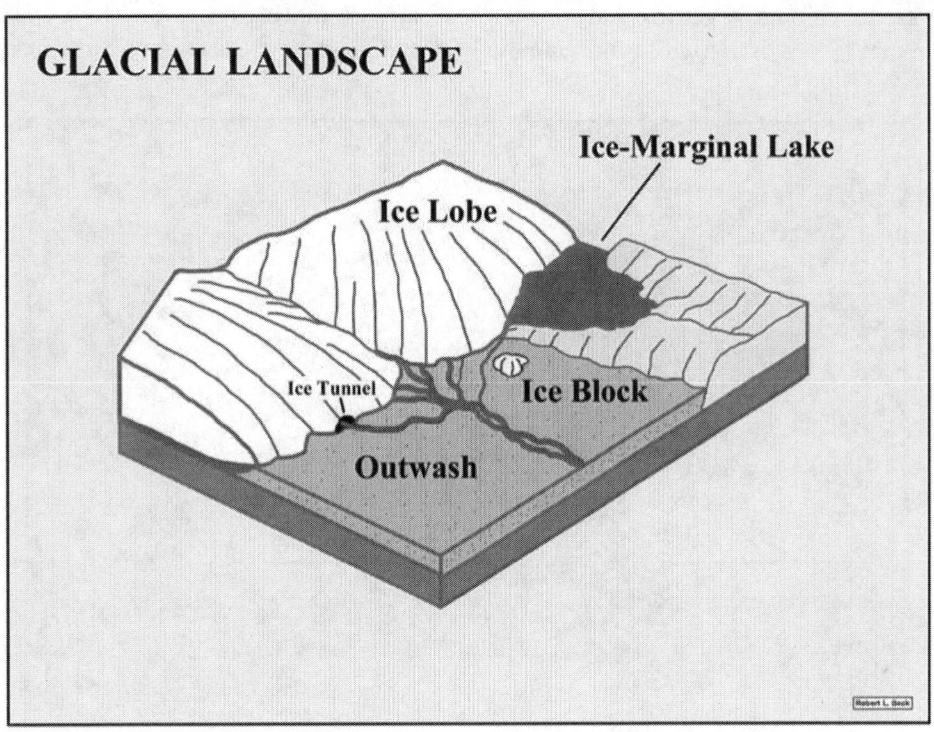

Figure 8.3a Glacial Landscape.

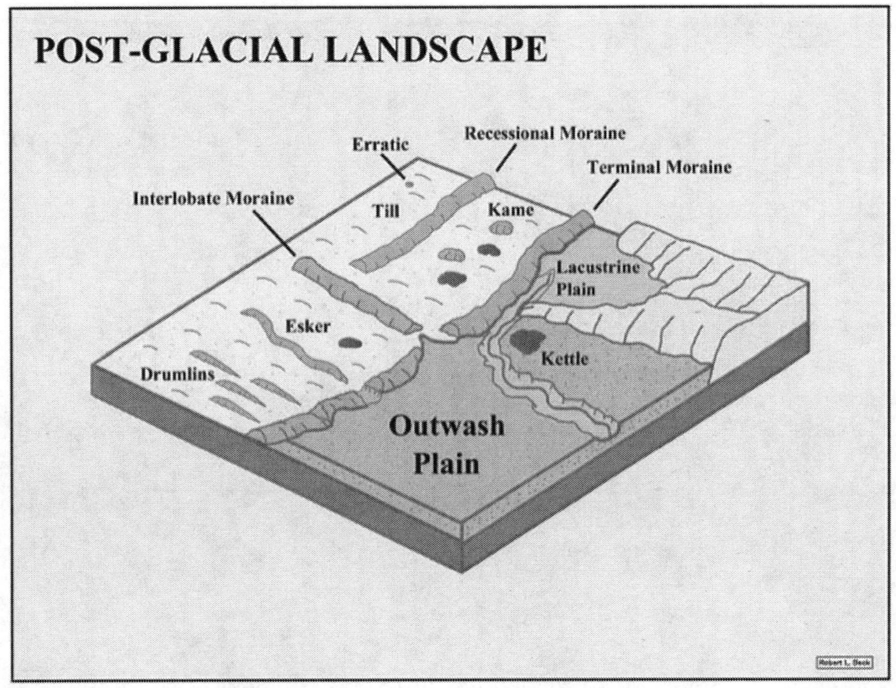

Figure 8.3b Postglacial Landscape.

line of maximum glacial advance, it is then known as a ***terminal moraine*** (Fig 8.3b).

If the glacier is in disequilibrium with its climate, it will either be advancing or retreating. If a glacier is advancing, its ice will be moving as the climate is getting colder, but if it is retreating, its ice might or might not be moving as the climate is getting warmer. For example, assume that the ice of a glacier is moving but that the climate is getting warmer. The warming climate causes the glacier to be in disequilibrium with its climate, so it starts to retreat because its ice is melting faster than it is moving, but it is still moving! Glacially borne debris will be pushed out the front of the glacier by the moving ice. ***Recessional moraines*** are produced by glaciers that are retreating (Figs. 8.3b and 8.4). As the climate warms, the glacier retreats back in the direction

Figure 8.4. Recessional Moraine, Northern Indiana.

Figure 8.5. Esker, British Columbia.

of its area of origin a few miles—to the point that it is back in equilibrium with its climate, this allows a recessional moraine to form, because the ice is moving but the glacier itself is not advancing.

Continental glaciers usually do not advance as a single sheet of ice. Instead they advance as separate ***lobes*** of ice that eventually might collide with each other. Sand, gravel, boulders, and other debris collects in the depressional areas between lobes. When the glacier melts this debris emerges as an ***interlobate moraine***, which points in the direction of the ice movement (Fig. 8.3b).

Streams flowing in, or on top of, the glacier also deposit earth materials that have been wrested from the ice by the action of liquid water. These streams often flow through tunnels in the ice, so the stream deposits are long and linear like the tunnels. When the ice melts, the stream deposited material emerges as a long, sinuous hill known as an ***esker*** (Figs. 8.3a, 8.3b, and 8.5).

When a glacier retreats rapidly or stagnates (stops moving), the material in the ice will be dropped to form ***ground moraine***, which is also known as glacial ***till*** (Fig. 8.3b). Till deposits tend to flatten out the topography of the areas in which they occur, producing ***till plains***. The central one-third of Indiana, including Marion County, lies in a till plain. In Indiana this plain is known as the "Tipton Till Plain" (Fig. 8.6).

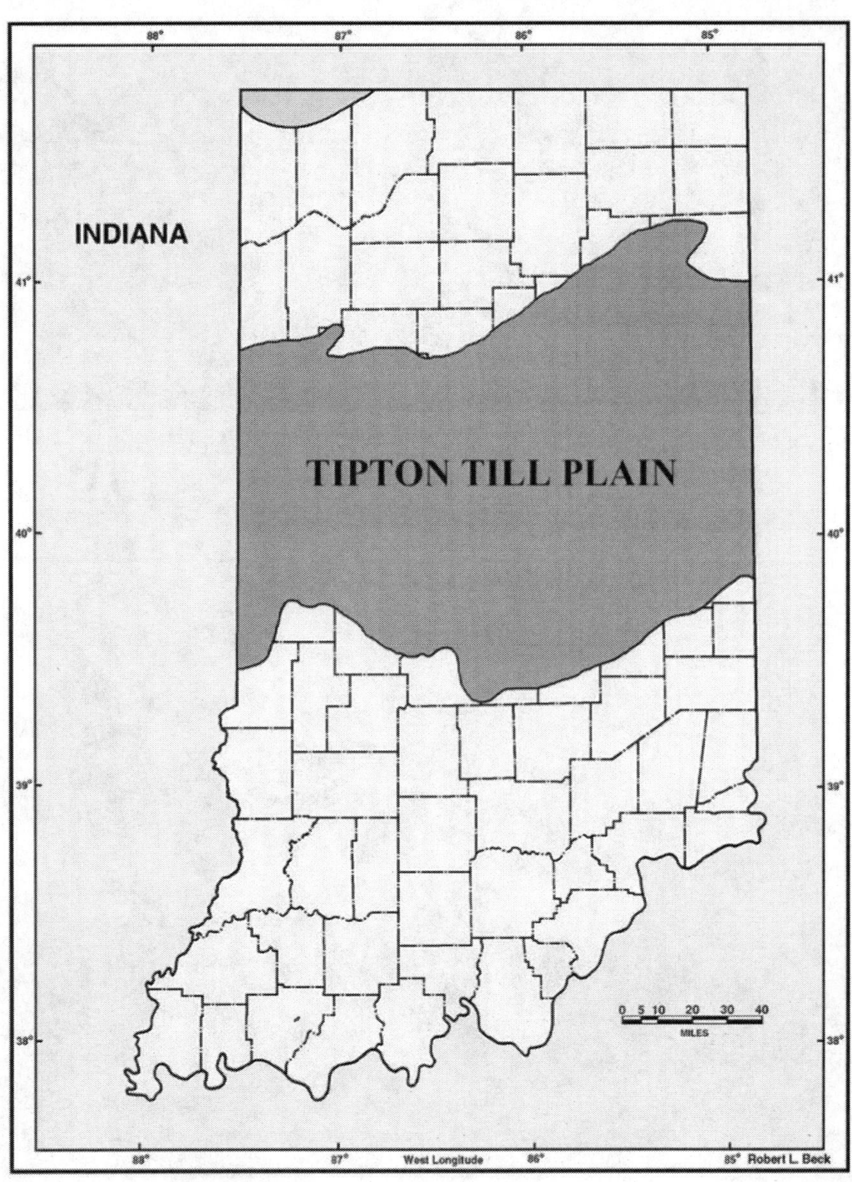

Figure 8.6 Tipton Till Plain.

It is named for Tipton County, the most featureless county in the state, which is situated near the center of the plain.

The till deposits of central Indiana have a lot of clay in them. During rainy periods the clay absorbs water and swells up, but during dry periods it loses most of its water and shrinks. ***Swell and swale topography*** is the name given to the topography of clay- dominated till plains. These plains are not totally flat, for when the clay swells up it produces a slightly undulating surface (Fig. 8.7). The swales are the wide, shallow troughs between the swells.

Stagnating and retreating glaciers leave blocks of ice strewn about the landscape (Fig. 8.3a) that often

Figure 8.7 Swell and Swale Topography, Tipton Till Plain, Central Indiana.

Figure 8.8 Kettle, Northern Indiana.

take a long time to melt, but when they do, the areas that they occupied become depressions, which are surrounded by till and morainal deposits. Water often fills these depressions, known as ***kettles***, to form small glacially formed lakes and ponds (Figs. 8.3b and 8.8).

Kettles are frequently found near ***kames***, which are conical hills produced by glacial meltwater deposition in close association with ice stagnation (Fig. 8.9). Kettles so often occur in conjunction with kames that the phrase, "kettle and kame topography" is commonly

Figure 8.9 Kame, Northern Indiana.

Figure 8.10 Kettle and Kame Topography, British Columbia.

used to describe the physical landscape where they exist (Fig. 8.10).

Water flowing off a glacier sometimes deposits huge amounts of sand and gravel in front of it to form an ***outwash plain*** (Figs. 8.3a and 8.3b). Such a plain is found between Indianapolis and Chicago in the vicinity of Rensselaer, Indiana.

Continental glaciers also produce ***drumlins,*** which are long, linear deposits that point in the direction the ice was moving (Figs. 8.3b and 8.11). The processes that produce drumlins are not known, but it is suspected they form when glacial ice reshapes deposits left by earlier glaciers.

Large rocks and boulders dropped by a glacier are known as ***erratics*** (Fig. 8.12). Erratics might be found

Figure 8.11 Drumlin, Northern Michigan.

Figure 8.12 Erratic, Central Indiana.

individually or in groups. In Indiana, they often mark the position of moraines. Farmers in the state pile them up in the corners of fields to keep them out of the way of farm machinery (Fig. 8.13). The fields behind our house in rural Putnam County were filled with crystalline erratics when we moved here in 2001. Indiana's bedrock consists of sedimentary rocks, so I knew these rocks had to have been carried in by a glacier and dropped when the ice melted. The abundance of them leads me to believe our house is situated on a moraine, probably the terminal moraine of the Wisconsin glacier. I asked the landowner if I could collect them to use around my flowerbeds. He readily agreed, for I was doing him a favor by supplying the labor to remove

Figure 8.13 Pile of Erratics, Northern Indiana.

Figure 8.14 Mountain Glacier, Alaska.

them from the fields. They are outstanding substitutes for plastic or wooden edging, for they don't rot, they are part of the natural landscape, and they are quite colorful and interesting.

MOUNTAIN GLACIERS

Glaciers that form in high altitudes are known as mountain glaciers, but some people prefer to call them ***alpine glaciers*** or ***valley glaciers*** (Fig. 8.14). These glaciers originate in ***cirques***, which are bowl-shaped depressions high in the mountains (Fig. 8.15). The growth of the glacier eventually causes its ice to move out of the cirque and down into a valley, hence the name ***valley glacier***.

Like continental glaciers, mountain glaciers produce distinctive landforms. Erosional, toothlike ridges that separate valley glaciers are known as ***arêtes*** (Fig. 8.16).

Figure 8.15 Cirques, Grand Tetons.

Figure 8.16 Arêtes, Western Canada.

If several cirques erode into a mountain from many sides, the isolated mountain peak is then known as a ***horn*** (Fig. 8.17). If two cirques erode through the ridge separating them they create a mountain pass known as a ***col*** (Fig. 8.17).

Glaciers moving through mountain valleys erode into the sides of the valley causing them to become quite wide. After the ice melts away it is easy to see where a mountain glacier has been, for the V-shaped valleys that were initially shaped by stream erosion will be replaced by ***U-shaped valleys*** shaped by glacial erosion (Fig. 8.18).

Glacial erosion of mountain valleys also tends to straighten stream eroded valleys. If the glacier melts

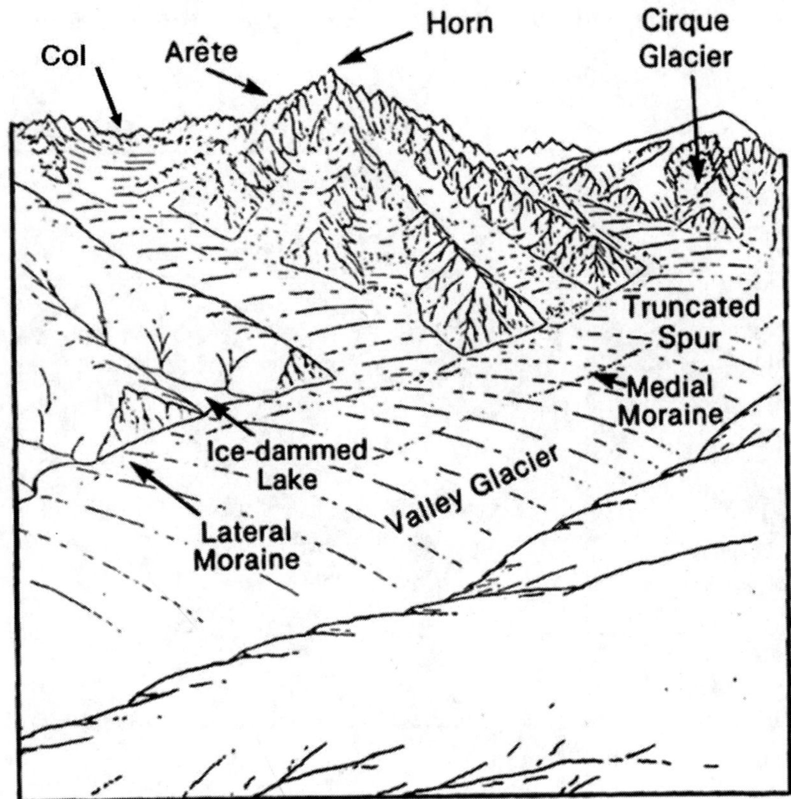

Figure 8.17 Mountain Glacial Landforms, Western Canada. Image is from http://rst.gsfc.nasa.gov/Sect17/Sect17_5a.html.

Figure 8.18 U-shaped Valley, Western Canada.

away completely, the cirque where the glacier originated is likely to have a depressional area near the center of it that was gouged out by the glacier. These depressional areas are usually filled with water to form high mountain lakes known as ***tarns*** (Fig. 8.19).

As a glacier moves down a valley it might run into another glacier that originated in a different cirque. The glaciers then join to form a larger glacier known as a ***piedmont glacier*** (Fig. 8.20). Often small glaciers joining a larger one do so at a high elevation in the mountains. The melting of the ice might reveal that the small glaciers formed in high valleys vertically separated from the valley in which the larger glacier was situated. These high valleys are then known as ***hanging valleys***.

Terminal moraines, recessional moraines, interlobate moraines, ground moraine, and outwash plains are also produced by mountain glaciers. ***Lateral moraines***, however, are only associated with mountain glaciers. These moraines form along the side of the glacier where debris lodges between the ice and the valley walls.

Figure 8.19 Tarn, Colorado.

Figure 8.20 Piedmont Glacier, Western Canada.

YOU SHOULD NOW BE ABLE TO:

- Explain why glaciers move
- List the two main types of glaciers and relate them to their areas of formation
- Discuss the *interglacial stage* concept
- Describe the difference between *glacial movement* and *glacial advance*
- Identify, and briefly discuss, ten types of landforms produced by *continental glaciers*
- Identify, and briefly discuss, eight types of landforms produced by *mountain glaciers*

Figure 8.21 A white skunk, Putnam County, Indiana, 2007.

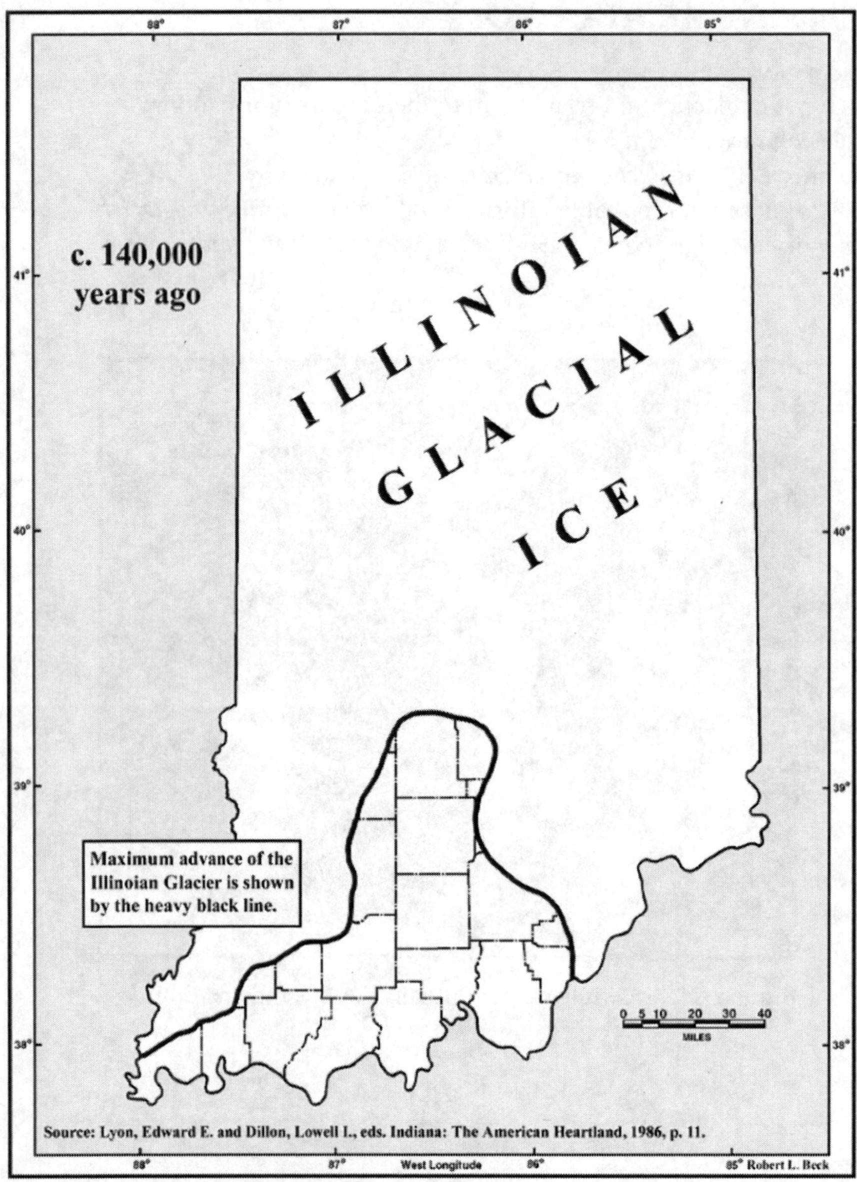

Figure 8.22 Maximum advance of the Illinoian glacier in Indiana. The Illinoian glacier was the third of the four major Pleistocene Ice Age glaciers, and it advanced farther south than any other Ice Age glacier. The hills of southern Indiana kept it out of the south-central part of the state. The lack of hills in the lower Wabash River valley allowed it to advance as far south as the 38th parallel in Indiana and Illinois.

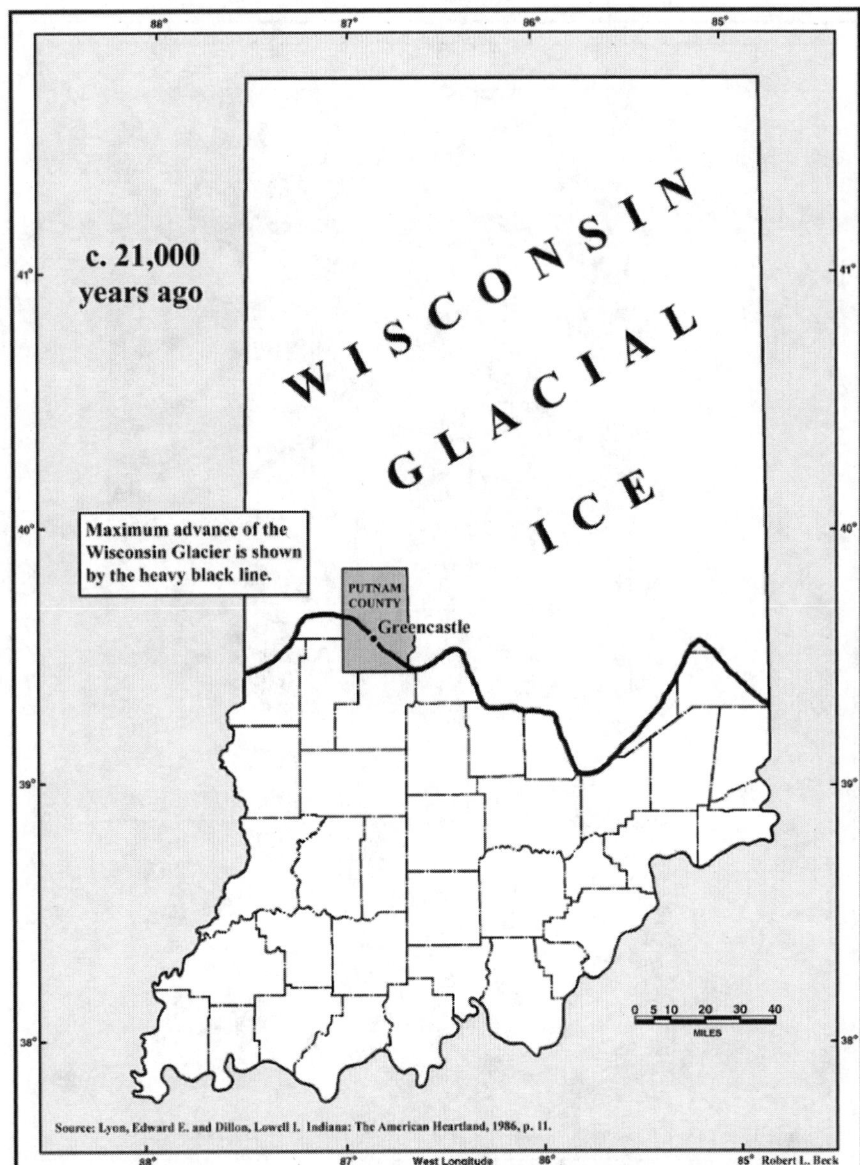

Figure 8.23 Maximum advance of the Wisconsin glacier in Indiana. The Wisconsin glacier was the fourth and last of the major Pleistocene Ice Age glaciers. One can see that southwestern Putnam County was covered by Illinoian ice, but not Wisconsin ice. The Sangamon interglacial stage was situated between the Illinoian and Wisconsin glaciers. The Wisconsin glacier was the one that created the Tipton Till Plain (Fig. 25-6). Northern and eastern Putnam County has gently rolling swell and swale topography, but southwestern Putnam County is hilly. The city of Greencastle is situated on the line of maximum advance.

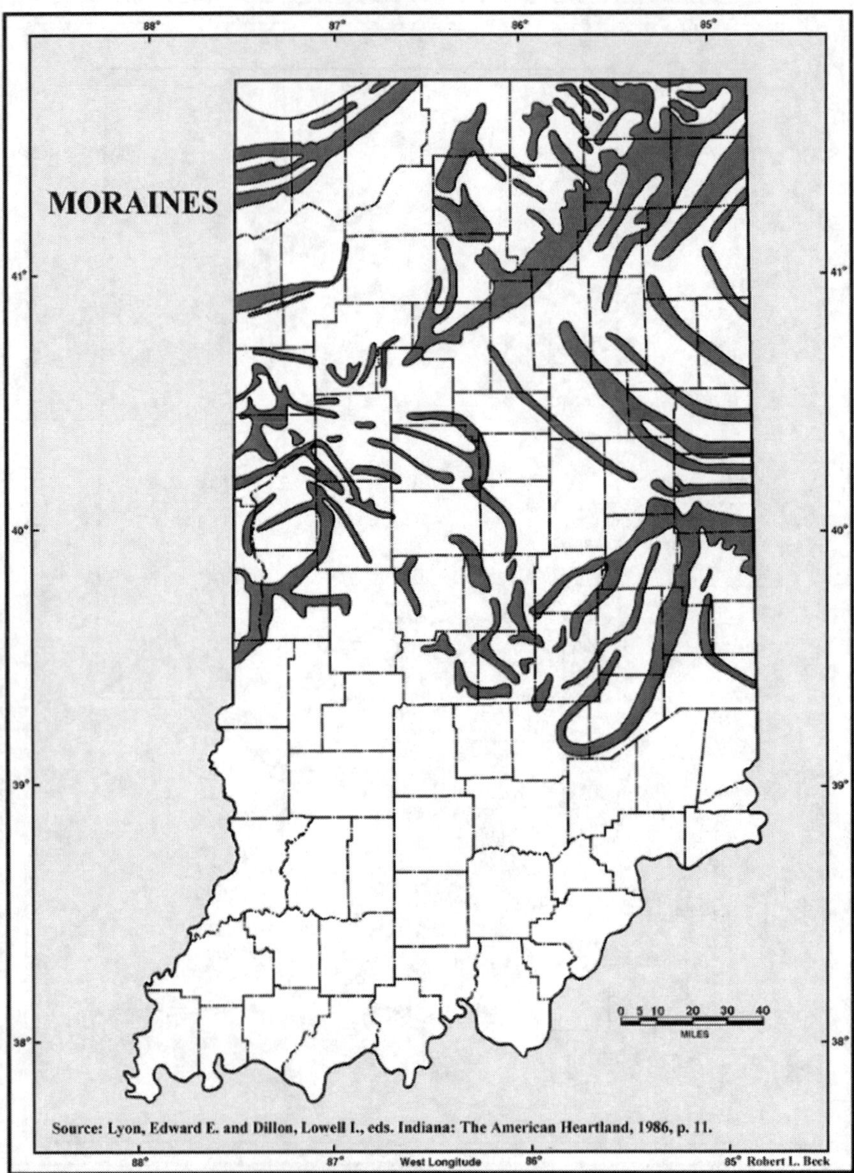

Figure 8.24 The recessional, interlobate, and terminal moraine deposits of Indiana are a legacy of the Wisconsin glacier. Many of these deposits are hard to see in the field, for often only subtle differences separate a morainal deposit from the areas of the landscape around it.

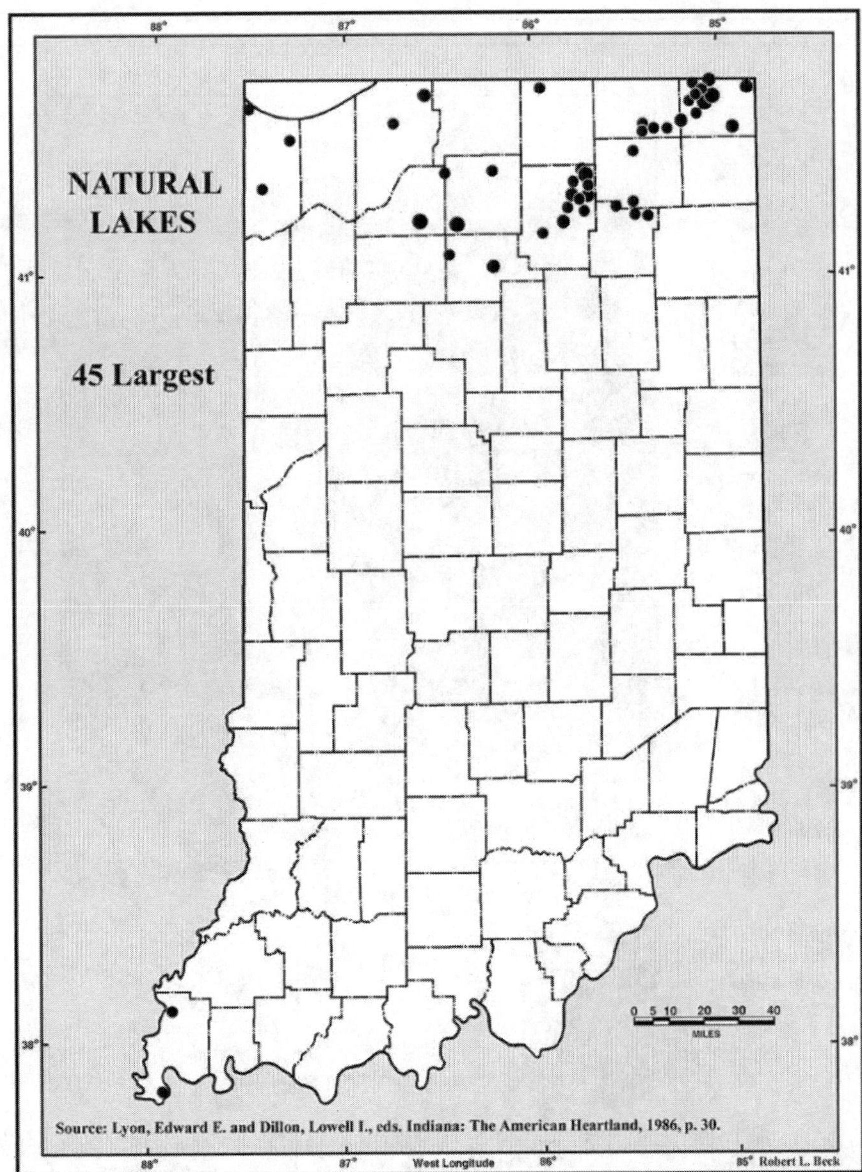

Figure 8.25 Forty-three of the 45 largest natural lakes of Indiana are a legacy of the Wisconsin glacier. The two lakes in Posey County, in the southwestern corner of the state, are oxbow lakes.

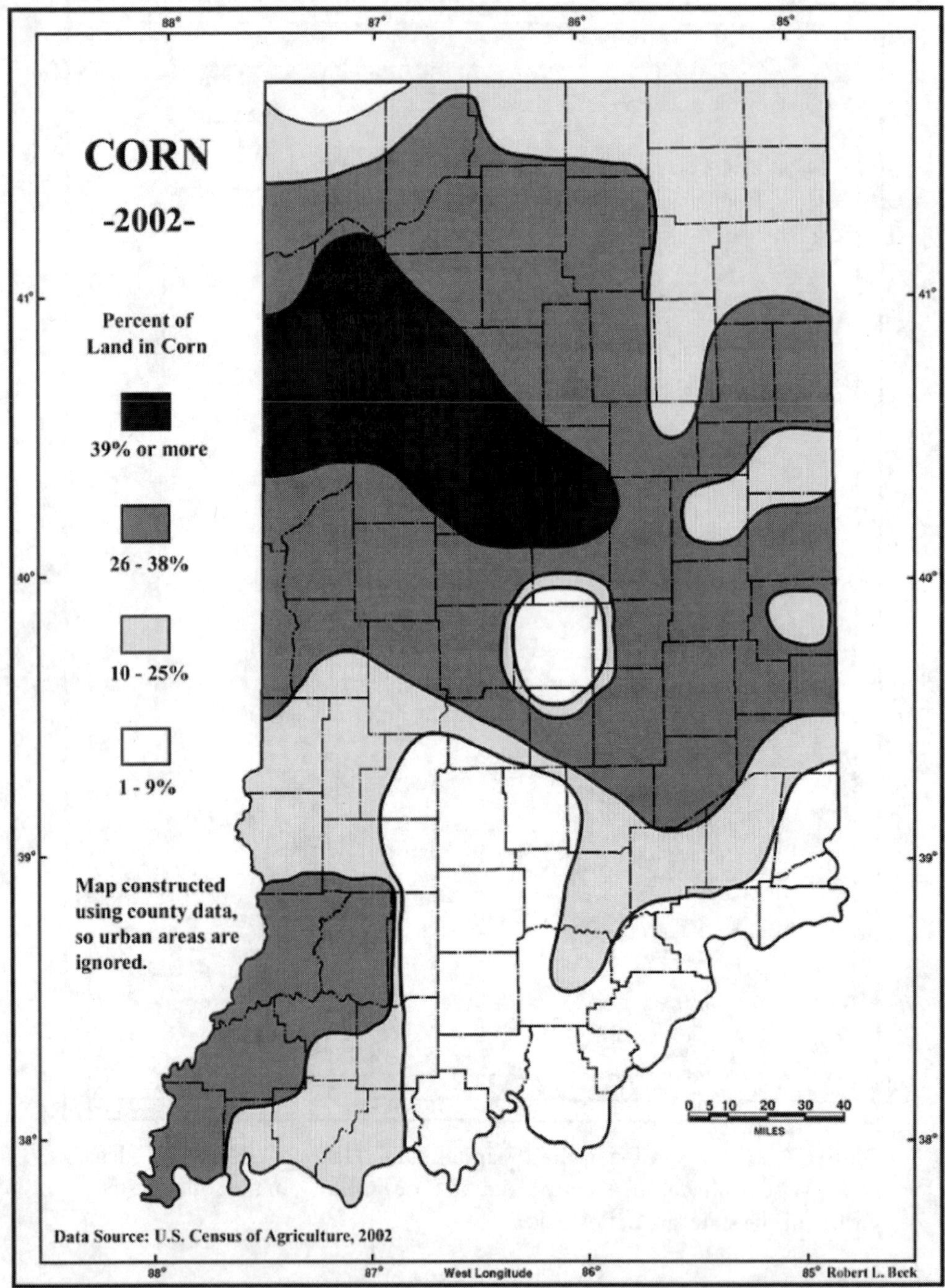

Figure 8.26 The Corn Belt stretches across Indiana from Ohio to Illinois and thence into Iowa and Nebraska. The southern margin of the Corn Belt in Indiana closely matches the southern margin of the Wisconsin glacier. Soils derived from glacial material in Indiana tend to be fertile, so the strong agricultural economy of the state is directly related to the physical geography of the state. One cannot fully understand the distribution of agricultural production on Earth while being blissfully ignorant of physical geography.

WATER PLANET VIDEO RESPONSE 5

Name: ______________________________

"Mystery of the Megaflood"

The scientific process often reveals unexpected results and this video looks at a flood that seemed to be of unimaginable size that in fact resulted from episodes of past glaciation.

1. What are the unusual landscape features in the U.S. Scablands?

2. What caused the flood that created the Scablands region? When did this event occur?

3. Why was this theory controversial?

4. What evidence now exists to support this theory?

5. What processes created the giant potholes in the valley floor?

6. How did this flood compare to the regular floods experienced around the world today?

7. Is a similar flood possible today anywhere in the world? Why or why not?

Chapter 9

FLOODING AND STREAMS

All climates, especially arid ones, are prone to flooding. Every year, numerous floods affect millions of people throughout the world. Weather systems can stall over an area and generate copious amounts of rainfall, causing streams and rivers to overflow their banks when too much water enters a drainage basin. Rapid melting of snow and ice also create abnormal water discharge. Areas that are most affected tend to lie toward the lower portions of a river system, as the topography there is less steep and the increased downstream flow cannot readily move water away from the affected region.

Floods can also be the result of poor urban planning or dam construction that causes water to flow unexpectedly in places where it was not meant to go. Coastal regions become flooded when maritime storms land ashore. The strong winds of hurricanes, cyclones, and typhoons generate storm surges that bring massive amounts of water inland, flooding low-lying areas. Tsunami although relatively rare, rapidly push sea water past beach zones, inflicting severe damage to communities in the path of the waves. Floods can also result from volcanic eruptions that melt snow and ice atop a volcano, the condition that contributed to the lahars of Mount St. Helens.

The U.S. Geological Survey (USGS) reports that flooding in the United States annually causes between 140 and 160 deaths and an average of almost $4 billion in damages. In many low-lying areas, home and landowners cannot purchase flood insurance and the losses they might sustain are not covered. Often the lower socioeconomic classes reside in these topographically lower locations and suffer immense losses in terms of property and human life. Although floods can be caused by storms, tsunamis, and volcanoes, this chapter will address flooding associated with streams.

STREAM PROCESSES

Earth's hydrosphere includes all water at or near the surface in addition to what is contained in the atmosphere. Water, which can be a liquid, a gas (water vapor), or a solid (ice), moves around in the **hydrologic cycle**—a continuous circulation of water around the globe. Solar energy drives this cycle; it stretches from the equator to the poles, where water movement is obviously slower but nevertheless part of the cycle.

Geologists define a **stream** as a body of water that flows within a confined channel on the surface. When several streams or **tributaries** join to produce a larger flowing body, the term **river** is then applied (**Figure 9.1**). Water that falls onto Earth's surface can produce **runoff**, which travels along the surface and ends up in a channel, or it can infiltrate into the ground, where it temporarily resides in underground collection areas before eventually finding its way into a stream system.

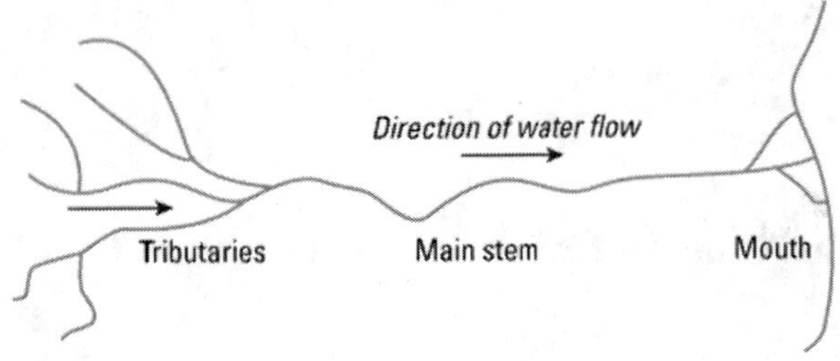

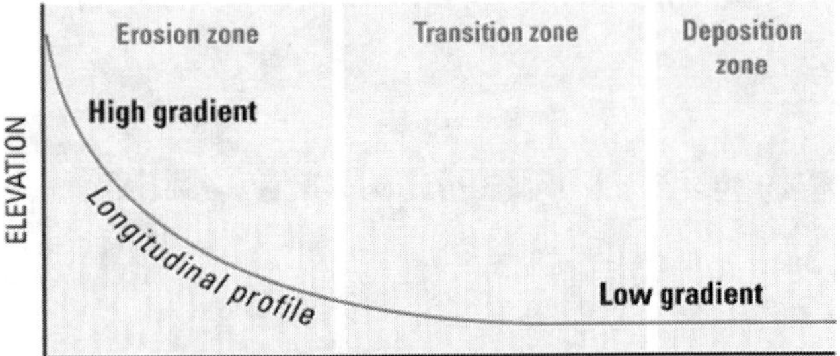

Figure 9.1 Streams flow from high to low elevations. In the upper portions, small streams form the tributary system to feed and create the trunk stream. The longitudinal profile shows the steep gradient, or slope, in the higher elevations becoming more gentle toward the mouth. Streams eventually feed into a sea or ocean.

In arid climates, infiltrated water often evaporates and reenters the hydrologic cycle as water vapor.

Drainage Basins

A **drainage basin** or **watershed** is an area on the surface that collects water that flows into a stream and forms a drainage pattern. Drainage divides, which are often ridges or a series of high points that divide downhill slopes, separate one watershed from its adjacent neighbors (**Figure 9.2**). The amount of water collected by a drainage system is dependent on the amount of precipitation, the size of the area, and the subsurface characteristics that control infiltration and runoff. As long as the amount of water flowing into streams and falling on the watershed is carried away by the existing system, water remains in the channels and does not present a problem.

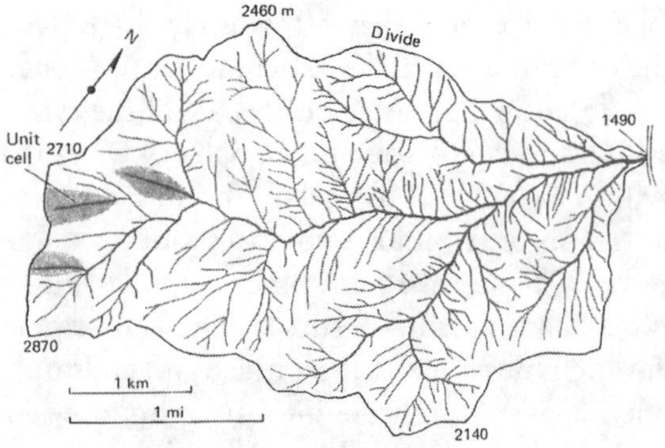

Figure 9.2 A watershed is outlined by its divide, which separates it from adjacent watersheds. Elevations are in meters. Notice how the stream patterns collect water and channel it into a larger stream downhill.

Think of a stream configuration as the transportation system that is moving water to some end point, either a temporary one, such as a lake, or the ultimate end point—a sea or an ocean. A stream begins to cut a channel into the landscape, thereby creating the "highway" that is allowing water to move through an area. Each channel has a cross sectional view, in which we see the width and depth of the channel. This area, coupled with the length of a particular stream segment and its drop in elevation, defines the volume or how much water is contained (and moved) by the stream and at what velocity (**Figure 9.3**). **Discharge** is the volume of water that flows downstream past a given point in a given period of time. We measure this volume in cubic feet per second (cfs) or cubic meters per second (cms), and the amount can vary widely depending on weather, surface conditions, and stream characteristics. The world's largest rivers move enormous volumes of water each second (**Table 9.1**). All of these rivers have very large watersheds and many of the rivers flow through regions that have wet, temperature climates.

Floodplain

A stream channel is bordered by its banks and the area to either side, which is termed the **floodplain**. When water spills over the banks, it is no longer moving in its channel. As it spreads out, the velocity of the water decreases rapidly, causing any sediment carried by the stream to be deposited. This process is repeated every time the stream floods. The continual buildup of sediment along the banks creates natural levees that increase in height, deepening the stream channel. Repetition of this process permits the stream to carry more water than before, because its cross-sectional area has increased. When water spills over onto the floodplain, it does not tend to drain back into the main river channel because the natural levees now act as a dam. This water slowly moves downhill on the floodplain until it finds a site where it can flow back into the main stream or off the floodplain (**Figure 9.4**).

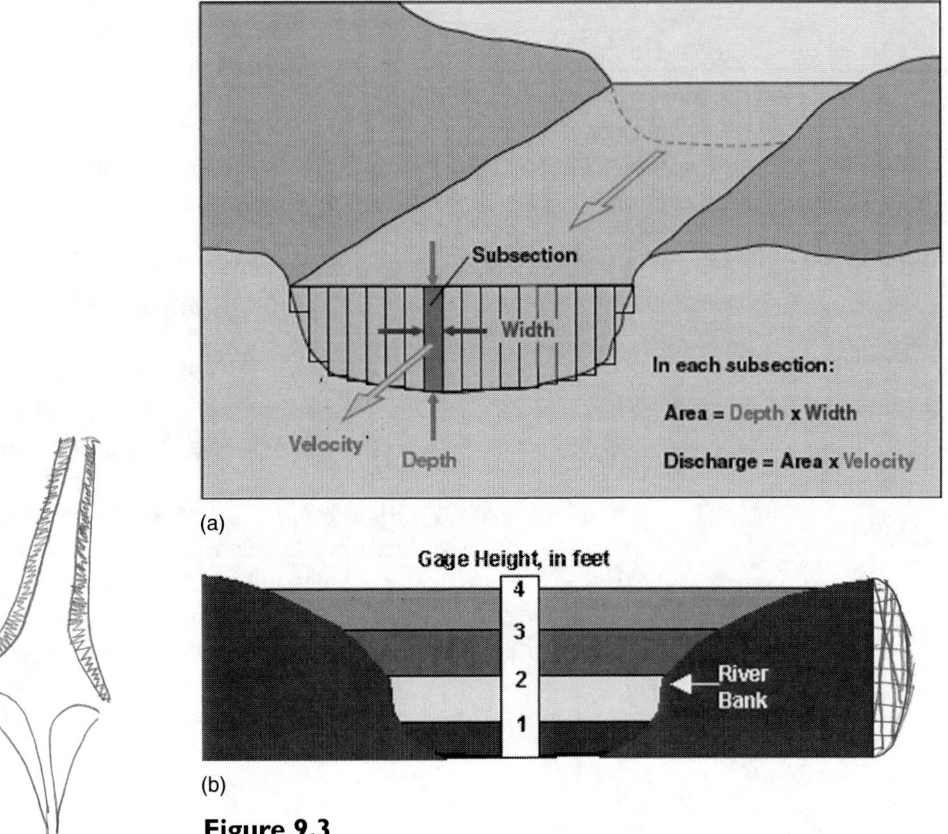

Figure 9.3

Streams provide water, transportation, food, irrigation, and soil to people living nearby. The finer silt carried by streams is deposited to create arable farmland, such as in the delta region of the Nile River in Egypt. Before the High Aswan Dam was built, these rich farmlands were frequently flooded, destroying crops, homes, and killing people, but also depositing valuable silt that enriched farming areas near the mouth of the river. Construction of dams lessened the occurrence of major floods, but the dams now hold back valuable silt, rendering many downstream regions unsuitable for growing crops.

TYPES OF FLOODS

Regional River Floods

Flooding that is related to seasonal rains or snow melts, or a combination of rain falling on snow, produces a large volume of water that cannot be handled by existing stream systems. Such flooding is common in wetter climates that have generally larger, more established rivers. Floods can occur anywhere along the length of a stream. In the upstream regions, such floods are caused by intense rainfall or snow melt over a watershed that flows into smaller streams and tributaries. When several watersheds feed into a larger stream, the volume of water can be immense and produce widespread flooding.

These vast amounts of water can have an effect on the landscape. One foot of water covering one acre is termed an **acre foot**. This amounts to 325,851 gallons of water, so for every inch of rain falling on an acre, there are 27,154 gallons that can flow across the surface. If one acre foot of water moves into a river, it will contribute 43,560 cubic feet (1233 cu meters) of flow to the stream's volume. Generally, these intense rainfalls are so rapid that very little water percolates into the subsurface, producing stream flows that become rushing torrents (**Figure 9.5**). As the gradient of the stream flattens out and the downstream river channels become wider, the velocity drops and the water becomes calmer. However, the volume of water continues to increase, especially if more streams are present in the system.

Table 9.1 World's 10 Largest Rivers by Discharge

River	Country	Average Discharge at Mouth (Cubic Feet per Second)
Amazon	Brazil	7,500,000
Congo	Congo	1,400,000
Yangtze	China	770,000
Brahmaputra	Bangladesh	700,000
Ganges	India	660,000
Yenisey	Russia	614,000
Mississippi	USA	611,000
Orinoco	Venezuela	600,000
Lena	Russia	547,000
Parana	Argentina	526,000

Source: http://www.waterencyclopedia.com/Re-St/Rivers-Major-World.html.

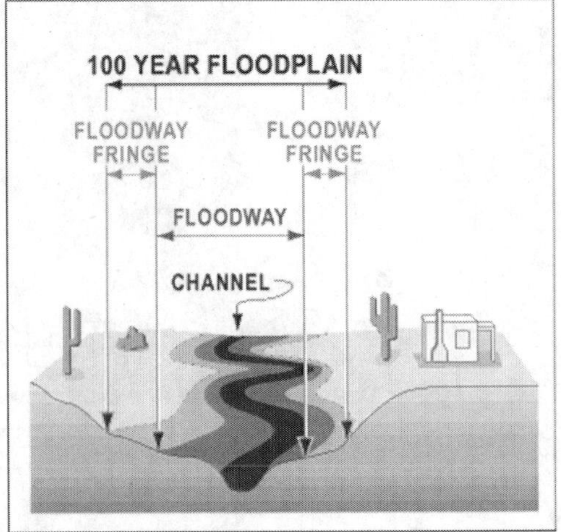

Figure 9.4 Notice how the shape of the channel dictates the velocity. (a) Water in a wide, shallow channel moves more slowly than in a narrow, deep one because of increased friction. (b) This stream has the same cross-sectional area as the one in (a) but there is less friction, hence a higher velocity.

FACT BOX Equivalent Measures and Weights of Water at 4°C.

1 gallon = 0.134 cubic feet = 8.35 lb (3.79 kg)
1 cubic foot per second (cfs) = 7.48 gal/sec = 62.4 lbs/sec (28.3 kg/sec) = 449 gals/min

Many watersheds consist of hundreds or thousands of acres, resulting in massive amounts of water moving downslope and downstream. The lateral and down cutting erosive power of the water causes dimensions of the stream channel to increase. Upstream regions generally have fairly steep slopes and the longitudinal profile of the stream shows a rapid drop in the elevation of the stream (refer to Figure 9.1). Therefore water will tend to move downslope quickly and generate large-scale flooding.

As higher elevation streams move water downstream, they join with other streams and increase the size of the trunk stream (in a fashion similar to the trunk of a deciduous tree having many branches that feed into the main trunk). If a widespread rain storm covers several different watersheds and feeds water into the trunk stream, the downstream region can experience flooding. Widespread saturation of the ground prevents water from percolating into soils, so the water must flow under the force of gravity to lower elevations. This downslope flow is not instantaneous, so there is often a lag that gives some warning to communities at the lower end of a drainage area. Downstream communities generally have some preventive measures in place in preparation for recurring floods. Increasing the height of levees and deepening the river channel help the river to handle a greater flow, thus preventing flooding. However, these measures are not always successful, particularly if there is a flow that greatly exceeds the normal amount. The result can be

Figure 9.5 The Reedy River in Greenville, South Carolina following a June thunderstorm.

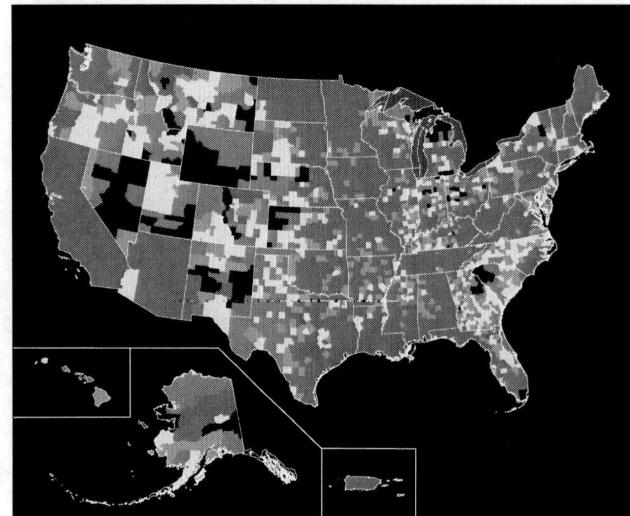

Figure 9.6 Presidential flood disaster declarations between June 1, 1965 and June 1, 2003, shown by U.S. county. Black represents no declarations, lighter gray represents 2 to 3 declarations, and medium gray (most of the map) represents four or more declarations. See http://pubs.usgs.gov/fs/2006/3026/2006-3026.pdf"

flooding so severe and widespread that the governor of the state requests presidential declaration of the region as a disaster area so that it can receive federal help (**Figure 9.6**). As we see from the map in Figure 9.6, very few regions in the United States are exempt from flooding over a period of several decades.

Other natural hazards play a role in changing the drainage regime of an area. The 1991 eruption of Mount Pinatubo, a volcano in the Philippine Islands, deposited massive amounts of ash across the countryside. Within a few months, copious rainfalls struck the region and moved the ash downslope as sediment. When flooding occurred in the streams, deposits were created along the banks and formed natural levees that increased the depth of the channels. After several episodes of this redistribution of the ash, streambeds were flowing at a level higher than the original surface. When the streams experienced later flooding, the water easily flowed into the lower lying areas adjoining the raised stream channels.

Flash Floods

Flash floods occur with little or no warning. They are usually caused by torrential rainfall that takes place over a very short time, often associated with severe, localized thunderstorms or from a series of storms continually soaking an area. Although flash floods can occur anywhere, they tend to be more devastating in two areas: (1) in mountainous areas, where steep slopes funnel water into narrow streams, and (2) in desert regions, where normally dry or low flow streambeds are quickly transformed into raging torrents. Rainfall does not have any chance of infiltrating into the subsurface and is often flowing in a rapid, sheet-wash manner across impervious surfaces to collect in dry stream beds. The intense nature of flash floods makes them capable of causing extensive damage and loss of life. When people drive their vehicles through normally dry washes and streambeds that are filled with fast-moving water, their vehicles begin to float, are pushed along by the flow, or are overturned, trapping the victims inside. The force with which fast-moving, sediment-laden water hits a surface is great (**Box 9.1**)

Winter Climate-Driven Floods

Ice-jam floods are a problem in regions where rivers freeze and then begin to thaw or receive surface water from rainfall or nearby melting. In the winter, some regions receive excessive snowfall, which rests on frozen ground. Rivers that normally drain the snowmelt freeze and cannot move any water downstream. Ice builds up whenever a small period of melting occurs and then refreezing takes place, thus making the drainage situation worse.

During the winter of 1996 and 1997, the watershed of the Red River of the North, which forms the state boundary of North Dakota and Minnesota, was besieged by excessive rainfall and a series of blizzards. Precipitation totals were more than three times normal and cold weather early in the winter froze the soil, preventing any percolation of water. In early April the region experienced record low temperatures along with

BOX 9.1 How One State Deals with Not-So-Smart Drivers

The State of Arizona has enacted the Stupid Motorist Law (Arizona Revised Statutes 28-910), which imposes a fine of up to $2,000 on drivers who have to be rescued from a flooded area. In spite of this law, people continue to drive around barricaded crossings and attempt to get through flooded roadways. A lack of adequate storm culverts causes water to flow across low points on streets and highways. The depth of water, even when it is flowing across a roadway that might be familiar to the driver, is very uncertain and the force of the water is much greater than one realizes.

DO NOT DRIVE THROUGH FLOODWATERS!

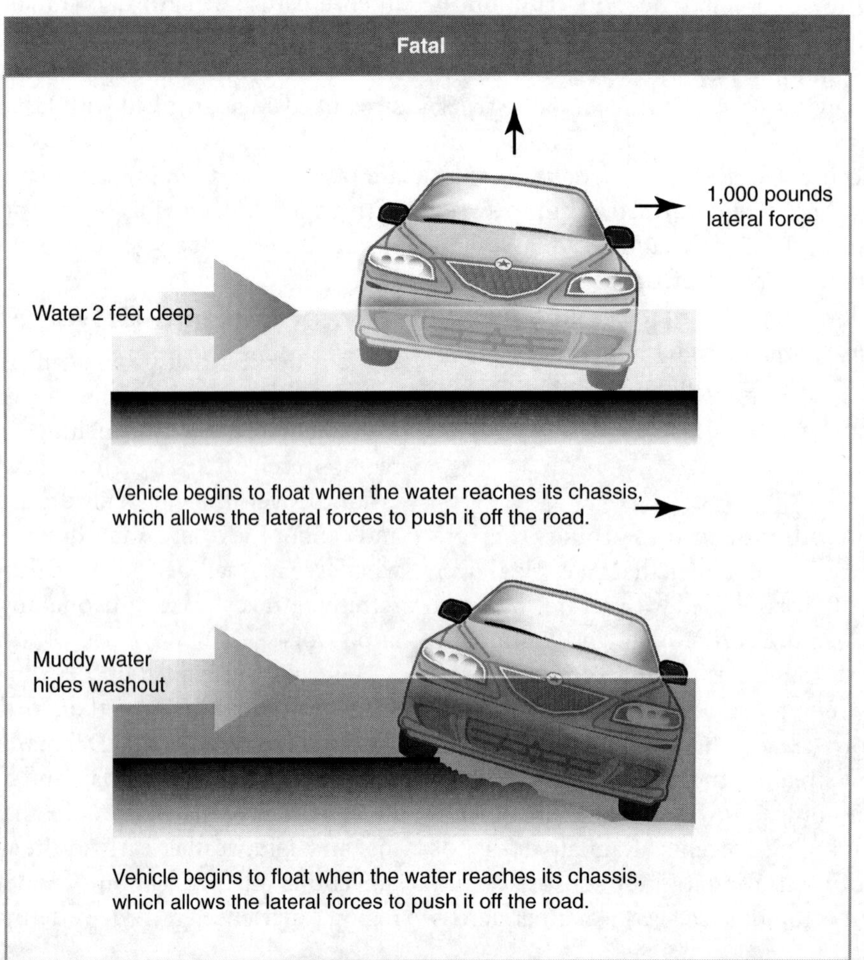

Figure 9.7 Sorlie Bridge, which connects Grand Forks, North Dakota, with East Grand Forks, Minnesota, lies under water in the April 1997 floods. Losses exceeded $3.5 billion in these cities.

another 10 to 12 inches (25 to 30 cm) of snow. Within a 10-day period, daytime temperatures swung from single digits to highs in the upper 50s (13–14°C). Rapid melting occurred that produced extensive flooding.

Because the Red River of the North flows north—one of few rivers in the United States to do so—the water was draining into an area where the river was still frozen. The surrounding farmland had a very low gradient (less than a few inches per mile), so the water had nowhere to go. The result was that almost 4.5 million acres were covered in water. Grand Forks, a city of about 48,000 on the banks of the river, was flooded (**Figure 9.7**) and more than 24,000 homes were destroyed. The downtown area was under several meters of water. News photos recorded fires burning that destroyed several key buildings in the downtown area. Farms were under water, major crops were lost, and more than 120,000 cattle died. Losses amounted to several billion dollars. The damage continued into Canada, where more than $800 million worth of property was destroyed.

DAM-RELATED FLOODS

Buffalo Creek

During a five-year period (1972 to 1977), several major dams failed in the United States. In 1972, a privately controlled, slag-heap dam on Buffalo Creek in West Virginia gave way following excessive rainfall, resulting in 125 deaths and more than $50 million in damage. After the main dam broke, water shot down the creek and destroyed two more dams downstream. In a matter of minutes more than 1,000 people were injured and 4,000 were left homeless. Interestingly, the U.S. Department of the Interior had warned officials in the state in 1967 that the potential for a disaster existed, but nothing was done to address the issues.

Teton Dam

On June 5, 1976, the Teton Dam on the Teton River in eastern Idaho, near the city of Rexburg, collapsed. The earthen dam was originally designed to serve as a multipurpose structure, providing irrigation water to agricultural land in the area, hydroelectric capabilities, recreational opportunities, and flood control. The dam was the subject of lawsuits in federal court during its planning and early construction, but it was completed and put into service in January 1976. It failed on the first filling of the impounded reservoir. In the end, the federal government paid out almost $400 million in damage claims, and the dam was not rebuilt. The final toll was 11 lives lost and 13,000 head of livestock drowned. Flaws in the design of the dam were considered the source of the failure.

Vaiont Dam, Italy, 1963

Completed in 1961, the Vaiont Dam, the world's sixth highest dam, was built to generate hydroelectric power for northern Italy (**Figure 9.8**). The region behind the 859 foot (262 m) high dam included steep hillsides that were underlain by sedimentary rocks, including shales, in the Dolomite region, about 60 miles (100 km) north of Venice. In October 1963, after the reservoir filled naturally, abnormal rainfall caused a block of approximately 270 million cubic meters (9.4 billion cu ft) to detach itself from one wall and slide into the lake at velocities of up to 30 m/sec (100 ft/sec) or (110 kph or 65 mph). This generated a wave 100 m high (325 ft)

Figure 9.8

that went over the top of the dam and blasted down the valley below. More than 50 million cubic meters (13.2 = 10^9 gallons) of water shot downstream. More than 2,500 people died in the disaster, which was very preventable. During planning and construction of the dam, geologists and engineers failed to note the potential of rock slippage. Fortunately the dam itself did not fail.

FLOOD SEVERITY

Some floods are accompanied by a slow rise in water level; others produce sudden raging torrents of water, silt, and other debris. Slow floods are generally forecast to happen whereas rapid ones provide little or no warning for people downstream. The degree of flooding is a function of the amount of water involved, the level it reaches, the expanse the water covers, and the slope of the land, which controls how rapidly an area might drain following an event. In addition to the damage caused by water, many floods deposit thick layers of silt and other debris. One of the major problems for homeowners is the pervasive nature of the mud that is left behind after a house is flooded.

Although flash floods are rapid and impart a great deal of damage, they are usually confined to relatively small areas. Large-scale flooding associated with major rivers or coastal areas affects huge areas and often is in localities that do not drain well, causing the water to linger for weeks. For anyone who has experienced a flood, the end results are personally devastating.

When flooding occurs in wet, humid regions, water takes a longer time to evaporate. Molds and mildew begin to grow and usually become a health hazard. Extensive flooding can also cause cholera and other water-related diseases to spread rapidly among the survivors of these disasters.

Evidence from the Geologic Record

Flooding has occurred on Earth since water began falling from the sky. As the continents began to form several billion years ago, water was an important part of the erosion that began to wear these landmasses down. Eventually, stream patterns formed that allowed water to move more efficiently downhill.

Dubiel and others (1991) reported that exposed continental land lay astride the equator during the Triassic Period (about 225 million years ago). Paleoclimate models showed a maximum effect of monsoonal circulation in the atmosphere. Their study pointed to climatic conditions similar to present-day moisture and circulation patterns of Asia and the Indian Ocean. We could employ the principle of uniformitarianism ("the present is the key to the past") and conclude that the possibility existed for cyclonic storms to develop as they do now, thus leaving their mark on coastal and adjacent low-lying regions. Many of those sedimentary environments are now situated well above sea level as a result of later activity that uplifted much of the continents through plate tectonics.

Lessons from the Historic Record and the Human Toll

Floods have affected Earth's surface for millions of years, just like the other catastrophes we cover in this book. Historians have documented the occurrence of floods worldwide during recorded history. From their reports we learn that no part of the globe is exempt from flooding.

Yanosky and Jarrett (2002) have been able to analyze tree rings for past records of floods to determine the frequency and magnitudes with which they occurred. In some instances, they could determine the date of a flood within a few weeks. One technique they used was to notice where trees were injured by stream debris. By counting the rings, they were able to determine the year, and sometimes the season, when the major flooding took place. Such studies are helpful in determining the recurrence interval for various levels of floods in given areas.

Thousands of major floods have occurred throughout history. Some have killed many people, some have damaged or destroyed cities and surrounding areas. Sometimes the floods could have been prevented or at least the damage minimized. Several noteworthy floods have occurred in the past 120 years.

Johnstown Flood

On May 3, 1889, an earthen dam failed, flooding the town of Johnstown, Pennsylvania. The dam, which was built in 1853 to hold water for the Pennsylvania Canal, had not received maintenance for several decades. After the canal changed owners, the spillway was altered and a grating was installed to prevent fish from escaping from the lake. This led to a build up of debris that eventually clogged the outlet.

In the early spring of 1889 the region received significant snowfall that was later followed by heavy rains that melted the snowpack. With a watershed measuring 657 sq mi (1,725 sq km), several billion gallons of

Figure 9.9 Debris flows were common in the region following the failure of the Johnstown dam in May 1889.

water flowed into the lake. By May 30 water was passing over the dam, and the following day the dam gave way with a flood crest of almost 40 ft (12 m). The estimated flow was approximately that of the water passing over Niagara Falls. Numerous debris flows resulted.

The town of Johnstown, located 15 miles (25 km) down the valley, was obliterated (**Figure 9.9**), and 2,209 people perished. Debates still continue about whether the townspeople were warned of the coming water or if they simply ignored the warning, having heard similar ones in the past when nothing happened. The event is memorialized at the Johnstown Flood National Memorial, part of the U.S. National Park system.

Florence, Italy

Rain began falling on Florence on November 2, 1966, and continued for two days. Early in the morning of November 4, the Arno River, which flows through Florence, burst its levees and the city began to be inundated with water. By midday the city was flooded, with water flowing through the lower floors of homes and buildings in the inner city. In sections of the city, water was more than 30 feet (10 m) deep. Numerous valuable objects of art and library volumes were damaged.

Within two days, the flood waters had receded and people began the restoration of millions of damaged items. Water was still almost five meters (16 ft) deep in places. With the assistance of many citizens from across Italy and other countries, life slowly began to return to normal. Volunteers came from many countries to help with the cleaning of the city and its valuable artifacts. Several countries contributed financial assistance and numerous world experts provided help with the restoration and repair of items damaged by water and mud.

Great Flood of 1993 in the U.S. Midwest

An unusual series of events produced the Great Flood of 1993, which resulted in the most catastrophic flooding the United States has ever experienced. At its peak, more than 15 percent of the contiguous United States was affected, more than 50,000 homes were damaged or destroyed, and water covered more than 400,000 square miles (1.04 million sq km) in Illinois, Iowa, Kansas, Minnesota, Nebraska, North Dakota, South Dakota, and Wisconsin. The infrastructure of America's heartland was disrupted and its economy was upset, affecting millions of people. For more than two months there was no barge traffic on the Mississippi and Missouri Rivers and railroad traffic stopped in the Midwest, one of the hubs of rail transportation in the United States. Because many highways and bridges were flooded, truck traffic came to a stop or had to be rerouted, delaying the delivery of many of the nation's goods.

Larson (1995) provides a good background for examining the conditions that led to the Great Flood of 1993. Flood forecasts are made by 12 National Weather Service River Forecast Centers located throughout the country. Components of the models used to forecast flood potential include temperatures, precipitation amounts, and the soil moisture content of various watersheds. Stream runoff is used to produce a flow model, which uses data from a unit hydrograph. The unit hydrograph represents one inch of runoff from a rain storm that evenly covers a defined headwater drainage basin over a given amount of time, usually taken as six hours. Data from different upstream drainage basins are combined to determine the amount of flow for a selected downstream location, allowing hydrologists to estimate the potential flooding severity.

The flooding that occurred in the Midwest in 1993 has been attributed by some researchers to El Niño, which is an oscillation of the ocean-atmosphere system located in the tropical Pacific Ocean (see **Box 9.2**). From January to June 1993, the upper reaches of the Mississippi River drainage basin received more than 1.5 times the normal rainfall (**Figure 9.10**). The continuing rains in July caused portions of North Dakota, Iowa, and Kansas to record more than four times their normal rainfall amounts. Rains fell often in very intense storms that passed over the region. Normally, floods only last a few days or perhaps a week or two at most. However, these prolonged rains produced supersaturated soils, causing subsequent rain to run off into the drainage basins and produce unprecedented flooding.

Box 9.2 El Niño and Its Effect on Climate

In normal conditions (non-El Niño years), warm surface waters in the western Pacific produce a convective rise of moisture that results in substantial rainfall in Indonesia and adjoining regions, while the trade winds blow to the west (Box Figure 9.2.1). Cooler, deep marine waters move eastward and their upwelling brings nutrient-rich water to the west coast of South America. This enriches the marine life and causes the region to have a major fishing trade.

During an El Niño year, trade winds in the western and central Pacific Ocean become weaker and a larger mass of warm water develops in the central Pacific. Atmospheric conditions change as low pressure exists in the eastern Pacific Ocean and high pressure dominates in the west. These conditions cause warm water to move toward South America. The colder waters at depth are unable to ascend to the surface. The increased atmospheric convection associated with the warm water along the eastern equatorial region produces more precipitation in the temperate latitudes of North and South America (Box Figure 9.2.2). Such was the case in early 1993 in the Midwest that led to the massive rainfalls that produced the Great Flood of 1993.

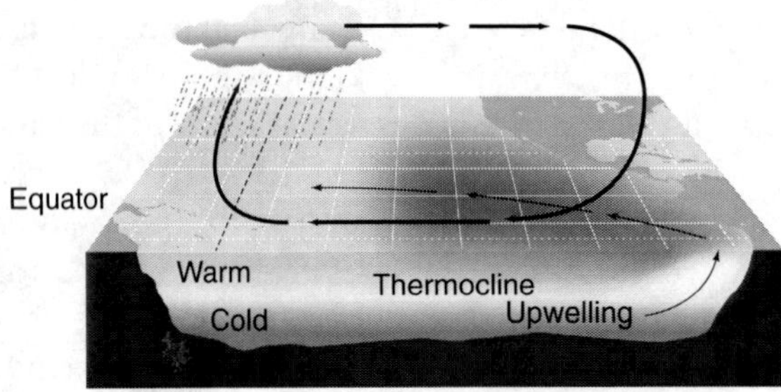

Box Figure 9.2.1 Normal conditions of atmospheric and oceanic conditions in the equatorial Pacific Ocean.

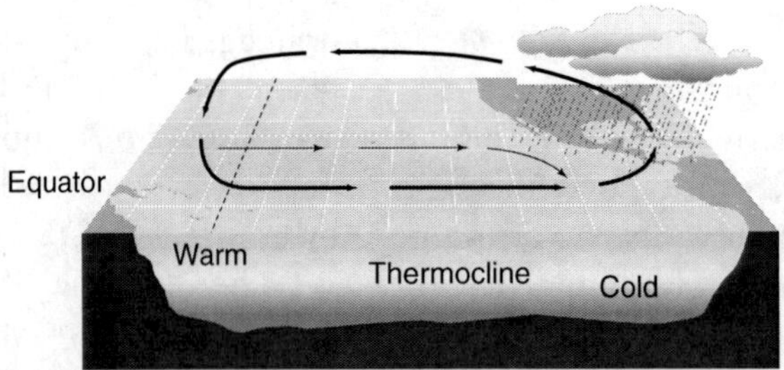

Box Figure 9.2.2 Atmospheric and oceanic conditions present during an El Niño event.

The Great Flood of 1993 lasted for months, with many locations experiencing flood stage conditions for five or six months. The duration of the regional flooding was caused by an extremely unusual set of weather patterns that kept the region very wet. Saturated soils could not absorb any rain, thereby causing it to run off into streams incapable of carrying the volume of water. Rainfall amounts set new all-time records for many recording stations, as the amounts recorded approximate those expected in a 75- to 300-year event (Larson, 1995).

With the continual rains and high humidity, very little evaporation occurred. The Mississippi River remained above flood stage in St. Louis, Missouri, for 146 days between April 1 and September 30, 1993 (**Figure 9.11**). In Cape Girardeau, a city located along

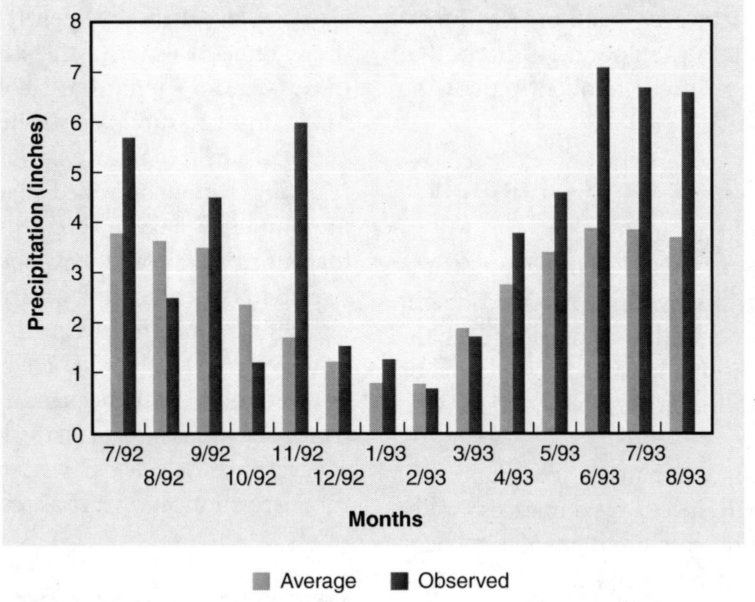

Courtesy of Earth Observatory, NASA.

Figure 9.10 Comparison of observed and average monthly precipitation totals for the Upper Mississippi River Basin.

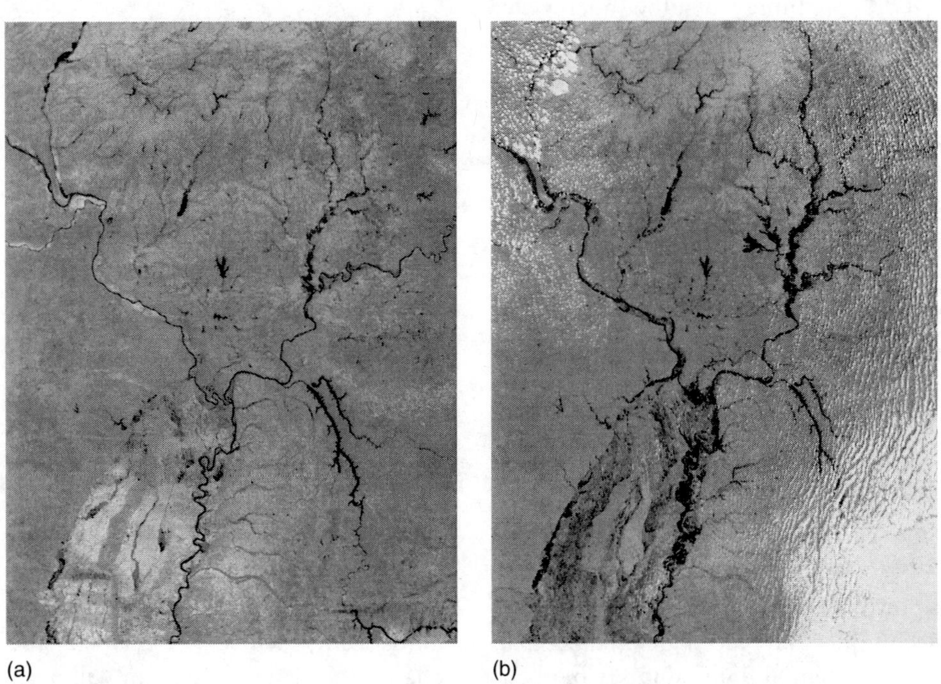

(a) (b)

Figure 9.11 A comparison of the river flows of the Illinois, Mississippi, and Missouri Rivers, August 1991 (normal conditions) and August 19, 1993 (full flood conditions).

the Mississippi River in southeastern Missouri, floodwaters crested 16.5 feet (5 meters) above **flood stage**. The river remained at flood stage in Cape Girardeau for 126 days. The floods of 1993 resulted in 50 deaths and damage estimates in the Midwest ranged between $15 and $20 billion.

HUMAN INTERACTIONS AND FLOODING

Streams will naturally flood at some point during their existence. Whether flooding occurs regularly or on a very periodic time scale, water will flow over the banks and onto a floodplain. However, mankind has introduced new parameters into the flooding process that create flooding conditions more frequently than the natural processes.

Construction of Levees and Channels

Construction of natural levees, although meant to allow a stream to flood in a natural way less often, upsets the normal balance of a stream system. Increased height of levees causes more water to flow in the deeper channel, so when it does occasionally break through, major problems develop. Water cannot easily flow back into the main channel.

Construction of concrete channels to contain flow through urban areas only speeds up any excess water from heavy rainfall or snowmelt that enters the channels. The Los Angeles River has been channelized. More than 60 percent of its watershed is covered by impervious material (asphalt and concrete), so infiltration is greatly reduced. Water is sent to lower elevations in the channel system. There are times when too much water accumulates at the lower reaches of these channels, and flooding results in extensive, unexpected damage.

When flooding occurs, sandbags are often used to contain the flow of water. Bags are placed along the banks of a river as temporary, "quick-fix" levees that hold most of the water in a channel. Bags are also used in low-lying areas to slow the flow of water into buildings and their doorways or low windows. Sandbags work well in the short term for localized flooding but do not help with major overbank conditions. Sometimes large sheets of plastic are placed over the bags but these sheets are not continuous and will allow leaks. All of these techniques are insufficient in solving the larger problem of streams overflowing their banks.

Flood Control

When water is out of control, it creates major problems. Several techniques have been devised to help control and channel potential flood waters. Channelization can involve the clearing or dredging of an existing channel to speed up the flow. Another method is to construct artificial cutoffs that shorten the length of a stream, increasing its velocity and gradient. The result is that more water flows through an area with higher velocities. The goal is to reduce the chances of flooding, but channelization has produced mixed results.

Recall that natural levees form along rivers and deepen the channel. Piling extra earth atop natural levees or putting earth alongside a river creates artificial levees that deepen the channel and increase the volume of water in the stream channel. However, these are only temporary solutions that eventually prove unsuccessful in controlling floods.

Dams help to reduce flooding by storing water and releasing it in a controlled manner. In addition to the impounded water, however, the dams collect sediment that normally would have been transported downstream to enrich floodplain farmland or to create riparian habitats along the stream. Dams create an imbalance in the ecology of the river environment, a fact that was not recognized until the past 20 or so years. On the other hand, the thousands of dams in the United States also generate hydroelectric power, provide water for agricultural irrigation, and serve as recreation areas.

PREDICTING FLOODS

The occurrence of floods depends on many variables, most of which we have little control over. Weather-related floods can be forecast with some detail in the short term, but over longer periods of time we cannot foresee their arrival. However, researchers can analyze flood frequency over longer periods of time, provided adequate data exist.

The USGS has a system of gauging stations situated all over the country that provide real-time data. Stream flow is constantly monitored and the data are available for researchers and scientists to analyze. For the data to be useful, researchers attempt to determine some type of recurrence pattern or interval for flooding events. The term *100-year flood* is a standard time period used to describe the recurrence interval of floods. As **Table 9.2** shows, the "100-year recurrence interval" means that a flood of that magnitude has a 1 percent chance of occurring in any given year. In other words, the chance that a river will flow as high as the 100-year flood stage in any given year is 1 in 100. Statistically, each year begins with the same 1 percent chance that a 100-year event will occur.

Even though a 100-year flood happens in one given year, its occurrence does not imply that another 100 years will pass before the water level would be that high again. Many variables are at work controlling the amount of moisture in an area so the event can indeed occur at any time, even twice within a given year. Should the 100-year flood begin to become more common, it will be necessary to reexamine all the data and redefine the 100-year flood, taking into account changes in the occurrence of such a flood level.

Table 9.2 Recurrence Intervals for Various Levels of Floods.

Recurrence Interval, in Years	Probability of Occurrence in Any Given Year	Percent Chance of Occurrence in Any Given Year
100	1 in 100	1
50	1 in 50	2
25	1 in 25	4
10	1 in 10	10
5	1 in 5	20
2	1 in 2	50

SUMMARY

Floods occur every day somewhere on Earth. When a drainage system receives more water than it can handle, the excess water flows over river banks and across the landscape, flooding farmland and communities. Drainage systems found in watersheds serve to remove water that falls in the area. As streams flow downhill, they gather more water and have a higher flow in the lower elevations. If the amount of water exceeds the capacity of the stream, flooding occurs.

Regional floods result from prolonged rainfall or excessive snowmelt. Such floods usually last several days or weeks and create widespread damage to a region. Usually the loss of human life is small in these events. Flash floods are fast to form and move through an area rapidly. They provide very little warning and are the primary cause of loss of human life. Floods caused by ice dams or the breaking of artificial dams have widespread effects. Failure of artificial dams is often traced to engineering problems. The effects of historic floods throughout the world indicate that many regions are affected by the influx of water. Low-lying areas suffer the most because flood waters are slow to recede.

Humans have attempted to intervene in preventing floods but generally the results are mixed. Channelization of streams and overland flow moves water through an area more rapidly than normal but can produce unexpected effects if too much water ends up at the end of the drainage system. The construction of dams for flood control is often a temporary solution as the dams tend to fill with stream sediment that eventually reduces their capacity to impound the amount of water for which they were originally designed.

The ability of researchers to predict floods is helpful in forecasting potential problems in a given area. However, the fickle nature of weather systems and climate changes makes the prediction of major events very difficult. It is necessary to use recent information when establishing future patterns of floods and related events.

REFERENCES AND SUGGESTED READINGS

Benito, G., V. R. Baker, and K. J. Gregory, eds. 1998. *Palaeohydrology and Environmental Change.* Chichester: John Wiley.

Dubiel, Russell F., Judith Totman Parrish, J. Michael Parrish, and Steven C. Good. 1991. The Pangaean Megamonsoon—Evidence from the Upper Triassic Chinle Formation, Colorado Plateau. *Palaios* 6: 347–370.

House, P. Kyle, Robert H. Webb, Victor R. Baker, and Daniel R. Levish, eds. 2002. *Ancient Floods, Modern Hazards—Principles and Applications of Paleoflood Hydrology.* Washington, DC: American Geophysical Union.

Larson, Lee W. 1995. The Great USA Flood of 1993. http://www.nwrfc.noaa.gov/floods/papers/oh_2/great.htm.

Lutgens, F. and E. Tarbuck. *Essentials of Geology.* 8th ed. 2003, Upper Saddle River, NJ: Pearson Prentice Hall.

Mayer, L. and D. Nash, eds. 1987. *Catastrophic Flooding:* Boston, MA: Allen and Unwin.

Yanosky, Thomas M. and Robert D. Jarrett. 2002. Dendrochronologic evidence for the frequency and magnitude of paleofloods. In *Ancient Floods, Modern Hazards—Principles and Applications of Paleoflood Hydrology,* ed. P. Kyle House, Robert H. Webb, Victor R. Baker, and Daniel R. Levish. Washington, DC: American Geophysical Union.

WEB SITES FOR FURTHER REFERENCE

http://pubs.usgs.gov.circ/2003/circ1245
http://water.usgs.gov/
http://water.usgs.gov/wid/index-hazards.html
http://waterdata.usgs.gov/nwis/rt
http://www.photolib.noaa.gov.historic.nws/index.html
http://www.usgs.gov.hazards/floods/
http://www.bt.cdc.gov/disasters/floods/index.asp
http://www.noaa.gov/floods.html
http://www.weather.gov/oh/hic

QUESTIONS FOR THOUGHT

1. How does the size of a drainage basin affect the amount of discharge in a stream?
2. How does the cross-sectional area of a stream affect its velocity?
3. What factors lead to flash floods? What would you do in case of encountering a flash flood?
4. What are ice-jam floods and during what part of the year are they most likely to occur?
5. Give two examples of how poor planning resulted in disastrous failures of dams.
6. Explain the role that levees play in major rivers.
7. How predictable are floods?
8. What would be the effects of a two-foot flood in your hometown? Where would such a flood come from and what would be the long-term effects? Look at your hometown's website to see if any plans are in place for such as disaster.

WATER PLANET EXERCISE 11

Name: ______________________________

Green Mill Run—River and Flood Process Field Trip

See Field Trip Map provided by your instructor and answer these questions after your trip.

1. How has this particular section of Green Mill Run been modified by people? Why?

2. How is this section of stream channel currently being used by people?

3. What evidence shows that the creek has moved position (or tried to) recently?

4. What evidence shows that humans are trying to prevent the creek from moving its position?

5. What are three potential sources of pollutants entering this section of creek?

6. What can be done to reduce stream pollution in this area?

WATER PLANET VIDEO RESPONSE 6

Name: ______________________________

Flash Flood Alley

This is a video that tells the story of an area that is particularly susceptible to flash floods. In addition to describing the physical characteristics that create this hazardous environment, human responses to the risk are depicted, including fear, denial, and acceptance.

1. Why is the region shown in the video so prone to flooding (think atmosphere and topography)?

2. List three examples of costs (in terms of dollar losses) associated with this flooding.

   a.

   b.

   c.

3. List three examples of non-monetary costs associated with this flooding.

   a.

   b.

   c.

4. Who learned from the experience and what did they learn? What actions do they plan to take?

5. Who didn't learn from the experience and will go back to the way things were? Why do you think that is?

Chapter 10

WATER RESOURCES

The sober citizen who would never submit his watch or his motor to amateur tamperings freely submits his lakes to drainings, fillings, dredgings, pollutions, stabilizations, mosquito control, algae control, swimmer's itch control, and the planting of any fish able to swim. So also with rivers. We constrict them with levees and dams, and then flush them with dredgings, channelizations, and the floods and silt of bad farming.

Aldo Leopold

Earth, the water planet. How incongruous it seems that "Earth" is both a word for soil and the name of our planet when oceans cover 71 percent of its surface! In addition to the water in the seas is that held in lakes, ponds, rivers, streams, marshes, bays and estuaries, as well as the water locked in polar ice caps and glaciers. Water so dominates the Earth's surface that it is responsible for the familiar image seen in satellite photos: a beautiful blue ball existing in stark contrast to the blackness of space. Vast amounts of water also exist in liquid form underground and as water vapor in the atmosphere. All of this water is linked in a continuous cycle of evaporation (from the surface to the atmosphere), precipitation (from the atmosphere to the surface), and runoff (from the land or beneath the land's surface). The hydrologic cycle (see Chapter 2) is driven by the sun's energy and has been recycling the same water through the millennia of the Earth's existence. Indeed, the water we bathe in today might have quenched the thirst of dinosaurs millions of years ago. In this chapter, we describe water resources and examine efforts to manage them.

DESCRIBING WATER RESOURCES

In this section, we look at how water supports life, how much freshwater is on Earth, and how water is classified. We also examine how humans use water and how those uses contribute to water pollution.

HOW DOES WATER SUPPORT LIFE?

Water is the largest constituent of living organisms, and it is also a habitat for a great diversity of life on Earth. Water is able to accomplish these dual roles because of unique physical and chemical characteristics (Table 10.1). For most of the Earth's existence, living organisms have been able to capture some of the water in the hydrologic cycle to maintain their internal environments. The human body is composed primarily of water (about 65 percent); there are about 43 quarts of water in a 150-pound person. Water makes up 83 percent of blood, helps digest food, regulates salt and mineral balances, transports body wastes,

Table 10.1 Physical and Chemical Properties of Water

Superior solvent. More materials can be dissolved in water than in any other solvent. Water can permeate living cell membranes; dissolved materials also diffuse through the membranes or are "pumped" through using respiration energy.

Strong attractive force. The strong attractive force between water molecules allows them to be transported through the spaces in soil, into roots, and through the conducting tissue in plants and then to be transpired through leaves and needles back into the atmosphere.

State changes. In the hydrologic cycle, the sun supplies the energy that vaporizes water to a gaseous state. When water vapor condenses to a liquid, energy is given off, helping to distribute the sun's energy across the Earth.

High specific heat. It takes substantial amounts of energy to raise the temperature of a body of water, and, conversely, water is slow to cool. This property protects aquatic environments against rapid temperature changes. The different heating and cooling rates of bodies of water and adjacent land masses help to circulate air, create winds, and establish weather patterns.

Expansion at freezing. Water is the only common substance that expands when it freezes. Other substances contract when they freeze.

Density at freezing. Water reaches its maximum density at 46° F (4° C), 14° fahrenheit above the freezing point. As water approaches freezing, it becomes lighter and moves toward the surface. When frozen, it floats on the surface as ice. Thus, streams, lakes, and ponds freeze from the top down, protecting aquatic environments from freezing solid in the winter.

Oxygen- and nutrient-holding capacities. More oxygen dissolves in cold water than in warm water, but warm water generally holds more nutrients. The largest populations of aquatic organisms are found where nutrient-rich warm waters and oxygen-rich cold waters mix.

Flow. Water tends to move easily downhill over land toward streams, rivers, lakes, ponds, and oceans. Bodies of water tend to flow downhill and toward larger bodies of water. Water also percolates through the ground, sometimes collecting in huge, slowly moving underground aquifers.

Aesthetic quality. Flowing water, shimmering water, cascading water, waves, small drops of dew collected on a spider's web, rainwater pattering on a roof or running down a windowpane, puddles, a single drop of water from a pond teeming with life, a tear: each affects the human psyche in ways science is unable to explain.

and lubricates joints. The body's internal water supply must remain constant and free from impurities to maintain health. Like all living organisms, we are intricately bound to the hydrologic cycle.

HOW MUCH FRESHWATER IS ON EARTH?

Most of the Earth's water (97 percent) is salty; only a small portion (less than 3 percent) is fresh. Three-quarters of all freshwater is found in polar ice caps and glaciers, and nearly one-quarter, known as **groundwater**, is found underground in water-bearing porous rock or sand or gravel formations. Only a small proportion (0.5 percent) of all water in the world is found in lakes, rivers, streams, and the atmosphere.

HOW IS WATER CLASSIFIED?

Water is classified as either fresh or salt (marine), depending upon its salt, or saline, concentration. The saline concentration of marine waters is generally fairly consistent, about 35 parts per thousand (ppt). On average, the saline concentration of freshwater is 0.5 ppt. The saline concentration of freshwater tends to vary more than that of marine waters because lakes, rivers, and streams are much more dominated by local environmental conditions, such as the lands they drain and the rate of evaporation.

Freshwater

Freshwater is found on land in two basic forms: surface waters and groundwater. The two are not entirely distinct. Some water from lakes, streams, and rivers may percolate downward to groundwater supplies. Similarly, during dry spells when surface runoff may be unavailable, groundwater may help to maintain the flow and/or level of rivers, streams, or lakes.

Surface waters

Surface waters are bodies of water (such as lakes and rivers) recharged by precipitation that flows along land contours from high to low elevations as **runoff**. Runoff makes its way into streams, rivers, ponds and lakes, eventually reaching the oceans. The entire runoff area of a particular body of water is known as its **watershed.** A watershed contributes water and dissolved nutrients and sediments to the body of surface water toward which it drains. The fertility of surface waters, then, depends on the fertility of the land in the watershed.

Surface water ecosystems include both standing water habitats (including ponds, lakes, reservoirs, and in some cases, wetlands) and running water habitats (including springs, streams, and rivers). **Standing water habitats** are relatively closed ecosystems with well-defined boundaries; generally, they contain both inlet and outlet streams. Standing water generally has a lower oxygen level than running water because there is less mixing of water. Water does move, or flush, through ponds and lakes, but at a slow rate—from one year or less in small lakes to hundreds of years in large lakes such as Lake Superior. With slow movement of water, pollutants have more time to build up to dangerous levels and to settle in sediments.

Lakes may be categorized according to the amount of dissolved nutrients they contain (Figure 10-1). **Oligotrophic lakes** contain a relatively low amount of dissolved solids, nutrients, and phytoplankton and are thus clear and deep blue in color. They lie in infertile watersheds, are cold and deep, have a high oxygen content, and usually have rocky bottoms. The low nutrient level of oligotrophic lakes results in a low production of organic matter, particularly phytoplankton, relative to total volume.

Compared to oligotrophic lakes, **eutrophic lakes** are warmer, more turbid, have a lower oxygen content, and often have muddy or sandy bottoms. They also are far more productive: Fertile watersheds supply eutrophic lakes with abundant nutrients, enabling them to support a large phytoplankton population and a rich diversity of organisms. Lakes undergo succession, becoming more eutrophic over time. Eventually, as eutrophic lakes and ponds grow warmer and shallower, they become weed-choked and more like marshes and dry land.

Lakes are composed of internal zones based on depth and light penetration. The **littoral zone** is a shallow, near-shore area where rooted plants grow because light can penetrate to the bottom. The **limnetic zone** is deeper water where light can penetrate and support populations of plankton. Below the limnetic zone is the **profundal zone**, into which light does not penetrate enough to allow photosynthesis to occur. Organisms of the profundal zone depend on food and nutrients filtering down from above.

Large lakes in temperate zones undergo **thermal stratification** (Figure 10-2). In the summer, surface waters heated by the sun become lighter and less dense and form a top layer, or **epilimnion**. Colder, denser water sinks to the bottom to form the **hypolimnion**. A sharp temperature gradient, or **thermocline**, exists between the upper and lower layers. Sometimes, especially in eutrophic lakes, all photosynthesis and oxygen production occur in the warm upper waters. The thermocline prevents the two layers from mixing, and the hypolimnion can become depleted of oxygen. Occasionally, late in the summer, the shallower areas of eutrophic lakes and ponds also can become completely devoid of oxygen. The lack of oxygen can stress fish populations and result in high fish mortality.

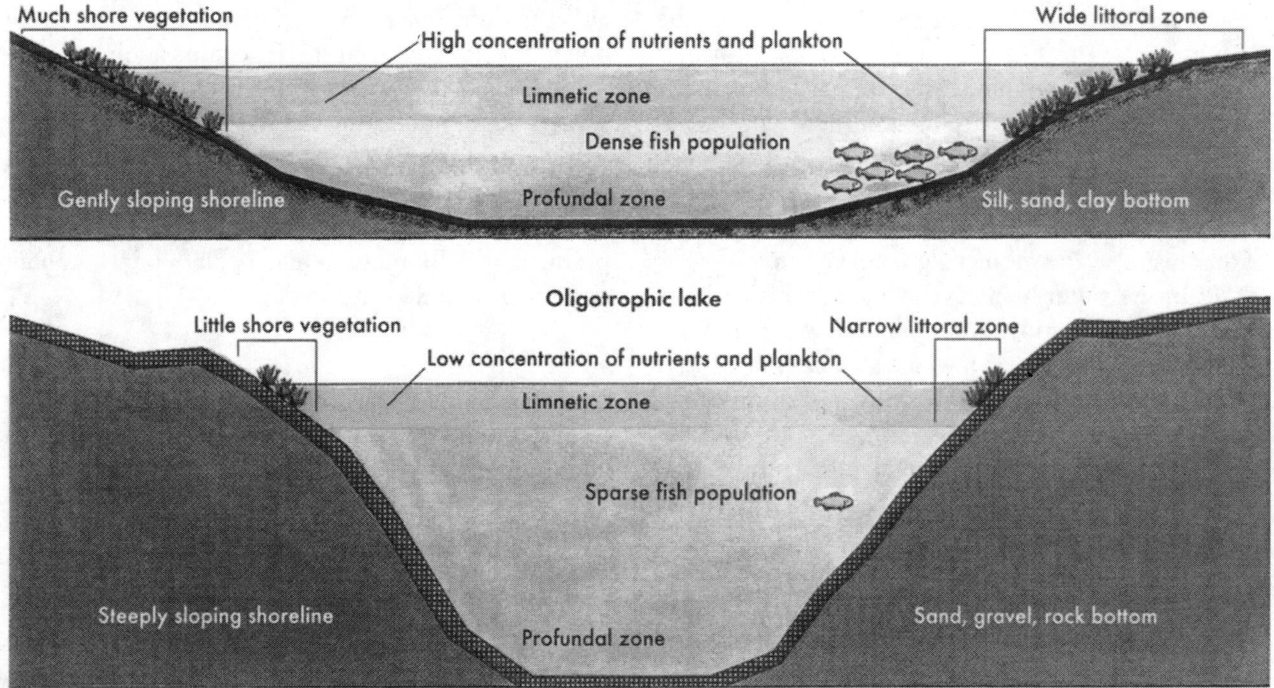

Figure 10.1 Eutrophic and oligotrophic lakes.

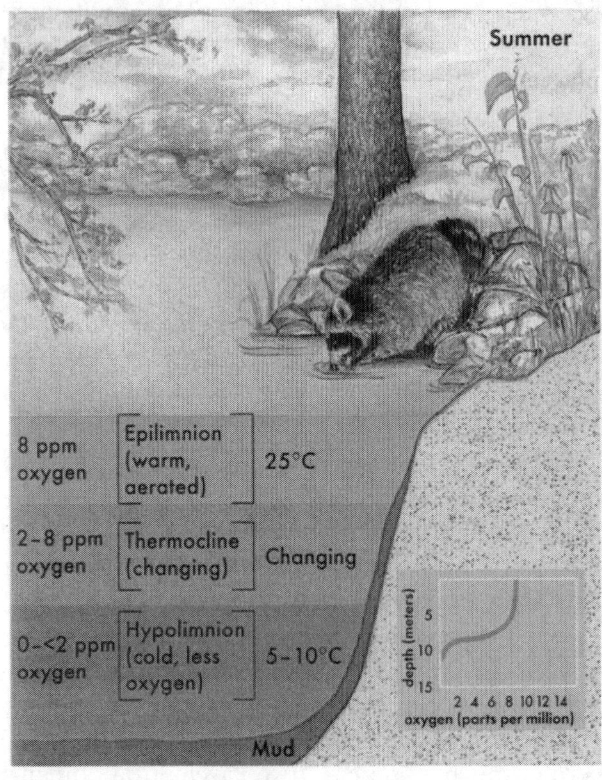

Figure 10-2: Typical pattern of thermal stratification in lakes. In summer, the thermocline separates the colder, oxygen-poor water in the hypolimnion from the warmer, oxygen-rich water in the epilimnion.

Generally, this phenomenon can be traced to very warm weather, little wind to mix the surface water, and a high decomposition rate of algae or other organic matter. In the autumn, when seasonal changes help to cool the surface water, the thermocline disappears and the top and bottom layers mix, returning oxygen to the bottom layers. This mixing is known as fall turnover. If the winter is cold and snow covers the ice for long periods, oxygen also can be depleted in the deeper areas. Spring warming causes the water to turn over once again, returning oxygen to the deepest levels and circulating both nutrients and the overwintering stages of organisms to the warmer, light-filled waters.

Running water habitats include streams and rivers, continuously moving currents of water that cut channels or beds through the land's surface. The speed of the current influences both the composition of the channel (such as rock, sand, gravel, or mud) and the oxygen content—and, consequently, the composition of the organisms found there. Fine-grained particles tend to collect in pools or shallows, while large rocks and boulders are found on the streambeds of fast-flowing waters. The oxygen content of fast-flowing streams is higher than that of slow-flowing ones.

Temperature also affects the composition of organisms in streams and rivers. In general, the temperature of small streams tends to rise and fall with the air temperature. Rivers with large surface areas exposed to the sun generally are warmer than those with trees and shrubs on their banks. Often, when streams are channelized or when surrounding land is cleared for farming, the water goes through large changes in temperature with subsequent drastic changes in species composition.

A look below the surface of a river or stream reveals many interesting habitats and associations of living organisms. Fast-moving rivers and streams usually contain two kinds of habitats, riffles and pools. Riffles, with a high oxygen content, tend to house the producers of biomass, while pools tend to contain consumers and decomposers.

Groundwater

As its name suggests, groundwater is freshwater found underground in porous rock strata. Imagine that you could contain all of the fresh surface water (from lakes, rivers, ponds, and streams) in the United States in one lake. Our imaginary lake would contain only a fraction of the water that exists underground. It would have to be 20 times larger to hold all of the groundwater! This huge amount, some 30 to 60 quadrillion gallons (114 to 227 quadrillion liters), represents 96 percent of the United States' freshwater.

Groundwater percolates downward through the soil from rain, snow, or surface water and is stored in an **aquifer**, a water-bearing geologic formation composed of layers of sedimentary material such as sand, gravel, or porous rock. Water fills the crevices of the rock and the pores between the particles of sand and gravel. The depth at which the aquifer begins is known as the **water table.** Before water reaches the aquifer, it passes through an unsaturated zone, where pores contain both water and air. Plants remove some of this water; the rest continues to move downward to the saturated zone.

Aquifers vary widely in terms of length and thickness. They can cover a few miles or thousands of square miles. For example, the High Plains aquifer underlies about 174,000 square miles (450,660 square kilometers) in eight states (South Dakota, Wyoming, Nebraska, Colorado, Kansas, New Mexico, Texas, and Oklahoma) and encompasses the 134,000-square-mile (347,060-square-kilometer) Ogallala aquifer. Because the Ogallala was formed long ago and is not significantly recharged by present precipitation patterns, the water in the aquifer is known as fossil groundwater. Aquifers can be several feet to several hundred feet thick; they may occur several hundred feet underground or quite close to the surface, perhaps emerging as a free-flowing spring or contributing water to a stream, river, lake, or wetland. If the material above the aquifer is permeable, allowing water to move freely downward to the water table, the aquifer is said to be **unconfined.** If an impermeable layer exists above the water table, thereby restricting the downward flow of water, the aquifer is said to be **confined**. Lacking a protective, impermeable rock or clay layer, unconfined aquifers are susceptible to contamination.

Groundwater flow also is highly variable, percolating from higher to lower elevations sometimes very slowly and sometimes surprisingly fast—anywhere from a fraction of an inch to a few feet a day (Figure 10-3). Groundwater flow is determined by the slope of the water table as well as by the permeability of the material through which the water is moving. The steeper the slope and the more permeable the substrate, the more rapidly the water flows. Usually, but not always, groundwater flows parallel to the aboveground flow. This may not be true, however, in the case of a confined aquifer, where an impermeable layer separates the surface water from the groundwater.

Aquifers supply drinking water for half of the U.S. population, including almost all rural residents. While groundwater is used to some extent in every state, it is the major source of drinking water in about two-thirds of them. In addition to its use as a source of drinking water, groundwater supplies over 95 percent of total rural household needs, 40 percent of agricultural demand, and 26 percent of industrial demand. It also helps to maintain water levels and the productivity of streams, lakes, rivers, wetlands, bays, and estuaries. Furthermore, mineral-rich groundwater helps to supply nutrients that nourish such aquatic ecosystems as Tarpon Springs and the Apalachicola River in Florida. These systems often support unique plants and animals and provide excellent fishing and recreation opportunities.

However, aquifers are slow to recharge after water is removed and slow to cleanse after they are contaminated. Contamination is becoming more significant as aquifers are increasingly threatened by pollution from sources as varied as municipal and industrial landfills, oil drilling, mining, urban and agricultural runoff, and leaking underground storage tanks for toxic substances.

Marine Waters

The oceans are one huge living system. Cradles of life, crucibles of diversity and nurturers of civilizations, they influence nearly everything we do. Constantly moving water currents operate under the influence of the sun's energy, the Earth's rotation, and the moon's gravitational pull. Currents move huge masses of water around the continents and across the vast open reaches, circulating nutrients that have washed in from the land. Further, the interaction of the oceans and the atmosphere affects heat distribution, weather patterns, and concentrations of atmospheric gases throughout the world. Because they are so expansive and deep, the oceans moderate climates and provide a sink for dissolved solids and gases. Beneath the ocean floor lies a rich storehouse of minerals, petroleum, and natural gas. Finally, hundreds of millions of people live near the ocean shores and on coastal plains. Even greater numbers depend upon ocean fisheries, energy, and minerals for their sustenance.

The ocean is divided into zones. As in a lake, the littoral zone is the area of shallow waters near the shore. The **euphotic zone** is the area of light penetration; here, phytoplankton exist in great abundance. Where light can penetrate to the ocean floor, attached plants like the giant kelps are found. The **neritic zone**, comprising seven to eight percent of the oceans, is the part of the euphotic zone over the continental shelf

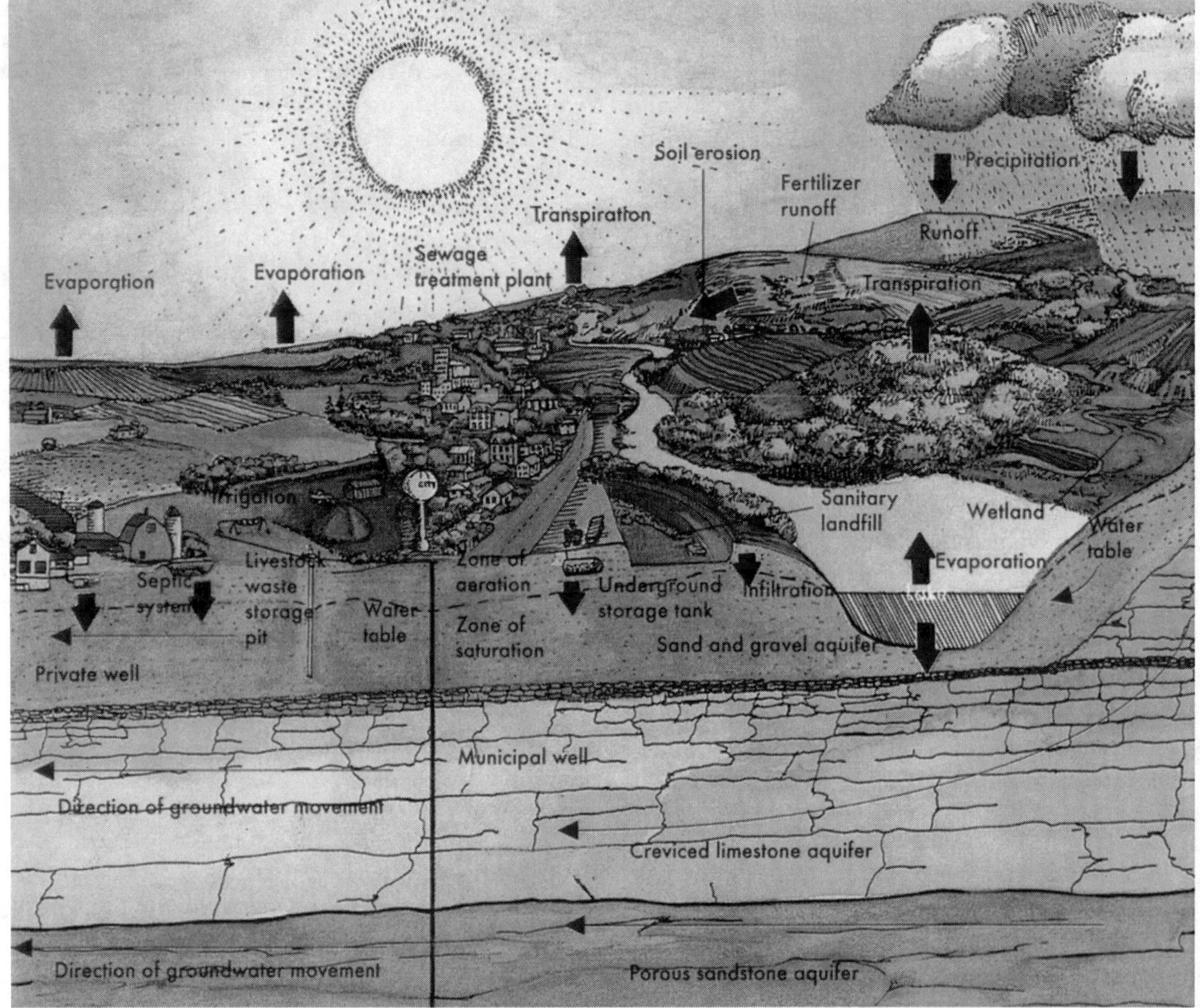

Figure 10.3 Generalized diagram of groundwater. Aquifers are recharged by precipitation that percolates through the ground or water that seeps down from lakes, rivers, streams, and wetlands. They are subject to many diverse sources of pollution.

and near-shore islands. The greatest variety of life is found in the neritic zone, where ocean waters mix with waters from the land, and this zone supports most of the ocean fisheries. The **pelagic zone** is the deep water of the open oceans. Below it lies the **abyssal zone**, the deepest part of the ocean.

HOW DO WE USE WATER?

We use water in countless ways: to drink, bathe, dispose of wastes, irrigate crops, support industry, and generate power. Some of the world's most important transportation corridors are waterways; many play a vital role in global economics and politics. Further, water provides many of our favorite recreational opportunities. Finally, water is a source of inspiration for poets, writers, artists, and others whose souls are stirred by the sight and sound of this most basic of all compounds.

Globally, agriculture is the single largest drain on water supplies; approximately 70 percent of fresh water withdrawn from lakes, rivers, and aquifers is used to produce food. By 1995, the total amount of land under irrigation worldwide was 625 acres (253 million hectares), approximately equal to an area the size of India. Industry accounts for about 22 percent of water use worldwide, and municipalities and households account for 8 percent.

Water uses may be nonconsumptive or consumptive. Nonconsumptive uses remove water from a river or lake, use it, and return it—usually altered in some way—to its original source. Municipal uses (such as drinking and bathing) and industrial uses (such as cooling and power generation) are included in this category. About 90 percent of the water used by homes and industry is available for reuse, although not all of this water will be suitable for use without extensive treatment. In contrast, consumptive uses remove water from one place in the hydrologic cycle and return it to another. For example, water withdrawn from a stream, lake, or aquifer to irrigate crops might not return to its original source; it might be "lost" through evaporation, or it might run off the land into a different stream or lake.

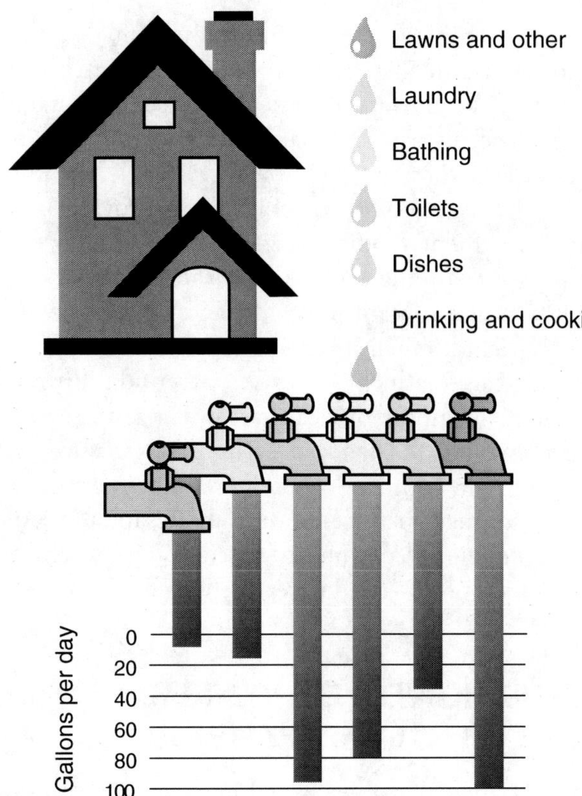

Figure 10.4 Water use by a typical U.S. family of four.

HOW DO WATER USE PATTERNS VARY WORLDWIDE?

Water resources are not evenly distributed; some areas have abundant water and others have little. In freshwater-poor areas, such as the Middle East and northern and eastern Africa, **desalination**—the process of removing dissolved salts from marine water or brackish groundwater—is used to provide citizens with water for drinking, cooking, and other needs. Even highly developed countries with seemingly adequate water resources can suffer from lack of rainfall and groundwater resources or from pollution that renders water supplies unfit for use.

The United States' current water consumption pattern is a mixed bag. In 2000, the nation as a whole withdrew 408 billion gallons (1.5 trillion liters) per day of freshwater; despite an increase in population, this amount is approximately three percent less than that withdrawn in 1990 and 14 percent less than in 1985. The U.S. Geological Survey attributes this decrease to better water efficiency in industry and agriculture. Yet, irrigation remains the largest use of freshwater in the United States; with 137 billion gallons (519 billion liters) per day withdrawn in 2000, it accounted for just over one-third of the year's total usage.

On an individual basis, water is becoming a resource Americans no longer can take for granted. Today, each citizen served by public supplies uses an average of 100 gallons of water (379 liters) per day, 70 percent of which is used in the home—mostly for flushing toilets. Figure 10-4 shows the daily water use of a typical U.S. family of four. If we calculate industrial and home use combined, each American consumes nearly 400 gallons (1,516 liters) of water per day.

The Pacific Institute for Studies in Development, Environment, and Security considers 15 gallons (57 liters) of water per day as the minimum standard for meeting four basic needs—drinking, sanitation, bathing, and cooking. Approximately 55 countries with a combined population of over one billion people cannot meet this standard; in fact, many of the world's people do not have access to even five gallons. This statistic means that one flush of a conventional toilet in the United States uses more water than many people in the developing world use in an entire day. In many less-developed countries (LDCs), clean drinking water and adequate sanitation facilities are unknown luxuries. Many areas do not have toilets, latrines, or proper drains; wastes are disposed of near or in the same rivers, lakes, or wells used for drinking and food preparation. Because developing countries dedicate most of their water resources to agricultural expansion, little remains for domestic use. India, for example, devotes 90 percent of all water to agricultural purposes, seven percent to industry, and only three percent to household use. Out of 3,119 towns in India, only 217 treat their sewage—8 fully, 209 partially. The untreated wastes threaten to contaminate surface waters with several waterborne diseases, such as cholera, typhoid, shigella, meningitis, and diarrheal disease. Worldwide, the lack of sanitary waste disposal and clean drinking water results in over 12 million deaths annually, most of which are in LDCs. Of the estimated four billion people who contract diarrheal disease (the major waterborne disease) each year, three to four million die, most of whom are children.

To increase water availability and provide basic waste treatment requires large sums of money and cooperation among nations. But the results—better health, reduced infant mortality, and population stability—yield a much better return than dollars spent on medical treatment. Disease prevention through an adequate supply of clean freshwater is the key to improving health standards. The greatest successes have come in countries where grassroots movements have encouraged better education about sanitation, the development of community-based water programs, and the use of low-energy treatment technology.

WHAT KINDS OF WATER POLLUTION ARE THERE?

Water pollutants can be divided into eight general categories: organic wastes, disease-causing wastes, plant nutrients, toxic substances, persistent substances, sediments, radioactive substances, and heat. These broad categories—and the interactions among them—indicate the complex nature of water pollution. Consider that one source may be responsible for more than one type of pollutant. For example, improperly treated sewage may contribute organic wastes, disease-causing wastes, plant nutrients, toxic substances, and persistent substances to a waterway. Likewise, a pollutant may fit in more than one category. For example, mercury and polychlorinated biphenyls (PCBs) are both toxic and persistent. Further, one type of pollutant may enter water attached to another type. For example, organic chemical pollutants often adhere to sediments. Many water systems are assaulted by pollutants from all eight categories, compounding the difficulty of clean-up not only by the magnitude of total pollutants but also by the need to use several different techniques. Effective clean-up is essential because a single pollutant may not be found in amounts necessary to kill organisms, but many pollutants acting together, or synergistically, may be deadly.

Organic Wastes

Organic wastes are small pieces of once-living plant or animal matter. They usually are suspended in the water column but sometimes can accumulate in the sediments of lakes or streams. Most suspended organic matter comes from human and other animal wastes or plant residues. Aerobic bacteria pull dissolved oxygen (DO) from the water to break down organic matter, a process called decomposition. Anaerobic bacteria, which often operate in the sediments, do not require oxygen to break down organics; they may emit noxious gases, such as hydrogen sulfide or methane, as a by-product of decomposition.

Decomposition by aerobic bacteria removes DO from the water to the detriment of other aquatic organisms, such as fish and shellfish. As the oxygen is depleted, the species composition of the area may change dramatically, as higher aquatic organisms (such as fish, oysters, and clams) die or leave the area, and organisms that can tolerate low oxygen levels (such as sludge worms and rattailed maggots) proliferate. If the oxygen depletion is drastic enough, it may cause many fish to die, an event known as a fish kill.

Biological oxygen demand (BOD) is a measure of the amount of oxygen needed to decompose organic matter in water. A stream or lake with a high BOD will have a low concentration of DO because oxygen is being used by bacteria to decompose organic matter. Accordingly, a body of water with a high BOD is also high in organic matter. Because DO is a major limiting factor in aquatic habitats, oxygen depletion contributes to the degradation of a stream or lake through the loss of species diversity.

About half of oxygen-demanding pollutants come from nonpoint sources, the most conspicuous of which is animal waste used as fertilizer. Sewage treatment plants and the food-processing and paper industries are notable point sources.

Disease-Causing Wastes

Untreated human or other animal wastes that enter surface waters increase the chance that infectious organisms (such as bacteria, viruses, and protists) will spread disease to humans. Disease outbreaks occur commonly in LDCs, where human sewage is treated improperly, if at all, before it enters an aquatic environment. Since millions of people in LDCs have no basic sanitation, providing adequate supplies of disease-free water presents a major challenge. Cholera, typhoid fever, hepatitis, and dysentery are some major diseases transmitted through drinking water supplies. Even in the United States, where the chlorination of drinking water helps to prevent major outbreaks, contaminated water causes some cases of infectious disease each year. Bacteria from human and nonhuman wastes is the number one contaminant in rural water supplies.

Water quality in the United States is also an issue outside of residential areas. Giardiasis, a disease caused by the protist *Giardia lamblia*, is the country's most common waterborne disease. It is known as camper's-, hiker's-, or backpacker's disease because of its high incidence in those groups. Even the most pristine lakes and streams can harbor these infectious protistans, which enter the water via animal wastes.

Many other diseases also are transmitted by organisms in water. For example, mosquitoes (whose larvae live in water) transmit the protist that causes malaria, and snails transmit the fluke that causes schistosomiasis. Both of these diseases are serious threats to human health in LDCs.

The presence of fecal coliform, bacteria normally found in the large intestines of humans and other animals, indicates the likelihood of contamination by waterborne diseases. Coliform standards for drinking water are stricter than those for water used for recreation. The International Food Policy Research Institute recommends that drinking water have a coliform count of no more than 100 organisms per 100 milliliters, but many waterways do not meet this recommendation. For example, several rivers in Latin America have coliform counts of more than 100,000 organisms per 100 milliliters. In the United States, despite attention to proper sewage treatment, many beaches are closed each summer because of high coliform counts.

Plant Nutrients

Algal and aquatic plant growth is normally limited by the amount of nitrogen and phosphorus in the water. The large amount of these nutrients contained in sewage—including the phosphates in some detergents and agricultural and urban runoff—stimulates massive reproduction and rapid growth in algae, known as algal blooms. Algae impart a green color to water and form a "scum" on the surface and on rocks near shore. When algae die and decompose, more organic matter is added to the water, increasing the BOD. Fast-moving water generally is not as affected by algal growth as slow-moving water. Ponds, lakes, and bays are most affected through the process of eutrophication.

Excess phosphorus generally is not a human health hazard, but excess nitrogen—in the form of nitrates—is. Found largely in fertilizers and organic waste from livestock feedlots, nitrates are soluble in water and do not bind to soil particles, making them highly mobile. As such, they wash into surface water supplies and percolate into groundwater. Nitrates in drinking water pose a significant health threat. For example, in the intestinal tract of infants, they are reduced to nitrites, which oxidize the hemoglobin in blood, rendering it unable to carry oxygen. This condition, called methemoglobinemia, can result in brain damage or death. Nitrates and nitrites also can form toxic substances called nitrosamines, which have been found to cause birth defects and cancer in animals. Still other studies have established a link between high nitrate levels and stomach cancer in humans.

Sediments

By weight, sediments are the most abundant water pollutant. With every hard rain, muddied streams and rivers are a visible reminder of the millions of tons of sediments that wash from the land into aquatic systems. Particles of soil, rock, sand, and minerals run off the land, enter waterways, and fill in lake bottoms and river channels.

Sediments contain nutrients, and natural erosion thus helps to maintain the fertility of aquatic ecosystems. However, a dramatic increase in the sediment load—from poorly managed agricultural lands and urban construction sites, for example—can cause problems. While the threat to human health is minimal because filtration easily removes sediments from drinking water, aquatic life often is adversely affected. Excess sediments smother fish eggs and prevent light from penetrating to rooted aquatic plants. Further, chemicals may adhere to sediments and accumulate on the bottom of bodies of water, where they can contaminate aquatic habitats. Some dredged sediments are so laced with dangerous chemicals that they must be treated like hazardous wastes. For example, polyaromatic hydrocarbons (PAHs), first identified in cigarette smoke, are carcinogens that bind to sediment particles. Major sources of PAHs include emissions from coke ovens, creosote plants, and coal gasification plants; sewage containing petroleum products; automobile exhaust; and oil leaked from boats.

Toxic Substances

Toxic substances have the potential to cause injury to living organisms and their cells. Toxic organic substances include oils, gasoline, greases, solvents, cleaning agents, biocides, and synthetics. Thousands of organic chemicals enter aquatic ecosystems every day. Most are by-products of industrial processes or are present in countless commonly used products. Some organic chemicals, such as dioxin, PCBs and trichloroethylene, are carcinogenic, meaning they cause (or are believed to cause) cancer.

Inorganic toxic substances include acids from mine drainage and manufacturing processes; salt from roads and irrigation ditches; brine from offshore oil and natural gas wells; and metals such as chromium, copper, zinc, lead, and mercury from industrial processes. Lead and mercury, in particular, have received a great deal of attention. In the United States, lead contamination from old pipes and solder joints caused the Environmental Protection Agency (EPA) to release an advisory explaining how consumers can reduce the lead content in their drinking water until new pipes and joints are installed. Also highly dangerous, mercury in water becomes methylated by bacteria; methylmercury accumulates in the fatty tissues of organisms such as fish and magnifies through food chains. In Japan, this process has led to a condition known as Minimata disease, which stunts the development of the brains and nervous systems of children who eat fish or shellfish contaminated with mercury.

Many rivers, lakes, and bays have thousands of toxic substances in their sediments. The increased incidence of cancers discovered in bottom-dwelling fish has been traced to contaminated sediments. Particularly affected in the United States are New York Harbor, Boston Harbor, Puget Sound, Ohio's Black River, and Michigan's Torch Lake. Further, the leaching of toxic chemicals from dumps and landfills into surface waters and groundwater supplies is a serious environmental problem in many industrialized countries.

Persistent Substances

As their name implies, persistent substances are pollutants that normally are not changed or degraded to harmless substances, instead persisting in their original form in the environment. Pesticides, such as DDT and chlordane, and organic contaminants, such as PAHs and PCBs, do not break down easily and tend to magnify through food chains. Consequently, organisms at higher trophic levels, such as the bald eagle and the polar bear, suffer the most serious effects of these persistent substances.

Many plastic products, such as bags, monofilament line and beverage six-pack rings, have a life expectancy of hundreds of years. Plastic pollution is particularly troublesome in marine systems. Plastic bags and balloons can become entwined in the stomachs and intestines of sea turtles and mammals, which mistake them for food such as jellyfish. Polystyrene plastic foam breaks up into pellets, which also resemble food. When consumed by sea turtles, the buoyant pellets can keep them from diving and clog their systems, causing them to starve to death. Parent seabirds also can feed these pellets to their young, inadvertently starving them.

Radioactive Substances

Radioactive isotopes, such as strontium 90, cesium 137 and iodine 131, enter water from several sources: the mining and processing of radioactive ores; the use of refined radioactive materials for industrial, scientific, and medical purposes; nuclear accidents; the production and testing of nuclear weapons; and the use of cooling water in nuclear power plants. Many of these isotopes magnify in food chains and can cause cell mutations and cancers. Water pollution from radioactive substances is so serious that when Soviet authorities found extensive groundwater contamination in the area around the 1986 Chernobyl nuclear accident, they sealed off over 7,000 wells within a 50-mile radius of the plant; drilled emergency wells into bedrock to provide water to bakeries and milk-bottling plants; and constructed an emergency pipeline from the uncontaminated Desno River.

Heat

Changes in water temperature can cause major shifts in the structure of biotic communities. Water is used for cooling purposes in manufacturing, industry, and electric power plants. The heated water then is returned to its source. Hot water holds less oxygen, speeds up respiration in aquatic organisms, and tends to accelerate ecosystem degradation. The relatively still waters of lakes and bays are particularly vulnerable to thermal pollution.

MANAGING WATER RESOURCES

In this section, we discuss problems surrounding the use of water worldwide, focusing on four "hotspots" around the globe. We also examine the legislation that guides the management of water resources in the United States. Finally, we look at how this country treats drinking water and wastewater, as well as how it manages and protects groundwater, surface waters, and marine waters.

WHAT PROBLEMS SURROUND THE USE OF WATER WORLDWIDE?

In 1998, Population Action International reported that eight percent of the world's population (nearly half a billion people) living in 29 countries are affected by **water stress**—the episodic lack of renewable freshwater—or the more serious condition of **water scarcity**—the chronic lack of renewable freshwater. Just five years later, in 2003, the United Nations' World Water Assessment Programme (WWAP) published the *World Water Development Report,* which found that a full two billion people living in 40 countries are suffering water shortages. Depending on future rates of population growth, between 2.7 and 3.2 billion people may be living under water-stressed or water-scarce conditions by 2025 (Figure 10.5). By 2050, one in four people will live in countries affected by episodic or chronic shortages of freshwater.

Globally, water resources are the source of hundreds of political tensions, economic concerns, and environmental problems. For example, some countries must share access to rivers, which generates political unrest. Further, many areas have been subjected to prolonged droughts; as the water table falls, streams and waterholes dry up, as do sources of groundwater. Yet, while drought poses a serious problem, many difficulties associated with too little water are of our own making. The combination of intensive agriculture and population growth places a great strain on water availability in arid climates such as the African Sahel, the Middle East, vast areas of the Asian continent, and the American Southwest. We examine each of these regions more closely in the paragraphs below.

African Sahel

Perhaps nowhere is water scarcity more severe than in the three principle countries of the Nile River Valley: Egypt, Sudan, and Ethiopia. Locked in the vise of water scarcity, these nations have growing populations and rely heavily upon the Nile River for irrigation. In 2004, Egypt supported a population of 73 million people and garnered much of the Nile's water. With its population projected to reach 127 million by 2050, Egypt's demand for water will rise dramatically. Likewise,

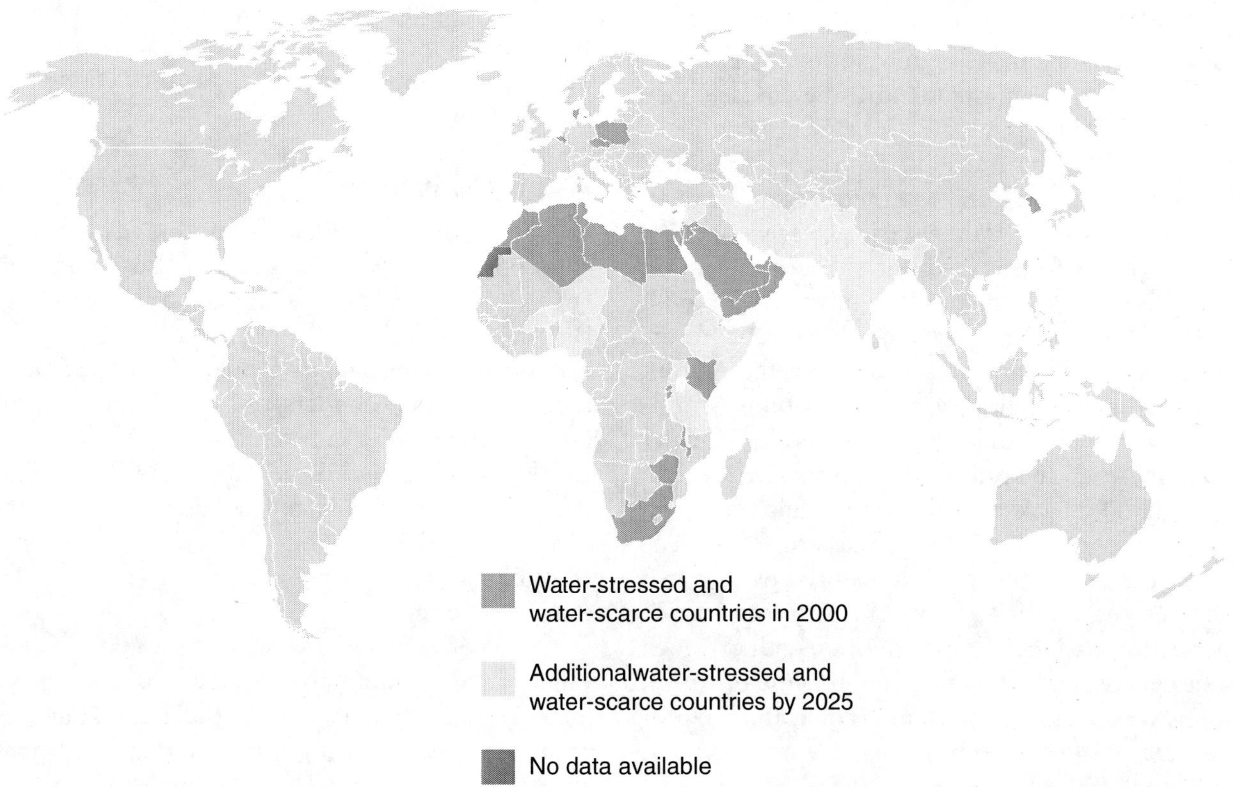

Figure 10.5 Water-short countries in 2000 and 2025. Areas most severely affected by water stress and water scarcity include the African Sahel, the Middle East, India, Haiti, and Peru. Source: *Population Action International,* People in the Balance: Population and Natural Resources at the Turn of the Millennium *(2002).*

Sudan—whose 2004 population of 39 million is expected to more than double by 2050—is becoming increasingly dependent on the Nile River. Even more startling, however, is the situation in Ethiopia, which controls 85 percent of the Nile's headwaters. A country whose current population of 72 million is expected to explode to 173 million by 2050, Ethiopia plans to recover from years of civil unrest by relying on the Nile River to promote economic development. In fact, by the end of 1998, Ethiopia already had constructed 200 small dams and designed extensive irrigation and power generation projects. As Ethiopia continues to increase its reliance on the Nile, less water will be available to Egypt and Sudan—just as their populations demand more. Yet, the difference in per capita gross national product between Egypt ($1,080) and Ethiopia ($100) emphasizes the very real need of Ethiopia to increase its use of the Nile River.

Middle East

Like the African Sahel, the Middle East faces the prospect of severe water shortages within the next several decades. In this region of political turmoil, water may be the resource that forges closer ties—or it may be the match that sets off the powderkeg. Syria's plight, especially, illustrates the difficulties of securing clean freshwater in a dry and fast-growing area. To examine Syria's situation, we must look to Turkey, its neighbor to the north. Since the 1930s, Turkey has been planning the Southeastern Anatolia Project, an ambitious effort to develop the nation's eastern region through a series of dams and hydroelectric power plants. The project's cornerstone is the gigantic Ataturk Dam on the Euphrates River, and in 1990, Turkey began to fill the Ataturk Reservoir to reach a volume equal to the Sea of Galilee. To carry this water from the Ataturk Reservoir to eastern Turkey, a series of tunnels measuring over 16 miles in length and 25 feet in diameter was built. When the project is completed in 2010, 22 dams will hold back the waters of the Euphrates and Tigris rivers, both of which rise in eastern Turkey. The flow of the Euphrates could be reduced by as much as 80 percent, creating a near-crisis situation for the downstream nations of Syria and Iraq, both of which are heavily dependent on the river. Because upstream nations are under no legally binding obligation to provide water to downstream nations, the only recourse open to Syria and Iraq (short of war) is to claim that they have historical rights of use and urge Turkey to honor those rights. Syria and Iraq both claim historical use of the Euphrates; Iraq also claims use of the Tigris. In advance of the completion of the Southeastern Anatolia Project, the project's Council of Ministers has ordered the development of a guiding document drafted with input from other governments. However, a technical committee comprising representatives from Turkey, Syria, and Iraq has been unable to agree on how best to meet the water needs of all three countries.

Even now, Syria is beset by serious water-related problems. Its population growth rate of 2.4 percent strains the nation's ability to provide water, food, and power for its people. Syria already has exploited its western farmland, which is fed by rain, and consequently finds that it must farm the arid eastern steppes in order to grow enough food to ensure self-sufficiency. Water withdrawn from the Euphrates River at the Euphrates Dam, located in Tabaq, Syria, irrigates some 500,000 acres (202,347 hectares). But feeding the country's population in 2050—an estimated 35 million people—will require cultivating millions of additional acres. Currently, there is only enough water in the Euphrates River to operate two of the eight turbines at the Euphrates Dam. One immediate result has been a reduction in power generation; the electricity in Syrian cities routinely is cut off for several hours each day. Although there was never enough water to power all the turbines, Syria maintains that it has even less water now, a consequence of the construction of the Ataturk Dam.

Asian Continent

Conflicts surrounding the distribution and use of water erupt not only between nations, but also within them. For example, the construction of the Three Gorges Dam across the mighty Yangtze River has caused internal discord among China's people. Though the dam is expected to supply one-tenth of China's energy output upon its completion in 2009, it also will flood prime farmland and thousands of villages, displacing more than 1.2 million people and threatening many other species, including the white-fin dolphin, the Chinese alligator, the finless porpoise, the white crane, and several species of monkey.

A major contributing factor to water stress and water scarcity, groundwater depletion is a problem in many regions of Asia. Parts of India and China, for example, are experiencing severe shortages as demand exceeds supply. Competition for the use of surface waters also has become increasingly intense. In 1960, the Aral Sea, located in Central Asia, was the fourth largest inland body of water (in surface area) in the world, behind the Caspian Sea, Lake Superior, and Lake Victoria. Now, it is about one-third its former size (in area) and one-eighth in volume, and its salinity has tripled. Wind blowing across the exposed sea bottom deposits salty grit throughout the region. The principal cause of the Aral Sea's decline is large-scale irrigation, which withdraws water from the sea's two major freshwater tributaries, the Amu Dar'ya and the Syr Dar'ya.

American Southwest

The water problems of the African Sahel, the Middle East, and areas of Asia are half a world away, but a growing population poses similar concerns in the American Southwest. Throughout history, cities in the United States have tried to balance population growth and water use by finding ways to increase quantity while still protecting quality. But today, the water wars in the American Southwest clearly indicate that water is a limited resource. Communities here always have had too little water, and continued growth only exacerbates the problem. The struggle over water often pits community against community, farmers against urban dwellers, and ranchers against wilderness preservationists. Water is power, particularly in this area where, as Mark Twain once noted, "whiskey's for drinken [sic], water's for fightin." Today's water wars are fought with legal suits, research papers, and blueprints rather than with six shooters and dynamite. For example, El Paso, Texas, sued for the right to sink wells into aquifers that traditionally have served other interests in New Mexico. The Central Arizona Pipeline, completed in the early 1990s, was intended to relieve the state's serious groundwater shortage by diverting billions of gallons of Colorado River water to Phoenix and Tucson. However, the water delivered to many Tucson residents was plagued by poor color, taste, and smell due to a combination of factors, including new treatment methods and the corrosion of old plumbing systems. As a result, the city continues to deplete its groundwater resources while attempting to devise a solution to its water dilemma. The Colorado, a once-mighty river, now trickles to the sea, laden with silt, pollution, and salts. From Utah to California, cities and irrigation projects drink the river dry.

Consider that from the one-hundredth meridian to the Pacific Ocean, rainfall averages less than 20 inches per year (with the exception of the Pacific Northwest and high mountains). Westerners live in a near perpetual drought. While Chicago receives about 40 inches of rain per year, Los Angeles averages just 9, and Phoenix averages 8. Many western areas do not receive enough rain to sustain agribusiness or rapid increases in urban growth. Yet, cities like Palm Springs continue watering dozens of golf courses, Arizona farms grow alfalfa in the desert, and dry towns like Phoenix experience phenomenal growth because federal support for large development projects makes water accessible at a low consumer cost.

As long as the price remains low, consumers have little incentive to evaluate future projects in terms of the actual availability of water or to conserve current supplies. For example, drip irrigation systems are more efficient than conventional systems, but because they are costly to install, they are used less frequently. But as demand continues to escalate, so, too, will the cost of pumping and transporting water. Moreover, future generations will not have the easy options that have been made available to us: aquifers to tap, rivers to dam, and lakes to drain.

WHAT IS THE SAFE DRINKING WATER ACT?

Underlying all water management legislation in the United States is the attempt to address one perennial question: How do we increase the quantity and protect the quality of water supplies to keep pace with increasing population? This question took on an added dimension in 1974, when the EPA announced that high concentrations of 66 human-made chemicals, including six suspected carcinogens, were discovered in the drinking water of New Orleans, Louisiana, situated on the banks of the Mississippi River. Many of the contaminants were traced to petrochemical businesses upstream of the city, agricultural operations, and numerous other industries based along the river and its tributaries. These discoveries focused attention on an entirely new water purification problem: removing substances toxic to human health.

In part, the condition of New Orleans' drinking water helped spur the passage of the Safe Drinking Water Act of 1974. The Act set national drinking water standards, called maximum contaminant levels, for pollutants that might adversely affect human health, and three years later, the first standards went into effect. It also established standards to protect groundwater from toxic wastes injected into the soil, once a common waste disposal practice.

In 1982 and 1983, the EPA established a priority list to set regulations for over 70 toxic substances that are likely to be found in drinking water. In 1986, when Congress reauthorized the Safe Drinking Water Act, it directed the EPA to monitor drinking water for unregulated contaminants and to inform public water suppliers of targeted substances. The 1986 reauthorization also instructed the EPA to set standards within 30 years for all 70 substances on its priority list. By 1995, the priority list had been expanded, and the EPA had set standards for 83 substances.

When the Safe Drinking Water Act was reauthorized again in 1996, the EPA was directed to regulate additional substances, including radon, sulfates, and arsenic. The amendments also instructed the EPA to identify and monitor at least five new contaminants every five years. To better familiarize residents with the water they drink, water suppliers must now provide customers with annual Consumer Confidence Reports that include information about several factors, including the sources of water, levels of regulated contaminants, and health concerns for any contaminants that are in violation.

WHAT IS THE CLEAN WATER ACT?

In 1972, President Richard Nixon signed the Federal Water Pollution Control Act, commonly known as the Clean Water Act. Amended in 1977, the Act divided pollutants into three classes: toxic, conventional, and unconventional. It stipulated that industries must use the best available technology (BAT) to treat toxic wastes before releasing them into waters. Conventional pollutants, such as municipal wastes, must be treated using the best conventional technology (BCT). All other pollutants, classified as unconventional, must meet BAT standards, though waivers can be granted for pollutants in this class. If the BAT will not protect certain waters, stricter standards (including "no discharge") must be enforced.

The Clean Water Act contained several stipulations pertaining to industry. It established pretreatment standards for industrial wastes that pass through sewage treatment plants. These standards require industries to handle toxic wastes rather than simply dump them into municipal sewers. In the past, such dumping resulted in the production of toxic sewage sludge. The Act also mandated that the EPA or state must grant a permit to allow the release of any pollutant into navigable waters. These permits define and limit the amount of pollutants that can be included in the wastewater and form the primary means for implementing the Clean Water Act. Discharges must meet the appropriate toxic, conventional, or unconventional standards. Unfortunately, the goal—to phase out toxic discharges by 1985—was not met, largely because the EPA allows local municipalities to enforce compliance with discharge standards.

The Water Quality Act of 1987, a reauthorization of the original Clean Water Act, provided $20 billion to curb water pollution, primarily through the construction of wastewater treatment plants. The federal government provides 20 percent of the money needed; local sources provide 80 percent. (Even so, the cost of building or remodeling existing sewage treatment plants remains prohibitive for many small communities.) The 1987 Act also provided money for nonpoint-source pollution programs, which afforded appropriations to help state and local governments improve the water quality of bays and estuaries. Through a National Estuary Program, money was earmarked to help clean up and protect San Francisco Bay, Puget Sound, and Boston Harbor. In addition, special appropriations have been made to monitor and control pollutants entering the Great Lakes and Chesapeake Bay.

Another provision of the reauthorization granted the U.S. Army Corps of Engineers the authority to regulate the dredging and filling of wetlands. That provision has proven controversial, with some landowners maintaining that limits on the use of private land amount to a "taking" by the federal government. They contend that landowners should be compensated financially for a portion of the development value of the land. Those who support the wetlands provision point out that draining wetlands adversely affects the entire community because it interferes with the invaluable ecosystem services they provide, including water purification and flood control. Therefore, when a private landowner develops a wetland, he or she alone realizes the profit, but the entire community pays an ecological and economic cost.

An extension of the Clean Water Act, the Great Lakes Legacy Act of 2002 was passed to address the growing problem of sediment contamination in the rivers, harbors, and other waterways that comprise the Great Lakes system. Persistently high concentrations of contaminants in sediments can make bottom-dwelling fish unsafe to eat and cause disease in aquatic and shore wildlife. The Act authorized $270 million for five years, beginning in 2004, to remediate contaminated sediments in the Great Lakes; this remediation also includes funds designated for research and public outreach.

HOW ARE DRINKING WATER SUPPLIES TREATED?

After water is withdrawn from a lake, river or aquifer, it is treated before being distributed to local destinations such as homes, businesses, schools, and hospitals. Most water treatment systems, large or small, include certain basic steps: A chemical such as aluminum sulfate (alum) is added to water supplies to create small gelatinous particles, called floc, which gather dirt and other solids. Gentle mixing of the water causes floc particles to join and form larger particles; floc and sediment fall to the bottom and eventually are removed as sludge. The water then is filtered through a granular material such as sand or crushed anthracite coal (carbon). Chlorine is added to kill bacteria and other microbes, and a chemical such as quicklime is added to reduce acidity and prevent corrosion in city and household pipes. Many municipal treatment plants also add fluoride to water supplies to prevent tooth decay.

Treated water is sent through a network of pipes to consumers. To ensure its quality, water must be monitored and tested throughout the treatment and delivery process. Generally, surface water is more complicated to treat than groundwater because it is more likely to be contaminated.

HOW IS WASTEWATER TREATED?

In rural (and some suburban) areas that have suitable soils, sewage and wastewater from each home usually are discharged into a **septic tank**, an underground tank made of concrete or fiberglass. Solids settle to the bottom of the tank. Grease and oil rise to the top where they are trapped and periodically removed to prevent them from clogging the tank. Through anaerobic respiration, bacteria in the wastewater feed on the sludge and scum and liquefy the waste products. The treated wastewater then filters out into a drain field. This process requires time, and septic systems must be large enough to accommodate the expected flow from each home (Figure 10.6).

Wastewater in urban areas must be managed much differently. Underground sewers collect wastewater from residences, businesses, schools, hospitals, industrial sites, and other buildings and transport it to sewage treatment plants. These plants are designed to make wastewater safe for discharge into streams or rivers or for reuse.

There are two kinds of sewer systems: combined and separate. A **combined sewer system** carries both wastewater and rainwater. Pipes that collect each type of water connect with an interceptor pipe that leads to a treatment plant. The interceptor pipe is large enough to hold several times the normal combined flow. But during storms, the rainwater flow might increase by a factor of 100. Since the combined sewer system is designed to protect the treatment plant, which can handle only a certain amount of flow, and to prevent flow from backing up into buildings, some of the combined flow (raw sewage and rainwater) may bypass the treatment plant and go directly into a receiving stream.

As the name implies, a **separate sewer system** consists of sanitary sewers, which carry only wastewater, and storm sewers, which carry only rainwater and melting snow. Rainwater follows a different route from that of wastewater, bypassing the treatment plant and going directly into a receiving stream. Separating sanitary and rainwater flow is costly, but it does significantly lower the volume of pollutants that enter a receiving stream after a storm. Unfortunately, separate systems have one significant flaw. Rainwater often picks up and transports sediments, oils, greases and other nonpoint-source pollutants, and because it is not treated, these pollutants are carried directly into the aquatic environment.

Once the flow enters a sewage treatment plant, it usually goes through a multistage process to reduce it to an acceptable effluent, the water that leaves the plant (Figure 10.7). Properly treating sewage maintains the integrity of the stream or river receiving the effluent.

Primary treatment is a physical process to remove undissolved solids. Screens remove sticks, rags, and other large objects. In some plants, the remaining sewage is chopped or ground into smaller particles, then passed to a grit chamber where dense material such as cinders, sand, and small stones settle out and are removed. Undissolved suspended materials, including greases and oils, are removed in a settling tank or primary clarifier. Greases and oils are skimmed off of the top; the undissolved organic material sinks to the bottom, where it forms a mass called raw sludge. This sludge is drawn off to a sludge digester where it is further reduced by anaerobic bacteria.

In plants that provide only primary treatment, the remaining liquid, called primary effluent, may be chlorinated and released to the receiver stream. Primary treatment is only about 50 percent effective at

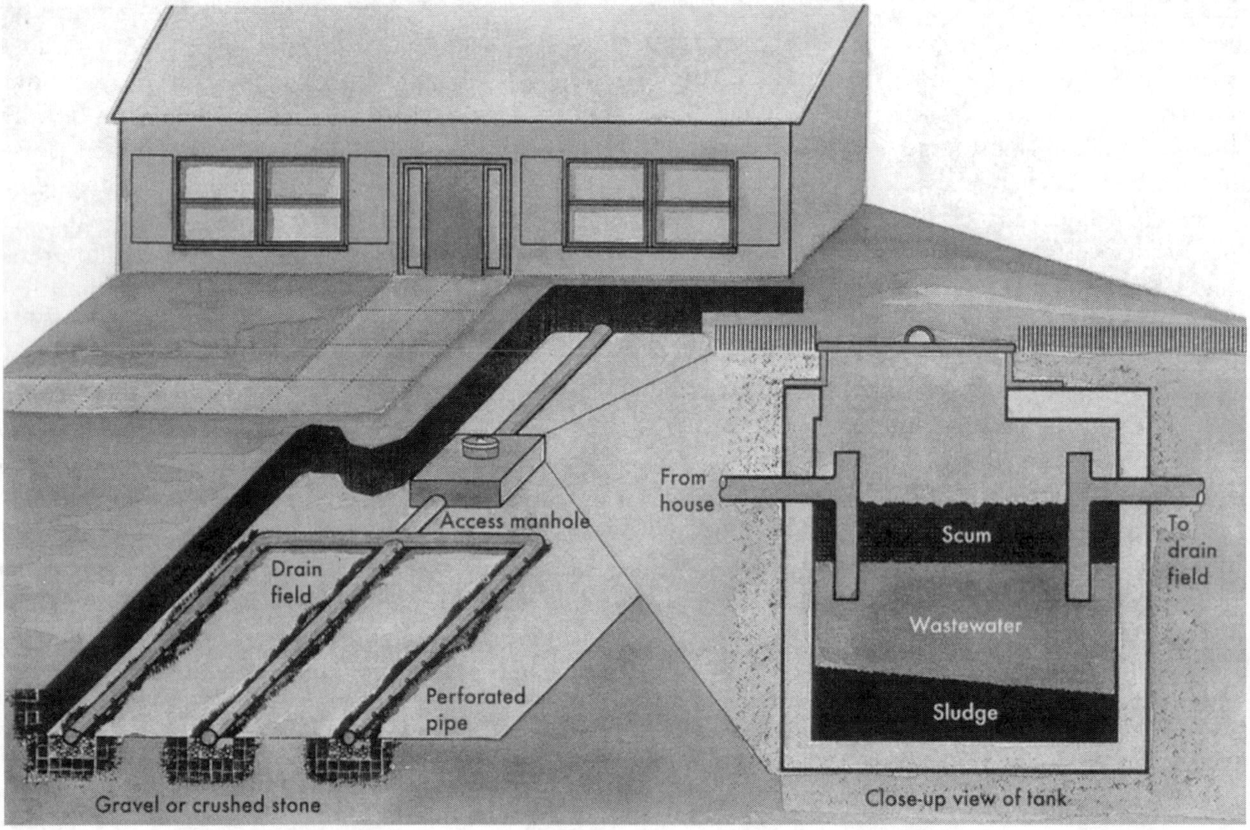

Figure 10.6 Septic tank system. In a properly functioning septic tank, only treated wastewater filters into the drain field. The drain field should be constructed so as to allow the water to drain properly and the soil to absorb the water and nutrients. For this reason, drain fields should not be placed in clay or sandy soils. When septic systems are not functioning properly, effluent (the water that leaves the tank) can be seen rising to ground level and drains or toilets operate slowly or not at all. Odors can often be detected near or below drain fields.

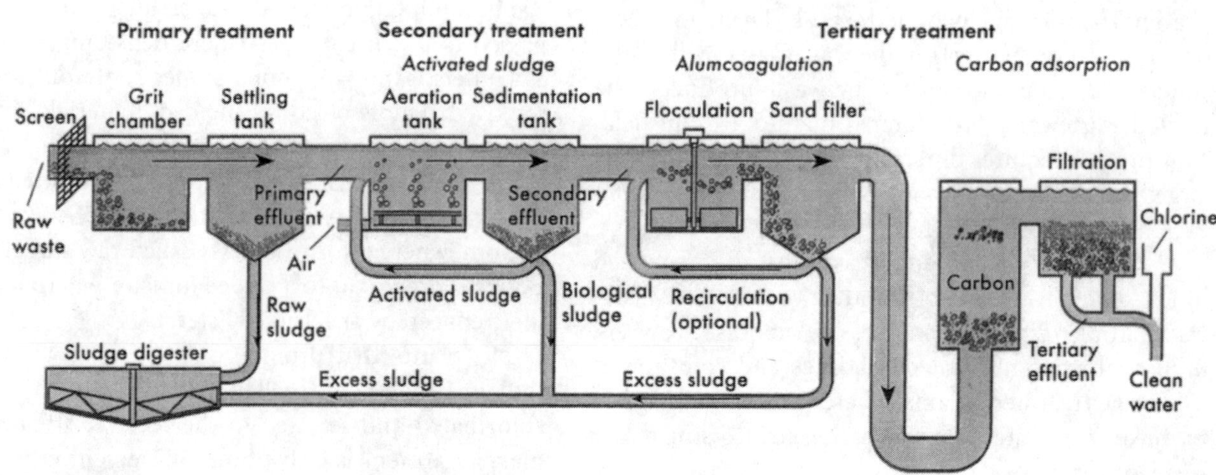

Figure 10.7 Multistage wastewater treatment process.

removing solids. It cannot remove excess nutrients, dissolved organic material, or bacteria.

Secondary treatment is a biological process. At sewage treatment plants, primary effluent is treated in one of two ways: trickling filters or activated sludge. Plants with trickling filters have tanks with beds of stones several feet thick. As wastewater passes, or trickles, through the beds, a diverse population of organisms living on the stones, including aerobic bacteria, protists, rotifers, algae, fungi and insect larvae, consume most of the dissolved organic matter. After leaving the filter, wastewater is allowed to settle in a secondary clarifier and then may be disinfected with chlorine and released to the environment.

In plants using activated sludge, primary effluent is pumped into an aeration tank (in which oxygen is added) and combined with biological sludge, creating a suitable environment for aerobic bacteria to digest the dissolved organic material still present in the wastewater. After aeration, the secondary effluent passes to a sedimentation tank or secondary clarifier where biological sludge is removed. Part of the sludge is recycled back to the aeration tanks, and the remainder is removed to the digester. The secondary effluent can then be chlorinated and released. Secondary effluent is usually considered to be 85 to 90 percent treated.

Tertiary treatment may be a physical or chemical process. It is designed to remove ammonia, nutrients, and organic compounds still remaining in the wastewater. Nearly all of the remaining solids or chemicals can be removed by sand filters, alum coagulation, or activated carbon **adsorption**—whereby organic compounds bind, or stick, to carbon particles but do not chemically combine with them. Tertiary effluent then can be disinfected and released to the environment. Tertiary effluent is considered to be 90 to 95 percent treated. In many instances, it is of a higher quality than the water in the receiver stream and is near drinking water quality. If phosphates are removed during this stage, such advanced treatment can render the water as much as 97 to 99 percent treated. However, because the cost of tertiary treatment is often prohibitive, most sewage treatment plants in the U.S. end the process with secondary treatment.

Proper sewage plant construction and operation are expensive, and for many towns and municipalities, the costs of upgrading are prohibitive. Large metropolitan areas also are struggling to pay for new plant construction to accommodate increased populations. Though the Clean Water Act aims to provide funds for maintaining treatment plants, more could be done on the national, state, and local levels to foster better wastewater management. Perhaps funding priorities should turn toward research and development: Effluent and properly treated sewage sludge can be resources used for constructive purposes. In addition, individuals should begin to realize that, once flushed, sewage is not merely "out of sight, out of mind." See *What You Can Do: To Protect Water Resources* (page 244) for ways to reduce the amount of wastewater leaving the home.

HOW IS GROUNDWATER MANAGED?

Groundwater withdrawal in the United States has increased 300 percent since the 1950s. As demand increases, both the quantity and quality of this essential resource are threatened. Our past use of groundwater supplies was based on two popular misconceptions: (1) there is an inexhaustible supply of groundwater, and (2) groundwater is purified as it percolates through the ground. Let's examine both misconceptions more closely.

It is difficult to imagine that the total groundwater supply in the United States, some 30 to 60 quintillion gallons, could be exhausted, but because groundwater is not evenly distributed and because all aquifers do not recharge in the same way, many aquifers experience overdraft. An **overdraft** is the withdrawal of water from a source faster than it can recharge; it is akin to writing a check for more money than you have deposited in your bank account. Recharge also is adversely affected by draining wetlands, clearing forests and diverting streams, all of which can reduce the amount of water absorbed by the soil. Paving for buildings, parking lots, and roads prevents water from entering the soil, as do prolonged drought and flooding.

In 2000, the USGS found that 68 percent of all groundwater extracted in the United States is used for agricultural purposes, particularly irrigation. Irrigation uses seven times more groundwater than all of our city water systems combined. Especially in the western and southern states, irrigation strains groundwater resources. Severe overdrafts, called **water mining**, can deplete aquifers, lowering the water table so drastically that further extraction is no longer economically feasible. The High Plains aquifer of the U.S. West has suffered water mining largely as a result of accelerated pumping for irrigation. In the early 1980s, about 16,000 square miles (41,440 square kilometers) of the aquifer experienced water table declines of more than 50 feet (15 meters), and an additional

50,000 square miles (129,500 square kilometers) fell more than 10 feet (three meters). Floyd County, Texas, endured the most severe decline—200 feet (60 meters). By 1994, water tables in parts of Texas, the Oklahoma Panhandle, and southwestern Kansas had declined by 140 feet (42 meters). Projecting continued population increases in the South and Southwest, the USGS forecasts widespread, severe depletions throughout the High Plains region by 2020.

Overdrafts can lead to land subsidence. Water pressure in the pores of aquifers helps to support the overlying material. When large volumes of water are removed without adequate recharge, the pores collapse, allowing the rock, sand, or clay particles to settle. If the affected area is large, the ground can collapse, or subside, and form sink holes, cracks, and fissures of varying sizes. Once the ground subsides, there is little chance for it to hold water again, as it generally becomes too tightly compressed to expand with new water. Dramatic effects of subsidence have occurred nationwide. For example, in parts of Florida, sink holes have swallowed trees, cars, and buildings.

In addition to problems of quantity, problems of groundwater quality also are becoming critical. For many years, we erroneously believed that groundwater was safe from surface pollutants. We thought that aquifers were deep enough so that contaminants would not reach them. Landfills were routinely located in abandoned gravel pits along rivers, enabling chemicals to leach into both surface and groundwater. Moreover, we thought that pollutants dumped on or near the ground's surface would be filtered out of the water as it percolated through soil, sand and rock layers, so that the water would be purified by the time it reached the water table.

Because groundwater usually moves slowly, the resulting pollution took a long time to show up. But now, groundwater contamination has reached such magnitude that surveys indicate it is a concern to people in all 50 states. Improperly treated sewage is a problem in rural areas nationwide, where septic tank systems are the norm. Thirty-four states have reported serious groundwater contamination from toxic chemicals. Pesticides, which have been found in groundwater in 25 states, are the major contaminants in agricultural states such as Iowa, Florida, Nebraska, Mississippi, Minnesota, Wisconsin and Idaho, all of which also are among the 10 states most dependent on groundwater for drinking water.

HOW ARE SURFACE WATERS MANAGED?

Pollution and development pose serious challenges to those responsible for managing the United States' network of lakes, rivers, and coastal areas. The Clean Water Act helped to protect the nation's tens of thousands of lakes by dramatically improving the treatment of wastewater (principally organic wastes), but toxic pollution remains a serious threat. Airborne toxins are thought to contribute significantly to the total contamination in the Great Lakes and are responsible for the acidification of lakes and streams in the Adirondack Mountains and parts of eastern Canada. Likewise, accelerated eutrophication is a problem in many lakes and reservoirs, which receive high inputs of nutrients from wastewater and agricultural runoff. In some lakes, such as Lake Erie, eutrophication has been slowed by banning phosphates in detergents, encouraging farming practices that reduce runoff, and improving wastewater treatment. Finally, development of coastal areas, especially along the Great Lakes and the Gulf of Mexico, can cause soil erosion, thereby contributing to water quality problems.

An extensive system of rivers crosses the United States. Thousands of rivers and streams flow year-round in the East. The Midwest also has many rivers, though some streams are dry for part of the year. In the West and Southwest, many waterways are dry beds for significant periods of time each year. Yet regardless of flow pattern, rivers throughout the country are besieged by numerous threats. In the West and Southwest, the Bureau of Reclamation began a desert reclamation project in 1902 to provide water storage and conveyance for irrigation projects in 17 western states. Proponents of the desert reclamation project maintained that it would pay for itself via increased use of public lands and a growing population. Unfortunately, low interest rates, water subsidies, and procedural loopholes delayed the payback, and the onset of cheap water discouraged conservation. In response, dams and water diversion became the order of the day across the country. On the positive side, dams control flooding, generate hydropower, and store water for a variety of uses. On the negative side, when unusually heavy rainfall causes a dammed river to rise, the build-up of energy can become so great that the river breaches levees and releases all of the energy—and water—in one devastating burst.

Dams, diversions, and channelizations have left few free-flowing rivers in the United States, largely the result of federal policy that puts power generation before environmental concerns. For example, the Federal Energy Regulatory Commission (FERC) grants licenses for hydroelectric plants on free-flowing rivers. FERC also can override states' designations of scenic rivers and permit the construction of dams to generate power. Further, in western states, water rights are guaranteed by law for hydroelectric, agricultural, municipal, and industrial use. Streams can be diverted to the extent that no water remains, leaving the streambed dry. In contrast, few water rights are granted for environmental purposes, including uses for wildlife, wilderness and human recreation, as well as the replenishing of groundwater.

Pollution from a variety of human activities has significantly altered most rivers and streams in the United States. Much of this pollution stems from nonpoint sources, including acid drainage from mining operations and agricultural and urban runoff. However, grassroots activists and responsible corporate citizens are rising to the defense of the nation's surface waters. For example, the two sewage treatment plants in Milwaukee, Wisconsin, flush approximately 200 million gallons (758 million liters) of wastewater into Lake Michigan each day. Included in that wastewater are hundreds of pounds of toxic chemicals generated by the more than 500 industries that use the Milwaukee District Sewage System. To address this issue, Milwaukee has developed a voluntary program that calls for companies to halt or minimize their toxic waste discharges. Participating companies realize economic savings while lessening their environmental impact. Likewise, in a first-of-its-kind action, the Pillsbury and Midbury Coal Mining Company donated its water rights (worth $7.2 million) for conservation purposes to help maintain flow through Black Canyon on the Gunnison River in Colorado. Black Canyon is considered one of the best natural trout streams in the West and is noted for its scenic beauty and populations of river otters and eagles. In addition, residents in many cities and towns are voting to enact river corridor management programs that create greenways and parkways, regulate flood plain development, and rejuvenate unused manufacturing areas. Similarly, communities in Oregon's Willamette River Basin are helping to protect the river and its watershed.

HOW ARE MARINE WATERS MANAGED?

Both pollution and overuse can result in abuse of the ocean ecosystem. Just as oceans are a vast sink for minerals, nutrients and gases, they also are a sink for pollutants. Eighty-five percent of ocean pollutants come from the land; 90 percent directly affect estuaries, coastal wetlands, coral reefs, and continental shelves. Indeed, humans dump thousands of chemicals into the most biologically productive ocean zones, where they slowly accumulate in aquatic food chains.

Our careless attitude toward the oceans—evident in our indiscriminate disposal of wastes, liberal use and release of toxic substances, and unwillingness to prevent erosion—has begun to exact a tremendous ecological toll on their vital life processes. In the United States, more than one-half of the coastal wetlands that existed at the beginning of European colonization have been dredged and filled, and entire communities have been eliminated from productive estuaries. We also have deposited billions of tons of sewage sludge, garbage, and dredge spoils into coastal and shelf waters. The magnitude of this pollution is so great that it often returns as "gifts from the sea," closing beaches and destroying shellfish beds all along the coasts.

Until recently, little thought was given to managing and preserving marine environments. However, the most promising trend in water resources management is the recognition that coastal zones and oceans are living ecosystems. Realizing the important role that each plays in maintaining the integrity of the biosphere, we are beginning to propose viable management strategies. For example, ongoing research that uses living organisms to biomonitor ocean and estuarine ecosystems appears promising. One such program uses mussels and oysters to record levels of pollution from heavy metals and petroleum hydrocarbons. Because these organisms concentrate and retain pollutants in their tissues, they can make detection easier and help researchers determine the effects of such substances on other constituents of the ecosystem.

Most scientists agree that we cannot afford to degrade our remaining coastal wetlands, estuaries, bays, and coastal zones rather, we need to seek new ways to demonstrate their importance. In Florida, where the population increases by some 6,200 residents each day—most of whom want to live near the coast—almost

WHAT YOU CAN DO

To Protect Water Resources

- Locate and correct leaks around your home. An estimated 50 percent of all households have some kind of plumbing leak. Worn-out washers and faulty tank valves are the prime culprits.
- To test for leaks in your toilet, add food coloring to the toilet tank. If there is a leak, color will appear in the bowl within 30 minutes.
- Look for dripping faucets. Consider that it takes about 11,600 average-size droplets to fill a one-gallon container. If your faucet is leaking at the rate of one droplet per second, and those droplets are of average size, about 7.5 gallons (28 liters) of water will be wasted each day. Over a year, the leak will send 2,700 gallons (10,200 liters) of unused water down the drain. Leaks are costly: A hot water leak increases your utility bill, and since sewer charges are based on water consumption, leaks also increase your sewer charge.
- Do not use detergents containing phosphates.
- When landscaping, use indigenous plants. For example, if you live in a dry climate, forego green lawns in favor of plants that do not require constant watering.
- Never throw garbage into a body of water.
- Read your water meter before and after a period of hours when no water is used in the house. If the meter shows a change, there is a leak in the house. Reading meters is easy: Most record gallons much as a car's odometer records mileage. For meters that show cubic feet of water used, you can convert it into gallons by multiplying the figure shown on your meter by 7.5, the approximate number of gallons in one cubic foot.
- Get to know a stream, river, pond, lake, estuary, or bay through observation and study; help to protect watershed or drainage basins.
- Become involved with a group or organization involved in restoring a body of water near your home.
- Make local and national politicians aware of your views.
- Install water-saving devices in your home or business:
  - Toilet dams block off a portion of the toilet tank, preventing water behind the dam from leaving the water closet. Properly installed, they reduce water use by about two gallons (7.6 liters) per flush.
  - Water-saving showerheads have a flow capacity of about 3 gallons per minute, compared to 6 to 9 gallons (23 to 34 liters) for conventional showerheads. Water-saving showerheads can be installed easily with a pair of pliers.
  - Low volume toilets use about 1.5 to 3 gallons (6 to 11 liters) of water per flush, compared to 5 or 6 gallons (19 to 23 liters) for conventional toilets.
  - Flow restrictors reduce the size of faucet openings, conserving water while maintaining the same pressure. They are inexpensive and easy to install on most faucets and showerheads.

unrestricted development has destroyed a third of the state's sea grass beds and more than half of its mangrove swamps. In response, Florida has taken several long-term actions to reverse these trends, including purchasing 70,000 acres (28,328 hectares) of shoreline for preservation and replanting mangroves in northern Biscayne Bay. In 1984, the Iron Bridge Sewage Treatment Plant, which serves parts of Orlando and neighboring communities, almost reached its capacity of 24 million gallons (91 million liters) a day, and the city faced building moratoriums unless capacity could be increased and effluent properly disposed. In response, the city established the Orlando Easterly Wetlands Reclamation Project, a 2.6-square-mile (6.6-square- kilometer) wilderness park that accepts treated effluent from the Iron Bridge plant. Already cleaned to secondary standards, the effluent filters through the reclaimed wetlands' three plant communities (deep marsh, mixed marsh, and hardwood swamp) and becomes "polished" before being discharged into the St. Johns River.

In recent years, the United States, as well as nations around the globe, witnessed a series of horrors on the oceans: hypodermic needles, catheter bags, and blood vials—some of which tested positive for infectious hepatitis and the Human Immunodeficiency Virus—washed up on beaches; fish with tumors and rotted fins; and marine mammals and sea birds maimed or killed by plastic debris. Perhaps these and other horrors best illustrate the immediate and ongoing need for individual, national, and international action to protect the Earth's life-giving waters.

SUMMARY

Most of the Earth's water is salty. Only 0.5 percent of all water in the world is found in lakes, rivers, streams, and the atmosphere. Water is classified as either fresh or salt (marine), depending upon its salt content. Freshwater is found on land in two basic forms: surface water and groundwater.

Lakes are categorized according to the amount of dissolved nutrients they contain. Oligotrophic lakes are cold, blue, and deep; often have rocky bottoms; and have a high oxygen content. They contain low amounts of dissolved solids, nutrients, and phytoplankton. Eutrophic lakes are warmer and more turbid, often have muddy or sandy bottoms, and have a lower oxygen content. They are far more productive.

Lakes are composed of internal zones based on depth and light penetration. These include the littoral zone, the area where rooted plants grow; the limnetic zone, deeper water where light can penetrate and support populations of plankton; and the profundal zone, where light does not penetrate enough to allow photosynthesis to occur. Large lakes in temperate climates undergo thermal stratification. In the summer, surface waters heated by the sun become lighter and less dense, rise, and form the epilimnion. Colder, denser water sinks to the bottom to form the hypolimnion. A sharp temperature gradient, or thermocline, exists between the upper and lower layers. In the autumn, the thermocline disappears and the epilimnion and hypolimnion mix, a process known as fall turnover.

Running water habitats include streams and rivers. The speed and temperature of the current affects the kinds of organisms that live in a habitat. Fast-moving rivers and streams usually contain two kinds of habitats: riffles, with a high oxygen content, tend to house the producers of biomass, and pools tend to contain consumers and decomposers.

The ocean is divided into zones. In the euphotic zone, light penetrates easily and phytoplankton are abundant. The neritic zone is that part of the euphotic zone over the continental shelves and near-shore islands. The neritic zone hosts the greatest diversity of life and it supports most ocean fisheries. The deep waters of the open oceans comprise the pelagic zone; below them lies the abyssal zone, the deepest part of the oceans.

The United States has about 20 times more groundwater than surface water. Groundwater percolates downward through the soil from precipitation or surface water and is stored in an aquifer, a water-bearing geologic formation composed of layers of sedimentary material. The depth at which the aquifer begins is known as the water table. Groundwater is the major source of drinking water in about two-thirds of the United States. In addition, it helps to maintain water levels and the productivity of streams, lakes, rivers, wetlands, bays, and estuaries.

Water uses may be nonconsumptive or consumptive. Nonconsumptive uses remove water, use it, and return it to its original source. Consumptive uses remove water from one place in the hydrologic cycle and return it to another. Worldwide, agriculture (a consumptive use) is the chief use of water.

Water pollution can be divided into eight general categories: organic wastes, disease-causing wastes, plant nutrients, toxic substances, persistent substances, sediments, radioactive substances, and heat. Biological oxygen demand (BOD) is a measure of the amount of oxygen needed to decompose the organic matter in water.

Globally, water resources are the source of hundreds of political tensions, economic concerns, and environmental problems. Water stress (the episodic lack of renewable freshwater) and water scarcity (the chronic lack of renewable freshwater) are at the heart of these problems. The African Sahel and the Middle East face an especially difficult situation, as rapid population growth further strains water resources already severely limited by arid climate and shared access to rivers.

Legislation, or the lack thereof, determines how water is managed in the United States. The Safe Drinking Water Act of 1974 set national drinking water standards, called maximum contaminant levels, for pollutants that might adversely affect human health. It also established standards to protect groundwater from toxic wastes injected into the soil. The 1986 reauthorization of the Act instructed the EPA to monitor drinking water for unregulated contaminants and to inform public water suppliers of targeted substances. The 1996 reauthorization built upon the 1986 regulations, requiring the EPA to identify and monitor five new contaminants every five years and to provide residents with annual Consumer Confidence Reports that detail the status of the water they drink.

The 1972 Federal Water Pollution Control Act, commonly known as the Clean Water Act, divided pollutants into three classes: toxic, conventional, and unconventional. The act stipulated that industries must use the best available technology (BAT) to treat toxic wastes before releasing them and the best conventional technology to treat conventional pollutants, such as municipal wastes. Unconventional pollutants must meet BAT standards. The 1987 reauthorization of the Clean Water Act granted the Army Corps of Engineers the authority to regulate the draining and filling of wetlands, though that authority remains contested by many landowners. An extension of the Clean Water Act, the Great Lakes Legacy Act of 2002 was passed to address the growing problem of sediment contamination in the rivers, harbors, and other waterways that comprise the Great Lakes system.

After water is withdrawn from a lake, river or aquifer, it is treated before being distributed. In areas that have suitable soils, sewage and wastewater from each home usually is discharged into a septic system consisting of an underground tank and a drain field. Wastewater in largely urban areas must be collected in underground sewers and treated in sewage treatment plants. These plants are designed to make wastewater safe for discharge into streams or rivers or to make it acceptable for reuse. Most sewage plants employ a multistage process to reduce wastewater to an acceptable effluent.

Fresh and marine waters worldwide are besieged by numerous threats. Many aquifers experience overdraft, the withdrawal of water faster than the aquifer can be recharged. Overdrafts can lead to land subsidence. When groundwater becomes contaminated, it is a costly, slow, and sometimes impossible task to remove pollutants. Toxic pollution and accelerated eutrophication are serious threats to the United States' lakes. Threats to rivers include dams, diversions, channelization, and pollution. Abuse of ocean and coastal ecosystems can result from pollution and overuse. Until recently, little thought was given to effectively managing and preserving marine environments.

19. Why do you think registration for these withdrawals is required from a quantity perspective?

20. Why do you think registration for these withdrawals is required from a quality perspective?

WATER PLANET VIDEO RESPONSE 7

Name: ______________________

"Flow"

Flow examines issues of water pollution, water projects, politics and human rights against an increasingly complex background of government and corporate influences.

As you watch the movie *Flow,* please answer the following questions:

1. How many kids die of water-borne diseases each year?
2. How many Americans get sick from dirty water each year?
3. What are the worst pollutants? ______________________
4. What is atrazine? ______________________

   ____
5. What does atrazine do to humans? ______________________
6. Where is atrazine banned? ______________________

   Where isn't it banned? ______________________

   Does this make sense? ______________________
7. Who are the Suez and Vivendi Corporations? ______________________

   ____
8. What are those corporations in business to do? ______________________
9. What is the problem with contracting water supply to private companies? ______________________

   ____

   ____
10. Who controls private water supply? ______________________
11. What is their role in private water supply? ______________________
12. What are the issues of getting water in Kwa-Zulu? ______________________

    ____
13. How has privatization affected water supply to the poor in undeveloped countries of the world? ______________________

    ____

    ____
14. What is the rationale for privatizing water supply? ______________________

    ____
15. As you look at the movie, who do you see going to get water for the household? ______________________

    ____
16. Where do they get water from? ______________________
17. Is the water they get treated? ______________________
18. Give some examples of simple, low-cost systems that can provide clean water. ______________________

    ____

    ____

19. What is the deal with bottled water? Why is it popular?____

____

What are the problems? ____

20. At their Michigan plant, how much water does Nestlé pump a minute? ______________________

How many gallons a day? ______________________________ A year? ________________________

21. Where do they get the water from?____

22. Who owns that water? ____

____

23. How did Nestlé get the right to pump the water?____

____

____

24. So this film raises the general question about who owns common property resources. How do private companies get the right to use them? Who is responsible for preserving those resources? Can they be used up? Who suffers when they are damaged or destroyed?

Chapter 11

URBAN-RURAL CALIFORNIA

Water, Land and Design

Early California Water Law—A Basic Primer

Under the Spanish and Mexican governments the missions and pueblo rights controlled water ownership and delivery. The missions had built their own waterworks to support human consumption but more importantly for irrigating agriculture. These water systems, some of which still operate today, remained confined to the mission buildings and immediate surrounding agricultural lands. In the pueblo, however, the ***zanjero*** (or water master) was a powerful person who controlled the system that supported settlement development in a dry landscape. This person controlled the development, operation and maintenance of the municipal and irrigation canals with regards to allotment of water, and he made sure the livestock stayed out of the series of ditches (***zanjas***). A requirement of the water master was to bring equality to the division of water for both the fields and the homes within the pueblos. Therefore, the Spanish and Mexican eras considered and promoted a communal use of water resources for the national interest. The Spanish *Law of the Indes* stated the communal decree for water, where water in a pueblo (municipality) could not belong to separate individuals, but rather passed from the Spanish Crown to the entire community as an incorporated body. When there was not enough water within the common lands granted to a pueblo to sustain the people and agriculture, it led to failure. For example, the Spanish era pueblo of Branciforte near Santa Cruz was a failure because of an inconsistent water supply for irrigating agriculture, as well as social problems.

The attitude regarding a communal and fair interest in water changed with the Gold Rush. **California Water Doctrine** became established under the U.S. era of development as a hybrid between prior appropriate and riparian water rights. Under prior appropriation, an unbridled individualism was dominant, allowing the creation of water companies that grabbed rights to impound and divert water. In the mid-1850s the courts upheld the right of companies to retail water not directly connected to hydraulic mining, and individualism led to corporations. The right to use water could be bought and sold like property; therefore it encouraged the swift diversion of water and the subsequent rapid development of land uses. Riparian rights, on the other hand, attached to the ownership of land adjacent to a stream or a river with the land owner being guaranteed the right to use the full natural flow less any upstream usage. Because the right of usage is limited to domestic needs, including livestock but not irrigation, it encouraged the acquisition of large land holdings.

The co-evolution of California's inhabitants and the waterscape is both dynamic and legendary in the American West, if not the world. California's spectacular growth is deeply linked to the creation and maintenance of the world's largest engineered water works. In 2007, four of the 20 most populous cities in the U.S.

were in California—two in Southern California (Los Angeles and San Diego) and two in Northern California (San Jose and San Francisco). The availability of water propelled urban expansion in this semi-desert in disguise. What will become clear to the reader is that the California story is one of constant water seeking, with support from the growing populations of urban dwellers, corporate agriculture, and strongly shaped by government policy and use directives.

> *". . . water issues are so closely intertwined with the core elements of California's (and the American West's) political, economic, legal and cultural evolution."*
>
> —Norris Hundley Jr., *The Great Thirst: Californians and Water, 1770s–1990s*, 2001

11.1 URBAN WATER IMPERIALISM: STORIES FROM THE SOUTH AND NORTH

The rapid spread of California's cities since the Gold Rush and their connection via the Transcontinental railroad during the first fifty years of the American era is unheralded. In these early years local sources of water for the major urban nodes of **Los Angeles** and **San Francisco** could sustain their growing populations, but by 1900 their booming populations and diminishing local supply met with the reality that a long-distance transfer of water would become a necessity.

11.1.1 Los Angeles: The Owens River Valley Saga

> "Few of the great cities of the land have had such humble founders as Los Angeles. Of the eleven pobladores who built their huts of poles and tule thatch around the plaza vieja . . . not one could read or write. Not one could boast of an unmixed ancestry. (Their only concern was water [sic] . . .)" J. M. Guinn, *Historical and Biographical Record of Los Angeles and Vicinity*, 1901.

The Spanish *Law of the Indes* granted Los Angeles **pueblo rights** to owning and thus controlling water under communal law, which also transferred in the Mexican era. The *Treaty of Guadalupe Hidalgo* with the U.S. preserved these pueblo rights, which the state upheld under the town's charter. Since the town council directly controlled the community's water system, a full time zanjero position was put in place to issue use permits, regulate water distribution, collect special water taxes and maintain and expand the system of aqueducts, canals and wells.

At the founding of Los Angeles, the main source of water was the **Los Angeles River**. Townspeople constructed a series of diversion canals (*zanjas*) to divert the waters. By the mid-1880s there were canals covering 93 miles working to support the water needs of Los Angeles, a far cry from its small pueblo days.

In the 1860s, however, the growing population required additional sources of water and methods of delivery. Residents used a thirty-year contract with a private water company to construct the city's first reservoir and brought the first use of above ground wooden pipes into the system for human supply. In addition, the city asserted its authority by making sure it fought against any water diversions along the Los Angeles River, which the town council believed the city fully owned under Spanish pueblo rights, supported by the *Treaty of Guadalupe Hidalgo*. Fights with upstream landowners over the rights to the full flow of the Los Angeles River (including surface and groundwater) went back and forth until the courts finally sided with the city in 1895. The legal authorities supported Los Angeles' right to become a "great city." The courts extended the pueblo rights once more in 1899 by allowing any annexed land by the city of Los Angeles to include ownership of the water. Annexation used to secure water rights became the Los Angeles strategy. By 1902 a series of ten canals and a newly installed system of underground pipes replacing the wooden pipes served the city.

During the Southern California boom period the population continued to increase at a rapid pace. Therefore the city continually sought new sources of water in the most imaginative of ways. In the late 1890s the city finally changed the city charter to require public control of the water system (thus eliminating the use of private water companies), by establishing the board of water commissioners to take a proactive and strategic course in the city's water searches. **William Mulholland** was appointed superintendent of the water system, head of the **Department of Water and Power**.

Guided by the former mayor of Los Angeles (who was also the superintendent of the private water company), the residents conceived the idea of bringing water from the Eastern Sierra Nevada—the fertile **Owens River Valley**. Mulholland considered the Owens River plentiful enough to provide enough water for all the city's future needs. He set out to build the **Los Angeles**

Aqueduct from the Owens Valley across the Mojave Desert over the San Gabriel Mountains and ending in the San Fernando Valley.

The construction of the Los Angeles Aqueduct was completed in 1913 with the support of the Bureau of Reclamation, the use of stealth in secretly buying options on land with riparian water rights in the Owens Valley, bond measures passed by Los Angeles voters and the grant by Congress of the aqueduct's right of way over federal land. Officials annexed land in the Owens Valley and the San Fernando Valley to Los Angeles, which extended its pueblo rights.

Once the ranchers and orchard farmers in the Owens Valley discovered what the City of Los Angeles was doing, resentment for their imperialistic ways built. The publication of *Land of Little Rain* by Mary Austin even generated national sympathy. It described in vibrant tones the landscape beauty and mystique of the Owens Valley and Mojave Desert—its flora, fauna and coexistence with people. While the project went through and was completed, the people of Owens Valley had an uneasy relationship with Mulholland's Department of Water and Power. Animosity escalated in the early 1920s when a drought led to increased water diversions by Los Angeles. The continuing loss of ranchers' livelihoods led to California's first "eco-terrorist" events when the ranchers dynamited the aqueduct in 1924. In the ensuing standoff, superintendent Mulholland refused to deal with the ranchers. The ranchers and their families then continued their battles by seizing the Alabama water gates, shutting the water off from the aqueduct and diverting the water back in-to the Owens River. In the mean time, Mulholland, worried about the continuation of water supplies to Los Angeles and built the St. Francis Dam in San Francisquito Canyon (just north of Saugus and Santa Clarita in Los Angeles County) to store water in case of more problems along the aqueduct. The dynamiting of the aqueduct and economic "battles" with the city continued into 1927. In a disaster that rivaled the 1906 San Francisco earthquake, the St. Francis Dam broke (they unknowingly built it on an earthquake fault and a water-swelling metamorphic rock type) killing 450 people and destroying over 900 buildings. While still reeling from the physical and public relations disaster of the dam, the stock market crash of 1929 occurred, which caused the collapse of Owens Valley banks that held properties and water rights the city needed to further secure the water and squeeze out the ranchers. This forced Los Angeles to buy much more of the Owens Valley, which entailed passing another bond to expand the aqueduct into the Mono Basin. By 1940 the extension was complete and the extended water diversions began.

11.1.2 San Francisco: Hetch Hetchy for a City with No Water Rights

San Francisco represents a far different starting story than Los Angeles but with a similar trend and long distance solution to its water problems. The location of the City of San Francisco was on a site that lacked substantial water sources and represented rather inhospitable geography. There was enough water in nearby springs and small lakes when the only population was the soldiers at the Presidio of San Francisco and the priests and neophytes at Mission San Francisco de Asis (Mission Dolores) during the Spanish era. After the securing of Mexican ownership and secularization closed the mission, American settlers arrived in small numbers and founded the settlement of Yerba Buena (around Portsmouth Square). A year after the Americans took California from Mexico, they renamed the settlement of Yerba Buena to San Francisco. The biggest legal difference between San Francisco and Los Angeles is that San Francisco never started as a pueblo chartered under the Spanish—therefore no pueblo water rights.

The Gold Rush brought in a flood of people who used San Francisco as their arrival and staging town before going to seek their riches. The population went from 1,000 in 1848 to 25,000 in 1849, which set off severe water shortages. During this period private entrepreneurs handled much of the development and distribution of water, as the social environment was virtually impossible for any local government authority to build a water strategy, let alone a system. Many groups competed to control the meager local sources that came from springs on Twin Peaks or were shipped in kegs from Marin County by barge and then sold door to door. The numerous fires that destroyed the city from 1850 to 1852 further exacerbated its water problems. Finally in 1857 another group of investors formed the San Francisco Water Works to take water from Lobos Creek, which was a free flowing stream on the presidio's property. They constructed five miles of redwood flume. Several years later the Spring Valley Water Works absorbed the San Francisco Water Works. It had created a monopoly of water sources along the peninsula (bought water rights) and received an exclusive franchise to provide water to the city in exchange for allowing its use for fighting fires.

Rather than San Francisco owning its own public water supply system, since it did not have pueblo rights, it was under the yoke of the Spring Valley Water Company to supply the city residents with water. By 1874 city officials convinced the state to approve its creation of a public water system, but it was unable to do so since Spring Valley Water Works owned the majority share of the water rights throughout the peninsula. The city tried to purchase the Spring Valley Water Company, but the owners wanted more than the city would offer, and these were powerful people in their own right—represented by the "Big Four" and Ben Haggin (i.e., *Miller-Lux vs. Haggin* fame). Fighting continued until 1900 when the city charter was changed to mandate a city-owned water system.

The city drew up a plan to circumvent the Spring Valley Water Works monopoly by obtaining water from a distant source outside the monopoly's domain. It considered a distant source on the Tuolumne River in the Hetch Hetchy Valley of Yosemite a promising area for a reservoir, plus it was accessible across the Central Valley via aqueduct. In 1906, the great earthquake struck, and the city blamed the Spring Valley Water Works for San Francisco's burning down by not supplying enough water to put out all the fires. The city pushed for a reservoir at Hetch Hetchy and got the Secretary of the Interior to grant access rights to build the reservoir in Yosemite National Park. Local and national politics delayed the process, with fierce opposition from Spring Valley Water Works, the **San Joaquin Valley** farmers and John Muir. San Francisco succeeded in receiving final approval in 1913. Despite further political and engineering problems delaying the construction, the city completed the **Hetch Hetchy Aqueduct** by 1934. In addition, San Francisco was able to buy the Spring Valley Water Works in the late 1920s. In a parallel process occurring across the bay, the East Bay Municipal Utility District built the **Mokelumne Aqueduct** by 1929, which also took water from the Sierra Nevada to support Oakland, Alameda, and Berkeley.

Courtesy of the U.S. Geological Survey

Figure 11.1 Hetch Hetchy Valley (1914) as it appeared before it was transformed into a reservoir. (Courtesy of the U.S. Geological Survey).

11.2 WATER PROJECTS: COLORADO RIVER, THE CENTRAL VALLEY PROJECT AND THE STATE WATER PROJECT

While the municipal projects conducted by Los Angeles and San Francisco were marvels and engineers and politicians admired them, an earlier project conducted on the **Colorado River** in conjunction with the Bureau of Reclamation showed both the prospects and the folly of large-scale irrigation projects. None of these projects though could match the breadth and sheer vast amounts of water transferred by the **Central Valley Project** that the federal government sponsored during the 1930s New Deal Depression era or the California-built **State Water Project**. In a state where inequality happens among cultures and economies, it is the regional inequality of water as a natural resource that these massive transfer schemes have ameliorated. In the water deficient San Joaquin Valley and in Southern California these transfers have supported large scale irrigation agriculture, urbanization, and industrial expansion. In the northern half of the state however, although the water capture and transfer process provided hydroelectric power, flood control and recreation, it has been detrimental to fish and wildlife protection. Engineering for extending natural carrying capacity has not been an easy road for California to follow, especially in a land of historical long term droughts, high biodiversity and boosterism policies that have brought multitudes of people to the state.

11.2.1 Controling the Colorado River and the "Accidental" Creation of the Salton Sea

The Colorado River is an exotic river, the "American Nile" according to some views. It is a moderate discharge river flowing through an arid region of the Southwestern U.S., and it creates part of California's southeastern border with Arizona. Its upper basin begins in the states of Colorado, Wyoming, Utah and New Mexico then flows south-southwest into the lower basins of Nevada, Arizona and California and on into Mexico to discharge into the Gulf of California. Hydrologists consider it a river of modest average flow, but it is highly variable throughout the year and over decades. Heavy spring rain and snowmelt in the upper part of the basin can lead to late spring-summer floods in the lower part of the basin, with late summer-fall being a very low flow period. Coupled with long-term drought cycles that punctuate the climatic record of the Western U.S., scientists consider the river to have both a large annual range and a very high inter-annual variability. The river also cuts through sedimentary bedrock formations owing to its steep gradient along its flow route (e.g., upper reaches of the Grand Canyon) resulting in erosion, entrainment, and transport

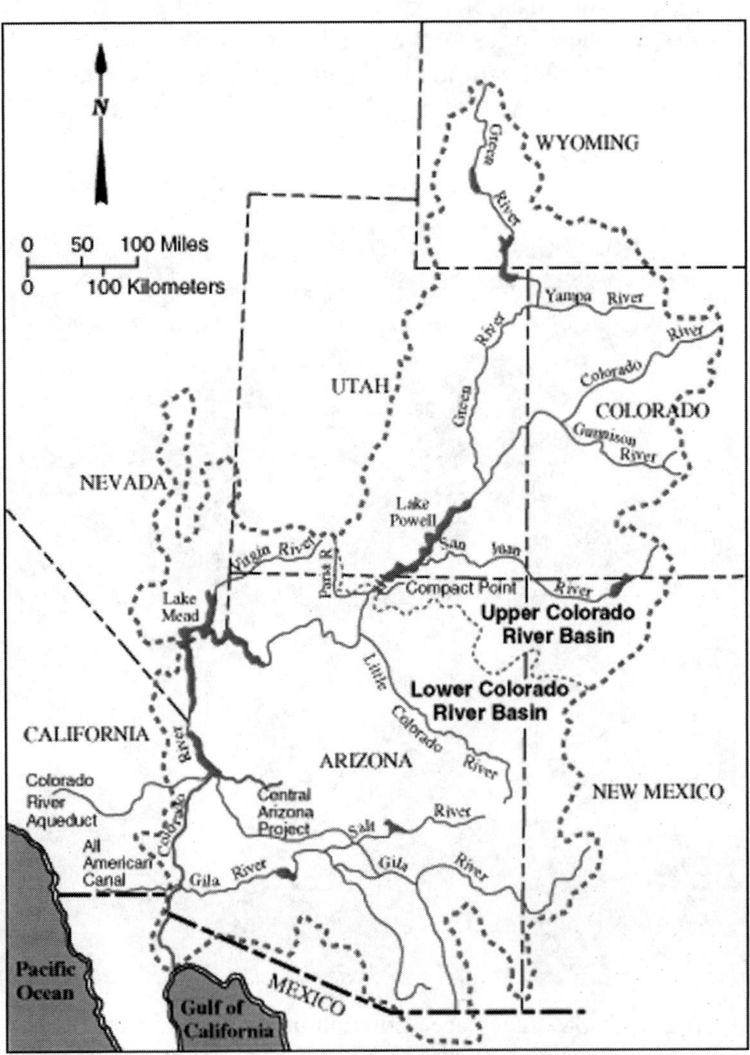

Figure 11.2 Colorado river drainage basin (Courtesy of the U.S. Geological Survey, http://geochange.er.usgs.gov/sw/changes/natural/codrought/fig_1.gif).

of a very large sediment load (i.e., 160 million tons per year of silt). The river's gradient flattens below the Grand Canyon, finally creating a large depositional delta in the Gulf of California.

Upon the passage of the **Reclamation Act** in 1902 the federal government wanted to approach the harnessing of the Colorado River to "green" the Southwestern desert "wastelands." The **Imperial Valley** (formerly named the Valley of Death) located in the Salton Basin of California's portion of the Colorado Desert in Southern California had already showed great potential as a fertile agricultural landscape. The valley consists of very fertile soils and a twelve month growing season, but there is an extreme lack of water. In 1901, a private diversion canal named the Alamo Canal was cut from the Colorado River and routed through Mexico. It then turned northward and entered the U.S. to support a highly successful irrigation agriculture project in the Imperial Valley. In 1904 the canal finally silted up due to the high sediment loads of the Colorado River. Two successive bypasses north of the border were cut, but they also silted up almost immediately.

In late 1904 a private water company received permission from Mexico to cut a new temporary canal, again south of the border. The company intended the construction work to be temporary so they installed flimsy control gates on the canal's entrance to the Colorado River. In 1905, the spring flood arrived early, and high water tore out the gates. Soon the full flow of the Colorado River surged through the diversion canal, swept northward and flooded the entire Salton Basin, transforming it into the **Salton Sea**. It took close to two years (1907) to close the gap, reroute the Colorado River back into its old channel and to restore its regulated flow through the Alamo Canal. By this time, the human-made disaster that is the Salton Sea had become part of the Colorado Desert landscape, along with the agricultural mosaic to the south of the sea that is the Imperial Valley. It has been shrinking with the high evaporative demand of the desert climate and swelling via agricultural runoff for

Figure 11.3 Satellite image of the Salton Sea, Imperial Valley and border with Mexico. Notice the differences in agricultural patterns on either side of the border. (Courtesy of the U.S. Geological Survey, http://terra web.wr.usgs.gov/projects/RSDust/WiFS/010may96_saltonsea_false_nojavascript.html)

over a hundred years, and therefore it remains highly saline and polluted.

11.2.2 Colorado River Compact and Boulder Dam

The Bureau of Reclamation saw the possibilities of the Imperial Valley and the disaster of the Salton Sea as a clear sign that it required a much larger framework to tame the Colorado River for resource use. While the Imperial Valley farmers wanted the irrigation canal to be on the U.S. side of the border—an **All American Canal**—the bureau saw the greater need for a dam to control the spring floods in order to effectively irrigate the lower basin. To make their plan work, however, required a water allocation agreement—"Law of the River"—among the seven states that contained the Colorado River drainage basin. The inequality of such a feat was apparent to most as the water comes from the upper basin states (Colorado, Wyoming, Utah and New Mexico), but the possibilities for agriculture and domestic uses are largely in the lower basin, especially California. Therefore in 1922 the states involved created the **Colorado River Compact**, based on an assumed average annual flow of 17.5 million acre feet, which unfortunately was based on a short record that turned out to be the wettest period in several centuries (i.e., we know this now after Southwestern tree ring analyses and archaeological research). The compact introduced the following allocations: 7.5 million acre feet to Colorado, Wyoming, Utah and New Mexico and 7.5 million acre feet to Arizona, California and Nevada, with the remaining 2.5 million acre feet left in the river for Mexico. Under the compact there was no further attempt to divide the allocations down to a states proportions within a basin. After much disagreement and lack of movement on the process, Congress took action in 1928 and authorized the building of **Boulder Dam** (i.e., also known as Hoover Dam) and the All American Canal to supply the Imperial Valley. The Congressional level set lower basin allocations by state as follows: California received 4.4 million acre feet, Arizona received 2.8 million acre feet and Nevada received 300,000 acre feet. Six states had to ratify the compact before construction began. Arizona refused, but the other six states agreed to the deal.

The federal construction of Boulder Dam (that created Lake Mead reservoir) began during the worst of the Great Depression in 1931with a majority of the labor coming from the devastated economy of Southern California. By the early 1940s the **All American Canal** to the Imperial Valley and the **Coachella Canal** to the Coachella Valley (i.e., the northern end of the Salton Sea) completed the modern irrigation system to California's Colorado Desert.

The final great Southern California tapping of the Colorado River came when William Mulholland convinced the citizens of Los Angeles to pass a bond in order to build the **Colorado River Aqueduct**. Construction began with the building of Parker Dam that created Lake Havasu reservoir in 1933, much to the anger of Arizona, which sent state national guardsmen to stop dam construction on their side of the river. The Supreme Court and the U.S. Congress acted in 1935 to allow the completion of Parker Dam, with the Colorado River Aqueduct being completed in 1941. The additional water source for Southern California helped major industrial and housing expansion during World War II.

Over the years since the 1940s Southern California has used more than 1 million acre feet over its original allocation of 4.4 million acre feet. Arizona has had numerous lawsuits against California since the 1930s. Finally, in a landmark decision the Department of Interior in 1998 ordered the Los Angeles Department of Water and Power to come up with a plan to reduce its usage back to the original 4.4 million acre feet allocation. In addition, the federal government has put rules in place regarding allocations during low flow drought years to protect the integrity of the river for endangered species and to honor the treaty with Mexico on their minimum allocation of 2.5 million acre feet. Drought years have allowed the government to cut back on the original allocations to any of the lower basin states, much to their dismay as their populations have boomed.

11.2.3 Central Valley Water Project: A New Deal in Water Delivery

The Central Valley consists of three major drainage basins: the **Sacramento River** in the north, the **San Joaquin River** in the south and the **Tulare Lake** basin between the San Joaquin basin and the Tehachapi Mountains in the south. Despite numerous rivers flowing through the valley, with sources in the Cascade and Sierra Nevada Mountain ranges, the usable surface water for irrigation agriculture and domestic needs is quite scarce. Floods in spring and early summer from snow melt create a swampy environment with subsequent loss of crop lands. By late summer and fall the region's extended drought leaves many of the riverine systems with low flow environments. In addition, the water availability is geographically biased towards the eastern side of the valley (windward slopes), as the storm track patterns across California leave the western and especially the southwestern portions (the rain shadow slopes) quite dry during the winter precipitation. The dry precipitation pattern and warm interior temperatures make the southwestern portion of the valley nearly similar in climate to the Mojave Desert.

Soils in the Central Valley are exceptionally fertile and consist of a balanced texture for agriculture. The type of agriculture available to California, outside of dryland farmed spring wheat crops is irrigated agriculture. To make it through the long extended summer drought Central Valley farmers started to tap the valley's enormous **groundwater** supplies. Researchers have estimated that there may be as much as 750,000,000 acre feet of water accumulated over hundreds of thousands of years as the miles-thick alluvial sediments have acted like a gigantic sponge. In the early 1900s farmers dug wells and used inefficient pumps to bring this water to the surface. In some cases the groundwater pressure was so great that they could easily tap flowing artesian wells and make access to the water easier (i.e., no pumping required). After World War I the development of efficient electric turbine pumps allowed irrigated acreage to rapidly expand three times the 1900 level of less than a million acres. The cost of over pumping the ancient aquifer in the San Joaquin Valley led to severe drops in the groundwater level, land subsidence and the death of deep rooted riparian trees.

Early state plans to bring water to the Central Valley, while mused about as early as 1856, took place as a proposal in 1919. The proposal called for a large dam on the upper Sacramento River and two aqueducts flowing south through the Central Valley with a spur to provide water to San Francisco Bay cities. The state promoted the Central Valley portion as providing controlled flows to the Sacramento and San Joaquin Rivers for improved navigation and to meter out the release of water into the Delta to prevent salt water intrusion. It also proposed a southern component that would divert the Kern River to Los Angeles via a tunnel through the Tehachapi Mountains. This plan, linked to riparian law, failed both in the legislature and with voters all through the 1920s. Recall that riparian users (owners of property next to a river) after 1902 could engage in irrigation as long as they understood that all riparian owners possessed the same right. Thus riparian rights holders had an obligation to use water reasonably, i.e., to share. Riparian rights users had a problem with this obligation to be reasonable when it came to those that had prior appropriation rights

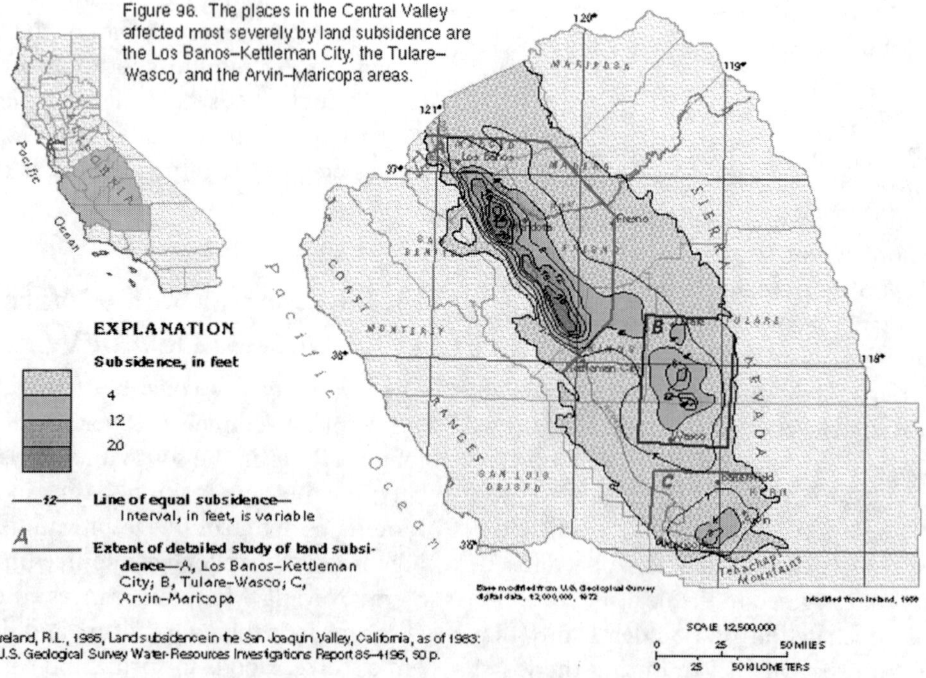

Figure 11.4 The places in the Central Valley affected most severely by land subsidence from intensive groundwater pumping. (Courtesy of U.S. Geological Survey, http://pubs.usgs.gov/ha/ha730/ch_b/gif/b096.gif).

on the same river. If they wanted to waste water they could do it just like the appropriators who ordinarily did not live on the rivers from which they took water. A 1926 State Supreme Court case upheld the riparian users' right to use water any way they saw fit. This decision also prevented appropriators from building dams and therefore trapping the spring flood waters vital to new development. The public was not happy with this ruling and in a ballot initiative passed an amendment to the state constitution to prevent the "*waste of water or unreasonable use.*" This amendment removed a significant roadblock to a statewide water plan and remains a central theme of California water rights law.

Because of the tremendous damage that Los Angeles caused to the communities in the Owens Valley, the Northern California counties wanted reassurance that they had superior water rights in relation to the massive transfer schemes being proposed by the state. Therefore in 1931 the state legislature passed the **county-of-origin law** that stated that counties could regain water rights to water originating within their borders if ever needed. Now the state could proceed with a scaled-down plan that only included the large dam on the upper Sacramento River, a canal and reservoir system to transport water south to the San Joaquin Valley, as well as the regulated releases to improve navigation and prevent saltwater intrusion in the Delta. The plan essentially became a Central Valley water plan.

California suffered a drought beginning in 1929 that continued until 1935. Thus in the depths of the Great Depression the state legislature and voters approved the **Central Valley Project** (CVP). Geographically it was an interesting mix of support. Northern California was in favor (the northern and central parts of the state were hardest hit by the severe drought), Southern California was against it as they saw no direct benefit for themselves, and the private electrical power companies (i.e., Pacific Gas & Electric (PG&E) and Southern California Edison) were against it because the plan had public power provisions. No one, however, would buy the $170 million in issued bonds needed to make the project happen. The federal government stepped in and took over the project as its own in 1935 for the Bureau of Reclamation to develop. The bureau began construction in 1937 and completed the system in the late 1950s. The project distributes more than 5,600,000 acre feet of water with 5,000,000 acre feet for farms (enough to irrigate about 33 percent of the agricultural land in California) and 600,000 acre feet for municipal and industrial use. The irrigation water is provided as a subsidy to farmers in the Central Valley. The project also generates 5.6 billion kilowatt hours of electricity that it sells to PG&E to supply to urban users.

The entire Central Valley Project consists of twenty dams and reservoirs, eleven power plants and five hundred miles of canals, conduits, tunnels, and so forth. The main components are Shasta Dam on the upper Sacramento River, which created **Shasta Reservoir**; **Clare Engle Lake** on the upper Trinity River (with an inter-basin transfer to Whiskeytown Reservoir); the **Tehama-Colusa canal** (that distributes water to agricultural users on the west side of the Sacramento Valley); the **Delta Cross channel** and the **Contra Costa canal** (keeps the Delta flowing to impede saltwater intrusion); **Folsom Dam** on the American River and **New Melones Dam** on the Stanislaus River (flood control and irrigation water storage); the **Delta-Mendota canal** (that moves water from the Delta to the San Joaquin Valley farmers); and the **Friant Dam** on the Kern River and the **Friant-Kern canal** (that moves water north along the east side of the San Joaquin Valley for farmers).

11.2.3.1 Irrigated Acreage Limitations: A Big Problem in California

Passage of the Reclamation Act of 1902 allowed homesteads to use water for irrigation, although it still limited irrigated projects to 160 acres per person (or 320 acres if married). In addition, the federal government was supposed to sell off excess land in areas being provided irrigation water through a Bureau of Reclamation project at pre-project prices. Other stipulations included that there was not to be absentee ownership of a farm, also known as "**paper farms.**" The government intended for all of these rules to foster the spread of small **family farming** areas in the Western U.S. and especially in California, with the support of federally subsidized water projects. Because the Bureau of Reclamation made no attempts to enforce the acreage limitation until 1943, largely in reaction to the portrayals of Okie farm workers in John Steinbeck's novels, farmers abused the 160 acre rule. Each member of a family could petition the government for 160 acres, which they cumulatively worked as a large land holding. For example, the number of farms increased from 75,000 in 1900 to 150,000 by 1935 in the Central Valley, while the average farm size dropped from 400 to around 200 acres during the same period. The percentage of the land in large holdings, however, remained high and continued to rise dramatically. Therefore by the

Figure 11.5 Shasta dam on the upper Sacramento River creating Shasta reservoir. Note the view of snow covered Mt. Shasta in the distance. (Image © Andy Z., 2009. Used under license from Shutterstock, Inc.).

mid-1930s, at the start of the Central Valley Project, two-thirds of the irrigable land was in land holdings larger than 160 acres. (For example, combine the 160 acres each of dad, mom, sister, brother, grandfather, grandmother, aunt and uncle to really farm 1,280 acres under one "farmer"). This exploitation led to 6 percent of the owners controlling 35 percent of the land in the Central Valley, and the Bureau of Reclamation was obligated to support irrigation to these lands under the revised Reclamation Act rules via the Central Valley Project water at a subsidized rate of payment. The idea of a true family farm in California as envisioned by the federal government never worked. It didn't help that the Bureau of Reclamation (by the late 1940s) tried to fix things for these large agri-business farms to continue to receive subsidized water by encouraging the farmers to develop technical compliance schemes. The farmers created corporations and "sold" pieces of land (160 acres or less) to each stockholder, but in reality they deeded the land back to relatives, children, employees and even pets! By 1982, after many decades of abuse, Congress passed the **Reclamation Reform Act** that recognized the reality of modern California farming operations. This showed that to make the economics work farms had to be bigger than the original 160 acres. The reality was that two-thirds of California farms were on less than or equal to one hundred acres, but 80 percent of the land was in holdings of over a thousand acres, and 75 percent of the agricultural production in the state came from only 10 percent of the farms. The acreage limitation was raised to 960 acres for subsidized federal water, and the act ended the residency requirement for farmers. The California agribusiness farm was here to stay.

11.2.4 State Water Project: World's Largest Water Works

To the large agri-business concerns in the San Joaquin Valley the technical compliance loopholes in reclamation law were ephemeral. Legislation could always be rewritten to truly enforce the acreage limitations that made the large corporate farm both dependent upon and wary of the Bureau of Reclamation. At one point they tried to push the state to buy the Central Valley Project from the Reclamation Bureau, but the price was too high for the state and the Bureau was not politically interested in giving up its expanding empire of controlled waterscapes. Corporate agriculture therefore got together to lobby for the state to underwrite, develop and own its own waterworks for the benefit of the whole state, not just the San Joaquin Valley. The beginning of the gigantic **State Water Project** was set, and with the post-World War II population booming across the state its proposal came at a most auspicious time.

The main proponents in the push for a State Water Project were located in the southern end of the San Joaquin Valley—Kings and Kern Counties—and especially the southwestern side of the valley known as the **Westlands** and the ancient **Tulare Lake** basin. These parts of the San Joaquin Valley are very dry with no useable surface water, very deep groundwater tables that were often brackish (this was an ancient seabed) and no connections to the Central Valley Project canals. Most of the owners held large land holdings ranging from 11,000 to 220,000 acres. These owners varied from the Kern County Land Company (cattle) to Standard Oil, Shell Oil, Richfield Oil, Belridge Oil, Tidewater Oil, Southern Pacific Railroad and Tejon Ranch (whose main owner was the publisher of the *Los Angeles Times*).

Even after the arrival of the Central Valley Project to the eastern side of the San Joaquin Valley the farmers continued to pump a tremendous amount of groundwater (i.e., 6,000,000 acre feet/year). All the Central Valley Project did was to cause the conversion of more lands to agriculture, rather than reduce pumping, and thus the water table continued to drop. The corporate landowners wanted State Water, at all cost, to avoid the acreage restrictions set by the Reclamation Bureau and to reduce some pressure on the groundwater system. To make the State Water Project work, the farmers needed urban buy-in as there was no way that the state could afford the project without this majority block of taxpayers. They had earlier support when the Water Resources Board issued a statement in the early 1950s stating that water was being "*wasted*" as it emptied into the ocean and that "The greatest challenge [facing the state] was redistribution of the water supply from areas of surplus to areas of deficiency." The plan developed in 1951 called for the world's highest earthen dam on the Feather River to apportion out water back into the Feather River, which was a tributary of the Sacramento River. The water was then to be pumped out of the Delta to be carried by an aqueduct along the west side of the San Joaquin Valley to the Tehachapi Mountains where it would then be lifted 3,300 feet over the mountains at a huge pumping station into Southern California.

The plan nearly sold itself when the state's worst flooding occurred in the winter of 1955–56 (i.e., a large pineapple express storm; on the Feather and Yuba Rivers inundating 100,000 square miles and killing people. A dam on the Feather River at Oroville could have prevented this, so the state established the **Department of Water Resources** to combine all fifty-two independent state water agencies under one roof for statewide planning. In 1959 the **Water Resources Development Act** passed the legislature and was put to a vote in 1960. It was written to authorize the selling of $1.75 billion in bonds with additional money coming from the state's share of royalties from offshore oil production for a total project cost of $2.5 billion. In economic terms, this bond issue nearly equaled the state's budget, was the largest bond issue ever considered by a state up until this time and represented a record sum for any water project. The true cost was still underestimated.

Gov. Pat Brown Sr. promoted the project, which San Joaquin Valley farmers (agri-businesses) backed heavily, but it had only moderate support from much of Southern California. There was a feeling in Southern California that they really did not need the extra water for urban use at this time, but they were worried that litigation with Arizona in the U.S. Supreme Court over the Colorado River was intensifying. The bond measure still passed by a 0.3 percent margin on a strong north-south split: north being against the project and the San Joaquin Valley and Southern California being for the project . . . barely.

The construction ran from 1962 to 1973 with the main components being the Oroville Dam on the **Feather River** that created the **Oroville Reservoir** and the **California Aqueduct** along the San Joaquin Westside. The aqueduct was lifted over the Tehachapi Mountains and then split into a west branch into Los Angeles County (**Lake Castaic**) and an east branch into San Bernardino County (**Lake Perris**). The water to supply the California aqueduct came from pumping the flows coming down from the Sacramento and Feather Rivers via the Delta. The latest addition to the project is the completion of the **Central Coast branch** that voters of San Luis Obispo and Santa Barbara Counties approved after the early 1990s drought. It was completed in 1997. The total water contracted

Figure 11.6 Aerial view of the California aqueduct carrying water south to Los Angeles and the rest of Southern California. (Image © iofoto, 2009. Used under license from Shutterstock, Inc.)

for deliv-ery consists of the following allocations: San Joaquin Valley (mainly Kings and Kern Counties—Westlands district) receives 1.35 million acre feet; Southern California receives 2.5 million acre feet; and the new Central Coast district receives 400,000 acre feet.

11.3 CALIFORNIA'S PERENNIAL WATER WOES: WHAT'S NEXT FOR THE DRY STATE?

Engineers identified the first big problem in California's waterworks in the 1970s—the **Sacramento-San Joaquin Delta**—but voters abandoned a solution in 1982 only to have it come back into focus as California experienced another drought (2007–2009 current). The Delta's fragile ecosystem is in decline, but, more importantly, the federal government's **Endangered Species Act** of 1973 must now dictate its management. The act (and the **California Endangered Species Act**) are strong pieces of policy adopted the same year completion took place of the main components of the State Water Project. The great pumps that pull the fresh water out of the Delta and into the California Aqueduct are severely threatening two state and federally listed endangered fish: the **Delta smelt** and the **Chinook salmon**. The California component of the endangered species legislation is more stringent than the federal as California requires that all losses be fully mitigated (avoid incidental take or fully replace taken species). The greatest threat to the conveyance of water supplies in California is the Delta. California voters in 1982 voted down the building of a peripheral canal that would have moved the pumps and built a canal farther north and around the eastern edge of the Delta to pump water from the Sacramento River. In 2007, a federal judge ordered that the southern pumps be shut down to stop the further destruction of the Delta smelt. This scared Southern California, which currently receives 30 to 40 percent of its water supplies via the California Aqueduct. In an act designed to revive the idea of a peripheral canal to solve the environmental problems, the state produced a report at the end of 2008 entitled the "Delta Vision Strategic Plan." The plan acknowledges that the Sacramento-San Joaquin Delta is caught in a toxic cycle of evolving conflicts concerning ecosystem decline, endangered species, flood control, water supply and quality, and drought. The co-evolving system has resulted in failed policies, numerous lawsuits, court orders and a renewed focus on conservation practices within the urban and agricultural systems that rely on the Delta as a critical link in the state's chain of water conveyance.

Second, the basis of the Central Valley Project and the State Water Project as well as with the local projects produced by Los Angeles and San Francisco was the substantially underestimated population projection numbers. The current systems are old and can barely keep up with the demand of 38.5 million people at the end of 2008. The projection is that the state will exceed 49 million people by 2030, while some estimates place the population at 90 million by 2100. The way California manages its water supplies has to change to a conservation driven and more sustainable path, as predictions indicate that the supplies will shrink rather than expand. Scientists don't even believe that the ocean desalination technologies touted in the Persian Gulf countries as a possible solution can produce enough supply to remotely meet future demand.

Finally, the issue of shrinking supplies is the third major state water issue. This brings to the fore the effect global **climate change** will have on California's regional climate and especially upon precipitation and snow pack. The tree ring record for the state has already alluded to large-scale and long-term droughts having occurred in the past. The natural range of variability, coupled with the effects of anthropocentric enhanced greenhouse gas emissions that cause the atmosphere to heat up faster than normal, will have a detrimental impact on California's water supply. These include the impounding of more water during mega-drought years, which deprives free flowing cold water for endangered fish species, combined with the potential rise in sea level of 55 inches by 2100, which will further exacerbate salt water intrusion into the Delta and up the Sacramento River. The prediction for the state's winters is not good as they will be wetter but have less snow pack (70–80 percent loss in the Sierra Nevada alone), thus leading to smaller spring and summer inflows to the rivers and reservoirs. For example, the upper American River has already witnessed a change in the snowline over the last thirty years of up slope movement of nearly five hundred feet.

California has some serious challenges regarding water. The development of reasonable solutions that rely on sustainable development values and serious conservation rather than upon voluntary public action are required, rather than just relying on more dam building. Are the citizens in the three large urban nodes of Los Angeles, San Diego and the San Francisco Bay Area able to come to serious, operational domestic water conservation agreements? Is agriculture, the largest user of water in the state, ready to confront its own wasteful practices to secure a sustainable food producing future? "*Where water flows, food grows*" is the rallying cry in the Central Valley farming communities, but those flows are not for certain. Sustainably designed urban and rural waterscapes for better land management will be necessary in the future if California is to move forward with an environmentally and socially secure future.

BIBLIOGRAPHY

Booth, S. (2008). *California Geography.* Course taught at Sierra College. [online] http://geography.sierra.cc.ca.us/ booth/ California/cal_index.htm.

Calisphere (2008a). *California Cultures.* University of California [online] http://www.calisphere.universityofcalifornia. edu/ calcultures/

Calisphere (2008b). *A world of California Primary Sources.* University of California [online] http://www.calisphere. universityofcalifornia.edu/

Carle, D. (2003). *Water and the California Dream: Choices for the New Millennium.* Sierra Club Books, San Francisco, CA.

Carle, D. (2009). *Introduction to Water in California.* 2nd edition. University of California Press, Berkeley, CA.

Chinn, T.W., ed. (1969). *A History of Chinese in California.* Chinese Historical Society of America, San Francisco, CA.

Cox, C.J. (2008). *California Geography.* Course taught at Sierra College. [online] http://faculty.sierracollege.edu/ccox/ california_geography/index.html.

Deverell, W. and D. Igler (2008). *A Companion to California History.* Wiley-Blackwell, New York, NY.

DeWitt, H.A. (1999). *The Fragmented Dream: Multicultural California.* Kendall/Hunt Publishers, Dubuque, IA.

DeWitt, H.A. (1999). *The California Dream.* 2nd edition. Kendall/ Hunt Publishers, Dubuque, IA.

Donley, M.W., Allan, S., Caro, P., and C.P. Patton (1979). *Atlas of California.* Pacific Book Center, Culver City, CA.

Durrenberger, R.W. and R.B. Johnson (1976). *California Patterns on the Land.* 5th edition, Mayfield Publishing Company, Mountain View, CA.

Fogelson, R.M. (1993). *The Fragmented Metropolis: Los Angeles, 1850–1930.* University of California Press, Berkeley, CA.

Guinn, J.M. (1901). *Historical and Biographical Record of Los Angeles and Vicinity.* Chapman Publishing Co., Chicago.

Hornbeck, D. (1983). *California Patterns: A Geographical and Historical Atlas.* Mayfield Publishing Company, Mountain View, CA.

Hundley, N. Jr. (2001). *The Great Thirst: Californians and Water-A History.* 2nd edition, University of California Press, Berkeley, CA.

Kelly, R. (1959). *Battling the inland sea: floods, public policy, and the Sacramento Valley.* University of California Press, Berkeley, CA.

Lantis, D.W., Steiner, R., and A.E. Karinen (1989). *California: The Pacific Connection.* Creekside Press, Chico, CA.

Larson, D.J. (1996). Historical water-use priorities and public policies. In *Sierra Nevada Ecosystem Project: Final report to Congress, vol. II, Assessments and scientific basis for management options.* University of California, Centers for Water and Wildland Resources, Davis, CA.

Leung, P.C.Y. (1984). *One Day, One Dollar: Locke California and the Chinese Farming Experience in the Sacramento Delta.* Chinese American History Project, CA.

McClurg, S. (2000) *Water and the Shaping of California.* Water Education Foundation, Heyday Books, Berkeley, CA.

McWilliams, C. (1973). *California, the Great Exception.* Peregrine Smith, Santa Barbara, CA.

Michaelson, J. (2008). *Geography of California.* Course at UC Santa Barbara, Dept. of Geography. [online] http:// www.geog.ucsb.edu/~joel/g148_f08/.

Miller, C.S. and Hyslop, R.S. (1983). *California: The Geography of Diversity.* Mayfield Publishing Company, Mountain View, CA.

Mitchell, D. (1996). *The Lie of the Land: Migrant Workers and the California Landscape.* University of Minnesota Press, Minneapolis, MN.

Mulholland, C. (2002). *William Mulholland and the Rise of Los Angeles.* University of California Press, Berkeley, CA.

Rawls, J.J. and W. Bean (2008). *California: An Interpretative History.* 9th Edition, McGraw-Hill Publishing Co., New York, NY.

Reisner, M. (1993). *Cadillac Desert: The American West and Its Disappearing Water.* 2nd edition, Penguin, New York, NY.

Rice, R., Bullough, W., and R. Orsi (2001). *The Elusive Eden: A New History of California.* 3rd edition, McGraw-Hill.

Righter, R.W. (2005). *The Battle Over Hetch Hetchy: America's Most Controversial Dam and the Birth of Modern Environmentalism.* Oxford University Press.

Starr, K. (2005). *California: A History.* The Modern Library, New York, NY.

State of California Resources Agency (2008). *Delta Vision Strategic Plan.* Blue Ribbon Task Force. Sacramento, CA. [online] http:// www.deltavision.ca.gov.

Stegner, W. (1992). *Beyond the Hundredth Meridian: John Wesley Powell and the Second Opening of the West.* Penquin, New York, NY.

Steiner, S. (1980). *Fusang: The Chinese Who Built America.* Harper & Row Publishers, New York, NY.

Wey, N. (1988). A history of Chinese Americans in California. In: *Five Views: An Ethnic Historic Site Survey for California,* pp. 105–158. California Department of Parks and Recreation, Office of Historic Preservation, Sacramento, CA.

Worster, D. (1992). *Rivers of Empire: Water, Aridity, and the Growth of the American West.* Oxford University Press, New York, NY.

WATER PLANET VIDEO RESPONSE 8

Name: ______________________________

"Cadillac Desert: Mulholland's Dream"

William Mulholland was the man responsible for providing water to the growing city of Los Angeles in the early 1900s and this video recounts his amazing success in buying the Owens River and redirecting it hundreds of miles across the desert in one of the nation's first broad-scale interbasin transfers.

1. Who was William Mulholland and what was his primary job for the city of Los Angeles?

2. What was the only source of water for L.A. in the early 1900s?

3. Who was using the Owens River before white settlers?

4. How did the city of Los Angeles go about securing the water rights to the Owens River?

5. Who really gained the most from the building of the Los Angeles Aqueduct as it passed through the San Fernando Valley?

6. Why was Owens River water used to irrigate the San Fernando Valley?

7. How did President Theodore Roosevelt help Mulholland's efforts in obtaining water from the Owens Valley?

8. How much more water was supplied to L.A. than they could use?

9. How did obtaining a steady water supply from the Owens Valley affect the growth of Los Angeles and its need for water resources?

10. How did Mulholland secure the rest of the water in the northern half of the Owens Valley?

11. Why did Mulholland build the St. Francis dam in San Francisquito Canyon?

12. After the Owens River, what was the second river L.A. obtained?

13. What are some of the other major plans that were discussed to provide for L.A.'s increasing water needs into the future?

14. What was the third river that LA acquired? What aqueduct was built to transport this water?

15. How did David Gaines and his fellow biologists stop L.A. from draining Mono Lake?

16. What movement in the United States contributed to stopping L.A. from draining Mono Lake, and its endless quest for more water?

17. What lesson can be learned from L.A.'s continual search for additional water sources?

WATER PLANET VIDEO RESPONSE 9

Name: ______________________________

"Cadillac Desert: An American Nile"

As seen in this film, large dams were vital for promoting growth in the drylands of the Western United States by providing water supplies and hydroelectric power, but they also create significant environmental impacts and are no longer considered beneficial water projects everywhere in the world.

1. What were the flow and sediment characteristics of the Colorado River before dams?

2. What were some of the questions that John Wesley Powell asked about the Colorado River that are still being discussed today?

3. Why was the first dam on the Colorado River built in the Black Canyon rather than Glen Canyon?

4. What were the benefits that were expected from Hoover Dam?

5. What was the general view of conservation just after Hoover Dam was built?

6. What were the more far-reaching effects of building Hoover Dam?

7. What was the purpose for building Glen Canyon Dam?

8. How did the building of Glen Canyon Dam actually encourage the beginning of the end of the era of dam building?

9. What environmental effects took place following the completion of Glen Canyon Dam?

10. What happens to the Colorado River in northern Mexico?

11. How did David Brower defeat the building of dams in the Grand Canyon?

12. What event occurred that made it possible for the dams proposed for the Grand Canyon not to be authorized by Congress?

13. What event was the beginning of the end of the age of dams?

14. What was the water project authorized by Lyndon Johnson in 1969?

15. What almost happened to Glen Canyon Dam in 1983?

16. Do you think the civilization we have created in the Southwest is sustainable?

17. What are some of the lessons learned from the manipulation of the Colorado River?

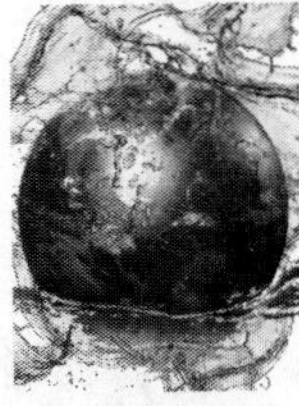

WATER PLANET VIDEO RESPONSE 10

Name: ______________________________

"Cadillac Desert: The Mercy of Nature"

Agricultural production uses more water than any other economic sector and this film examines a unique historical relationship between water supplies, water projects, politics, and farming.

1. What percentage of the food grown in the United States comes from the Central Valley in California?

2. What is the biggest disadvantage for agriculture in the Central Valley?

3. How did California pass Iowa as the country's leading farm state?

4. How far below the surface had the aquifer been drawn down in the San Joaquin Valley by 1930?

5. Where did the migrants from Oklahoma (Okies) during the Great Depression go?

6. Why would the Central Valley Project not have been built if it hadn't been for Franklin Roosevelt?

7. What was the purpose of the Central Valley Project?

8. What was the purpose of the Reclamation Act of 1902?

9. Who was the largest land owner in California who eventually benefited the most from government-subsidized water?

10. What was the largest freshwater lake west of the Mississippi River? What happened to it?

11. What is the driest part of the San Joaquin Valley called?

12. Who was supposed to settle the Westlands according to a local congressman?

13. What were some of the negative effects of large-scale farming in the Central Valley?

14. What did President Carter do that no other president had attempted?

15. What was the environmental time bomb that went off that changed the political history of the Central Valley Project?

16. What were the poisons that contaminated the Kesterson Wildlife Refuge and where did they come from?

17. What did President Bush do before he left office that changed farming in the Central Valley?

WATER PLANET VIDEO RESPONSE 11

Name: ______________________________

"Cadillac Desert: The Last Oasis"

Many common water project technologies such as dams are no longer viable or desirable for meeting water needs. This video looks at some of world's water problems and also identifies several places implementing new technologies and conservation methods to address those needs.

1. What is the simple equation that Sandra Postel describes that has been used in the past to make water resource decisions?

2. Why doesn't that equation work anymore?

3. What are the primary purposes for which dams are built?

4. Why has the dam building era in the United States come to a close?

5. What is schistosomiasis?

6. Where are the world's largest dams being built?

7. What is the world's largest hydroelectric project? What are the reasons given for wanting to build the dam? What are the some of the drawbacks for building the dam?

8. Why are parts of Mexico City subsiding as much as 12 inches per year?

9. What does Mexico City lose one-third of its water to?

10. Eighty percent of the illness in developing countries can be traced to what two causes?

11. Israel gets one-fourth of its water from where?

12. What percentage of its water does Israel recycle?

13. What is the main problem with irrigating agricultural land over time? Where is the well-known historical example of this?

14. What is the problem with desalinization?

15. What are some of the factors that have changed our attitudes on building dams?

16. What were some of the concerns that stopped Two Forks Dam in Colorado from being built?

17. How did opponents of Two Forks Dam show that the dam was unwise?

18. What are some of these conservation measures?

19. What is the single greatest waste of household water?

20. What activity uses the most water globally?

21. Why is saving just a little water in agriculture so important?

22. What is the fundamental problem with the Colorado River? Why doesn't it reach the Gulf of California?

23. What has happened to the Colorado River delta?

24. Why do you think this last segment of the Cadillac Desert video series is called the Last Oasis?

Chapter 12

OUR FUTURE WATER PLANET

We have learned a great deal about water—its properties, its availability, its benefits to us and our uses and our abuses of it, its ability to sculpt the landscape, and its ability to create disasters. It should be clear by now that water is essential, but at the same time, it can be a problem. In other words, this critical resource is very complex. We cannot live without it, but we overuse it and pollute it. We want to live near it, along coasts and rivers, but the extreme events associated with weather systems and climatic patterns put us at risk in these locations. We continue to understand more about how water moves through the hydrologic cycle and how its importance to ecosystems creates both environmental quality and recreational opportunities. But, there is much that we do not understand, including the extent and impacts of climate variation, patterns of extreme events, and how population and land use changes will affect demand patterns in the future. We have addressed these and other issues throughout the semester, but there is more to consider.

In 2009, the United Nations issued *Water in a Changing World*, the third UN report focusing on world water development (as of this writing, a new report is underway). The Secretary General of the United Nations, Ban Ki-moon, states in the foreword to this document, "There has been a widespread failure to recognize water's vital role in providing food, energy, sanitation, disaster relief, environmental sustainability and other benefits. This has left hundreds of millions of people suffering from poverty and ill health and exposed to the risks of water-related diseases." Unless water is managed with these needs in mind, the impacts on the environment, on human livelihoods, and on economic welfare are potentially devastating and irreversible. You have learned through the semester that water management is very difficult because water is not always available where and when we need it, and both natural and human-induced pressures on this critical resource are extreme. When these are combined with varying demands for water associated with such factors as population size, density, and distribution, and the importance of water to economic development, the complexities are increased significantly.

The diagram in Figure 12.1 illustrates the relationships among the various components that we have discussed all semester. The interactions among the boxes are complicated in and of themselves. However, we also have to recognize that different elements within each box may interact with individual elements in other boxes, and this will vary from place to place and from time to time. For instance, land use affects and is affected by the availability of water. It affects water resources by influencing permeability of the surface, thus altering groundwater supplies and by affecting runoff, thereby defining the location and amount of runoff that gets into surface sources. Land use, in turn, is affected by the availability of water, which is an important determinant in how much water can be applied to irrigation, for just one example.We understand these relationships between the physical and human environments, but we do not always translate that understanding into long-term decisionmaking.

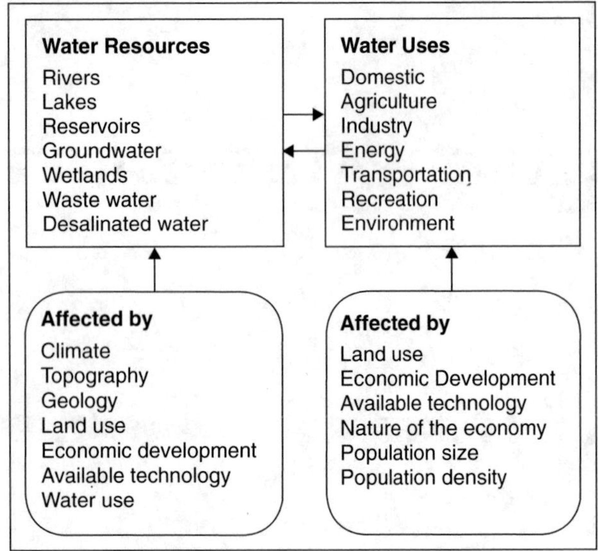

Figure 12.1 Components of water resources management.

There are many people making decisions about water use, and they do so to achieve different goals (Figure 12.2). Many times, the decisionmakers coordinate their efforts, and their goals support one another. An example of this is politicians and business leaders deciding to allocate funds to treat polluted water in order to provide higher quality water for industries. This, in turn, may help to alleviate poverty if more jobs are available in those industries and if higher quality water leads to improvements in public health. Other times, the efforts are not coordinated and the goals conflict. This would be the case when, perhaps, upstream decisionmakers dam a river to provide water for urban and agricultural uses, while restricting flows to downstream users. The objectives and the decisions are very heavily influenced by water availability (for instance, when there is less, more is sought) and by existing patterns of water use (when, as an example, much has been used for agriculture, but growing urban areas need more). Figure 12.2, then, represents the interactions between the physical and human environments that determine how much water is available, how much is used, and for what uses. It also represents a rather static situation, which is obviously an oversimplification, and it does not truly reflect the impacts of how differing goals and objectives of different decisionmakers can lead to problems that adversely affect not only water uses, but also the hydrological systems that provide the much-needed resource in the first place.

We already know that water availability varies seasonally, as do some uses, such as more water being used in irrigation when precipitation is lower. Other uses depend on the consistent availability of water, as is the case with industrial and energy uses, as well as domestic demands. To meet these needs, we have developed the means to store water from season to season, as illustrated by the dams and reservoirs discussed earlier in the semester. All of this is based on current patterns of water availability, which we know

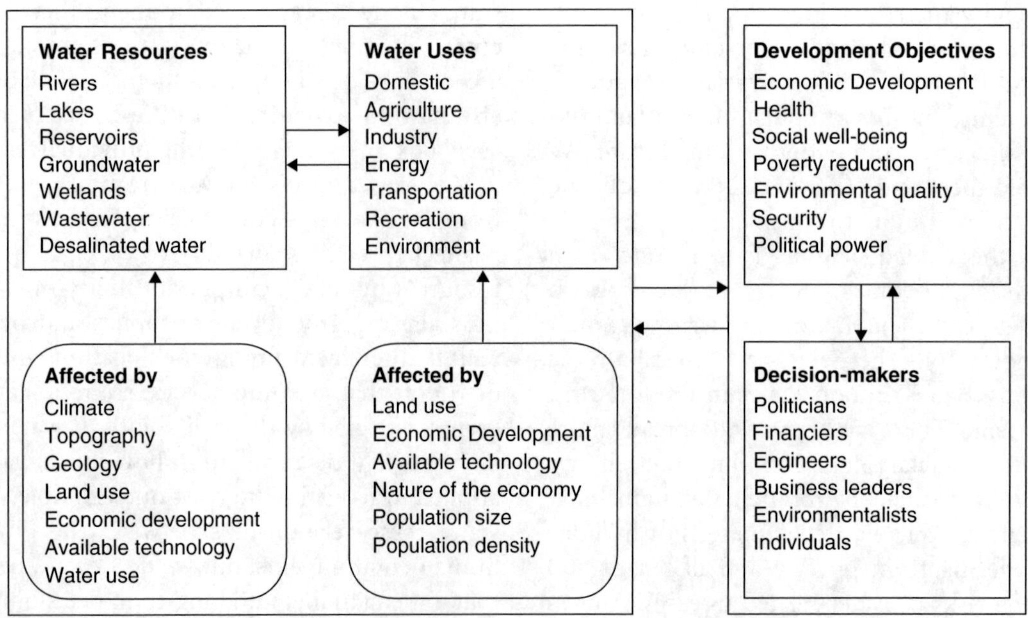

Figure 12.2 Adding decision making to the management framework.

are affected by climate change. This alone is an area of extreme uncertainty that requires us to rethink our current use patterns and our traditional responses to water extremes. These extremes can lead to too much or too little water. Yet, there are other changes and uncertainties that will affect all of the elements shown in Figure 12.2, and thus will influence water management for the foreseeable future. We use these to conclude this book because they illustrate the challenges that water managers of the future will face, and thus, the mix of disciplinary expertise needed to meet these challenges. While many of these challenges may seem far removed from us, they are not, as we experience all of them in one way or another in the United States and in North Carolina.

POPULATION GROWTH AND MOVEMENT

It is estimated by the Population Reference Bureau that the world's population is growing by about 78 million people each year, with much of that growth occurring in less-developed regions. This is problematic for several reasons. First, water demand will increase each year simply because there are more people. This translates to an additional 64 million cubic meters of freshwater demanded each year on a global basis. Second, much of this population growth will take place in areas that are either water-scarce or water-stressed. Part of the lack of water is due to climate, because some regions, such as sub-Saharan Africa and South Asia, where much of the population growth is expected to take place, have relatively high evapotranspiration rates. But it is not just climate, and this leads us to the third reason. Because of the largely rural nature of many of these regions and little economic development, there is a lack of infrastructure to provide adequate supplies of water of reasonable quality. As a result, currently some 1 billion people lack access to adequate water supplies, and more than 2 billion people lack access to improved sanitation. These numbers are expected to worsen in the near future with anticipated population growth.

Even while population is growing, it is also moving. International migration is on the rise, but what is particularly relevant to water management is rural to urban migration, both in terms of magnitude and the speed at which it is occurring. Asia and Africa are seeing the greatest increases. African urban populations are projected to see almost a fourfold increase between 2005 and 2050, moving from just under 350,000,000 to 1,234,000,000. Asian cities are expected to more than double during this same time period, increasing from just under 1,500,000,000 people to over 3,300,000,000. This 45-year time frame is insufficient for water managers to keep up, even if there were sufficient money to provide the necessary infrastructure. As a result, increased numbers of urban inhabitants will not have access to safe water or to adequate sanitation.

Growing urban areas put additional strains on water resources. More people means more water withdrawal, which in turn means an increased need for water storage to provide a consistent supply for the population and for the economic development and industry that support that population. Frequently, this translates to more dams and more diversions of water from the source to the users. And, once used, the water is polluted, requiring increased investment in wastewater treatment facilities. Growing populations, whether urban or rural, lead to other demands for water, particularly for agriculture. As the demand for food increases, so too does the need for water for irrigation—a consumptive use of water, particularly in areas of high evaporation.

There has also been a trend of movement to coastal areas. Throughout the world, many large cities are near the coast for some very logical locational benefits. But, it isn't just migration to coastal cities that is problematic. In the United States, we have seen a trend of increasing populations in coastal counties for decades (Figure 12.3), many of which do not have large cities. Not only does this put these populations at risk (as was discussed earlier in the semester), but it also puts a strain on water resources, as frequently adequate freshwater is not available in these locations, often leading to saltwater intrusion into groundwater and to large expenses to obtain adequate water supplies to support the growing population.

It is not difficult to see the impacts of increased population growth, whether we look at absolute numbers, distributions, or specific locations. More people means greater demand for water, which requires an investment in water infrastructure. Without such an investment, either insufficient amounts of water will be available or water that is available will be of poor quality, or both. As is discussed next, making such an investment can be difficult.

INFRASTRUCTURE INVESTMENT

Water does not come cheap—at least not water in sufficient quantity and of suitable quality for consumption and for other uses. Engineered works to capture, store, and distribute water, such as dams and

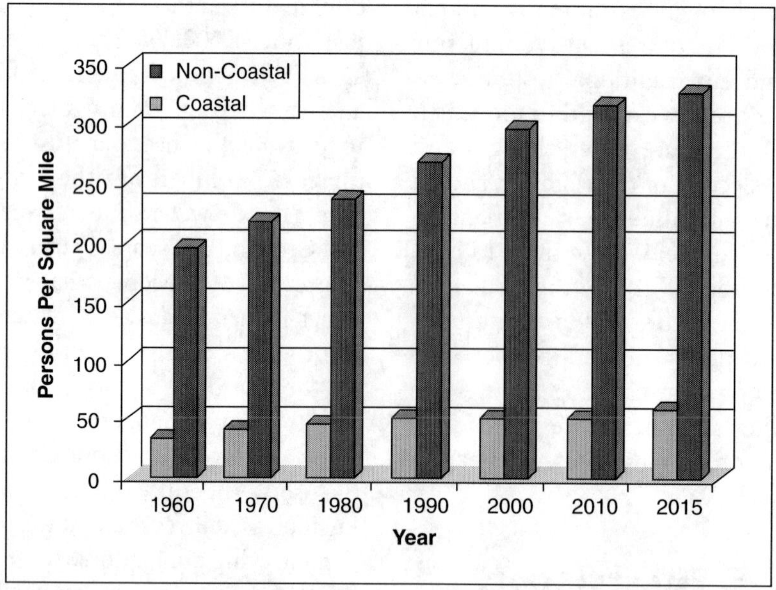

Figure 12.3 A Comparison of Changes in Population between Coastal and Non-coastal Counties
Source: www.csc.noaa.gov/coastal/images/NeedFig1.gif

reservoirs, drilled wells, and water pipelines, require up-front investment. Such an investment is usually quite substantial given the quantities of water that are required for the uses shown in Figure 12.1. Then there is the investment required to ensure that the water that is supplied is of the appropriate quality for its intended use, so some sort of filtration or treatment may be required, leading to additional investment. Finally, water that is used must be treated before it is returned to the system, further increasing the costs through building and operation of wastewater treatment facilities. Each of these can be small or large (or anything in between), depending on need, but as was shown above, those needs can change. And, they can change quickly. Much of this was discussed in Chapter 10, but no consideration was given to costs for building and maintaining such systems.

In less-developed countries where financial resources are particularly scarce, there is tension between those who advocate investing in water development in rural areas and those advocating investment in urban areas. Both çite direct and indirect benefits. The rural proponents argue that a very small change in water availability has a huge impact on health, quality of life, and economic well-being. Because less water is used in rural villages than in urban areas, the necessary investment is much lower, yet it results in a large positive impact. Women and children, the ones who traditionally get the day's water, will be relieved from the need to walk long distances to find adequate, but frequently poor quality, water. That time can now be spent in other, more economically productive activities. Further, the increased health of rural residents resulting from consuming water of higher quality will also allow them to be more economically productive. Better living standards, resulting from improved access to good quality water, may also help to stem the tide of rural-to-urban migrations, thus indirectly helping urban areas.

On the other hand, urban proponents contend that the situation is much direr in cities, and particularly in urban squatter settlements. Access to any water is severely limited, and population pressures, both in terms of absolute numbers and concentrations, continue. As a result, water-borne illnesses can spread through urban areas quickly and debilitate many. Those favoring investing in urban water infrastructure argue that many can be served by a relatively modest investment.

An obvious solution to the dilemma might be to invest in both. However, the costs are high and there are many demands on what money is available. So, decisions for allocating funds to various projects have to be made based on social, economic and political objectives, such as those shown on the right side of Figure 12.2. Which objective dominates at any given time depends on many factors, too complex and frequently too numerous to discuss here.

In developed countries, including the United States, water infrastructure has been in existence for, in some cases, hundreds of years. As examples, New York City began developing its reservoir and aqueduct system in the 1840s; the City of Chicago started laying pipe to supply water in 1851; and the Hoover Dam has been in operation since 1936. While these engineering works have been repaired, replaced, and maintained over time, much of our water-related infrastructure is deteriorating. The American Society of Civil Engineers has reported that some 3,200 dams are designated as "unsafe," and the number of miles of unsafe levees in the United States is unknown. Many of these unsafe structures are due to aging of the infrastructure and, in some cases, a lack of maintenance. As is the case in less developed regions, decisions have to be made about priorities for spending scarce dollars, and the same factors are considered in the United States as elsewhere. These are very difficult choices.

CONFLICT

As we have learned, despite the vast amount of water that exists globally, there are regional and local shortages. Some of these shortages are due to climatic factors, and some are due to how water is used. With these shortages, whether they are stem from less water available overall or insufficient water available for a specific use, conflicts arise. These may be conflicts between water users in a region or they may be between regions. Because water is necessary for economic development and for life and livelihoods, sorting out conflicts becomes very difficult, often embedded in the different political and economic interests of the parties involved.

An example of conflicts among users can be seen in the western United States (Figure 12.4). It should not be surprising that many of the areas of anticipated conflict are near urban areas—particularly those that are experiencing population growth and sprawl. Some of these cities, such as Las Vegas, Nevada, and Phoenix, Arizona, are in desert regions. Water provided by damming rivers (remember the *Cadillac Desert films* and Chapter 11) made these urban centers possible and the warm, dry climates made them attractive places to live. In this region (and elsewhere throughout the United States), irrigated agriculture is critical to the economy. As a result, the competing demands for water to meet growing urban needs and to support the agricultural base of the region are substantial. The situation has been exacerbated by drought. For example, along the Rio Grande, there are legal battles for the water that involve the city of Albuquerque, New Mexico, farmers, environmentalists who are trying to protect endangered species, and local Native Americans. There is no simple solution because each has a compelling interest in and need for the water, but supply is simply not sufficient to meet all needs.

While many of the problem areas shown in Figure 12.4 are within one state, there are several that cross state boundaries, bringing sovereignty into the conflict. This can pit state against state, and it is not restricted to the western United States. Indeed, North Carolina and South Carolina had been in a three-year legal battle over North Carolina's diversions from the Catawba and Yadkin Rivers. An out-of-court agreement was reached in January 2011, but the potential remains for conflicts in the future as water demand and supply change. Thus, conflicts occur even in areas that tend to have plentiful water resources.

Water is also the cause of international conflicts. Look again at Figure 12.4. The numerous conflicts along the border of the United States and Mexico, especially Texas, show that the potential for conflict is either substantial or highly likely. We have, in fact, addressed some of the water conflicts with Mexico, but others remain and additional ones will surface as urban development in this border area grows and as demands on both sides of the border increase. You might also notice some areas on the map that suggest the potential for conflict with Canada. Although we have had our differences with our neighbors to the north and south, we have, for the most part, been able to address our water issues through negotiation and diplomacy. This has not been the case everywhere.

There are many examples throughout history of water management decisions by one country causing significant political turmoil. One current example is the Greater Anatolia Project (GAP) in Turkey that controls the Tigris and Euphrates Rivers. To make a very long and detailed story short, Turkey, which is located in the upper reaches of both rivers, decided to develop a series of dams to provide both irrigation water and hydroelectric power to fuel its economic development. This is a logical decision for a country, but it has deleterious effects on downstream countries in this arid (and politically volatile) region of the world. Iraq, Iran, and Syria are all affected by this project, which they see as hindering their abilities to develop economically. There are also political motivations that perhaps have underlain some of Turkey's decisions. Whatever the case, Turkey's actions have sparked a regional controversy that has not been resolved to the satisfaction

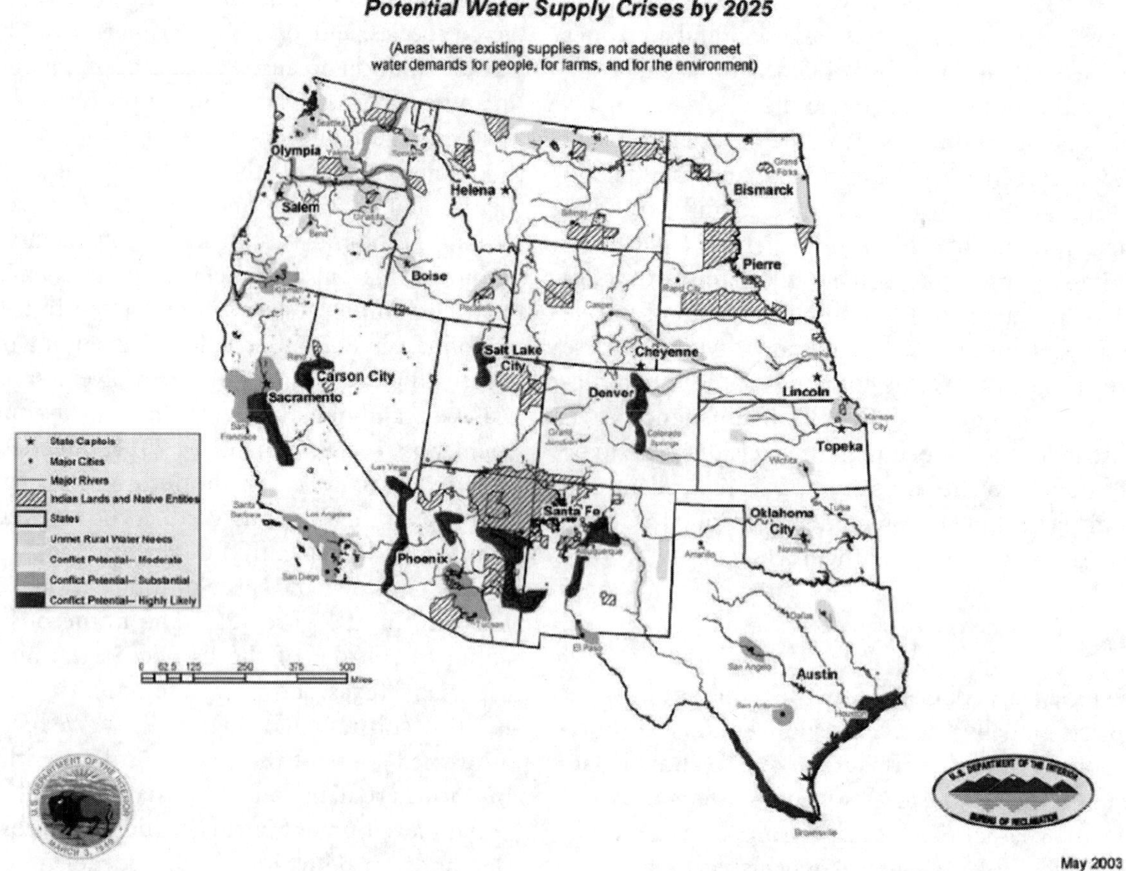

Figure 12.4 Areas of Potential Conflict in the Western United States
Source: U.S. Department of the Interior, 2005

of all countries involved. And this is just one example. Although not always the root of conflict, water "wars" have been associated with controversies between Israel and Palestine, between China and downstream countries on the Mekong River, and India's management of the Ganges River. As the availability of water changes with a changing climate, it is anticipated that such conflicts will be both more frequent and more volatile.

THE CHANGING ENVIRONMENT

Although this topic has been talked about all semester, and it is emphasized throughout the book, climate change and subsequent altered weather patterns promise to pose significant challenges to people and water managers everywhere. Some will be slow in coming and cumulative, meaning that the changes will perhaps be small so that they may go unnoticed except by a few experts. However, because they accumulate or build on one another, once we recognize it, responding to it may be very difficult. Sea level rise is a good example. As shown in Figure 12.3, coastal populations are growing rapidly so development of coastal areas is growing rapidly. Building is taking place based on current sea levels, and therefore on current high tide measurements and on current estimations of storm surge levels. How will these built-up areas change with rising sea level? And how does this increase risk to existing and anticipated future coastal populations? These are questions we need to address. Our experience with such issues suggests that while we may be able to answer these questions, making hard decisions about how to respond is much more difficult. Another example in North Carolina has to do with agriculture. Our agricultural patterns are well established, with, for example, tobacco and cotton in the eastern part of the state and apples and Christmas trees farther west. Our agricultural economies are developed around these patterns. Climate change and associated changes in precipitation and temperature may well require shifts in these patterns, but will not necessarily be noticeable immediately. So how do we deal with it? Again, the science may be straightforward, but the impacts remain uncertain, which means the political will to take action before a crisis occurs may be lacking.

With or without climate change, the environment is dynamic. For very good historic reasons, we developed in floodplains, but most of those reasons no longer apply. Over time, these floodplains have changed, partly because of hydrologic processes, partly because of the natural evolution of watersheds, and partly because of land use changes and the draining of wetlands. Upstream changes such as these put more water into rivers more quickly, thereby increasing the extent of downstream flood-prone areas. Though a changing climate may exacerbate these processes and impacts, the environment is different now compared with even the recent past. How we understand these changes and respond to them is important and involves all of the elements in Figure 12.2. The key here is that each element is subject to change, but not at the same time or at the same geographic or time scales. Clearly this presents challenges, but not ones that are insurmountable as long as we recognize the factors involved and the relationships among them.

It would be remiss of us to omit mention of the massive tsunami that struck Japan in 2011. While this natural event is the result of tectonic, rather than hydrologic, processes, it is impossible to ignore the impact that water had. This event showed the world the destructive power of water, probably even moreso than did Hurricane Katrina in 2005. What is particularly important about this event is that the Japanese government was well prepared for earthquakes and resulting tsunamis. Indeed, Japan was, and probably still is, a world leader, in earthquake engineering and preparedness. What we were reminded of by this event, among other things, is the fact that natural events can exceed our preparation levels, no matter how well developed our preparations are.

WHERE TO FROM HERE?

The challenges presented in this chapter are complex because they reflect the necessity, utility, and complexity of water. Meeting these challenges will require professionals with an interdisciplinary foundation. Understanding the characteristics of water as well as how the physical environment influences where, how, and in what quantity and quality water is available is a critical part of addressing the issues. So, too, is understanding how humans interact with the hydrologic environment, for better and for worse. We have addressed these topics throughout this course, and by now you should have a grasp of the physical, environmental, and human factors that affect water and therefore our choices in managing water. We cannot have healthy lives and livelihoods and, thus, economic viability, which everyone wants and deserves, without water. With a dynamic climate, the situation is changing, and it is up to those of us with training in the physical, environmental, and social sciences to avoid the potentially devastating and irreversible impacts about which the United Nations is so concerned.

These issues and challenges probably seem very far away and removed from your everyday lives. But they are not. We need to think about how we behave as users of water and as citizens of wherever we live and how we can be effective stewards of the environment.